DEPARTMENT OF THE ENVIRONMENT

Waste Management Paper 26B

Landfill Design, Construction and Operational Practice

D1612557

London: HMSO

Recycled Paper

6.9.96.

Contents

List of Figures

Foreword

Purpose and readership

This Waste Management Paper (this Paper) provides guidance on the overall development of landfill sites, encompassing landfill design, construction and operational practice. The guidance is set in the context of the Government''s commitment to sustainable development and the developing strategy for sustainable waste management. This context includes considerable developments in landfilling techniques, practices and waste management legislation over the last decade.

The guidance emphasises an engineering approach to landfill design and construction based on site-specific risk assessment, underpinned by quality management and good operational practice, to achieve a high standard of implementation and environmental protection. It is aimed at professional practitioners and operators in the waste management industry, and all those in planning and waste regulation who play a part in pollution control and the regulation of landfill sites.

Relationship with other Waste Management Papers

This Paper replaces guidance given previously in Waste Management Paper 26 (1986) and forms one of the Waste Management Paper 26 (WMP26) series. It should be read in conjunction with the other WMPs in the 26 series.

WMP26A   Landfill Completion (published)

WMP26D   Landfill Monitoring (in preparation 1995)

WMP26E   Landfill Restoration and Post Closure Management (in preparation 1995)

WMP26F   Landfill Co-disposal (in preparation 1995).

In planning the overall design and operation of a new landfill or extension to an existing site, the reader should have particular regard to the interface with afteruse and restoration, and should consult both WMP26B and WMP26E. For guidance on the specific aspects of landfill completion, monitoring and co-disposal, WMPs 26A, D and F respectively should be consulted. Waste management licensing is addressed in WMP4.

Contents

This Paper has ten chapters, a set of appendices, a glossary, a list of abbreviations and a bibliography for further reference and guidance. The Paper is arranged in three main parts as follows

Part 1 (Chapters 1 and 2) explains the background and legislative framework for landfill design, construction and operation.

- **Chapter 1** describes the purpose, scope and context of the guidance and the basis of the approach to landfill design.

- **Chapter 2** provides an overview of the legislative framework for the planning and regulation of landfill sites.

Part 2 (Chapters 3 to 7) provides more detailed guidance on the engineering principles and approach to landfill design and construction.

- **Chapter 3** describes the objectives and key principles for landfill design, and provides guidance on standards to be adopted in preparing a design.

- **Chapter 4** describes the principles of a quality approach to landfill development and emphasises the importance of quality assurance and quality control throughout design, construction and operation. It also gives guidance on contract arrangements for construction on landfill sites.

- **Chapter 5** contains advice on the site investigation information that is required to design a landfill on a particular site and sets out the objectives and methodology for geotechnical, hydrogeological and hydrological site investigations.

- **Chapter 6** provides guidance on the overall criteria for the engineering design of a landfill site and describes the topics and information to be included.

- **Chapter 7** focuses on landfill liners and gives guidance on the selection of liner systems, materials and construction methods which may be utilised, and their appropriateness to specific circumstances.

Part 3 (Chapters 8 to 10) provides guidance on landfill operation including the planning and design of operations, details of operational practice and capping.

- **Chapter 8** discusses the general principles of site operation including the approach to operations, the required skills and experience for operators; the mechanisms for transfer of information between the design, construction and operational stages, general legal and landfill safety requirements and performance monitoring.

- **Chapter 9** sets out specific guidance on individual aspects of landfill operations, illustrated with examples of good practice.

- **Chapter 10** considers the design and construction of capping systems for completing the landform.

A fold out *User Guide* is provided to assist the reader through the stages of landfill design and operational practice, together with a full index listing for individual topic areas.

Review

The Department is considering mechanisms to ensure that the Paper is reviewed regularly to incorporate new research findings and developments in landfill practice.

Acknowledgements

This Waste Management Paper has been produced by the Department of the Environment in consultation with the Scottish and Welsh Offices and with other interested parties.

In preparing this paper, the Department of the Environment's Wastes Technical Division received invaluable help from the waste management industry, regulatory authorities and consultants who contributed text, advice and comment. The Department is particularly grateful to Aspinwall & Company Ltd for drafting and editing the core text, figures and annexes, and to members of an advisory group who provided assistance throughout the production process. The advisory group members were:

Mr J Ablitt	Northumbrian Environmental Management Ltd
Dr P Collinson	Rust Environmental
Mr D Greedy	Greenways Waste Management
Mr B Griffiths	Biffa Waste Services Ltd
Mr R Lucas	Shanks and McEwan (Southern) Ltd
Mr M McNulty	Cleveland County Council
Mr P Quinn	Warwickshire County Council
Mr R Wilkins	Greenways Waste Management
Mr P Coulter	Department of the Environment
Mr R Watkinson	Department of the Environment.

It is intended to revise and update this paper. Readers with enquiries, comments or suggestions about this paper are invited to write to:

Department of the Environment
Wastes Technical Division
43 Marsham Street
London
SW1P 3PY

Part 1
Background and Legislative Framework

1 Background and Concepts

Introduction

1.1　This chapter provides an essential background to the overall aims and applicability of the guidance contained in this Waste Management Paper. It explains the approach that has been adopted to the development of landfill sites, encompassing landfill design, construction and operational practice, in the context of the current UK position on landfilling and developments since Waste Management Paper (WMP) 26 (1986) was published.

Aims

1.2　The overall aims of the guidance in this WMP are

- to illustrate the process for determining the design, construction and operation of landfills on a site specific basis consistent with the need to protect the environment

- to improve the overall standards of landfill design, construction and operation in the UK in accordance with best current practice

- to acknowledge the aims of sustainable development in the design and operation of new landfill sites.

Scope and applicability

1.3　The Paper is applicable to the design and operation of new sites involving landfill or landraising, to discrete new lateral extensions at existing sites and to vertical extensions where a change in design and operational philosophy is intended. The guidance on operational practice is also applicable to existing landfills where there is opportunity to adopt improved standards in line with current best practice. The risk assessment approach that is embodied in this Paper can be applied to all landfill activities.

1.4　The guidance is applicable to all types of solid waste, incorporating household, commercial, industrial, construction and other wastes, which have been identified as suitable for landfill disposal[1] These include

- *inert wastes,* which will not chemically react, undergo biodegradation or leaching within the landfill environment, and which may incorporate the products of pre-treatment

- *bioreactive wastes,* which will undergo biodegradation within the landfill environment to varying degrees depending on their physical and chemical composition

- *hazardous wastes,* some of which will be acceptable at co-disposal sites[2].

1.5　The general principles of design, construction and operation set out in this Chapter apply to all types of landfill site. The guidance should be applied at a level appropriate to the type of waste and site, consistent with a site specific risk assessment. The principles of this Paper apply equally to co-disposal sites. However, additional provisions are necessary at such sites and these are set out in WMP26F.

1.6　This Paper takes as its starting point the conceptual design of a landfill. The type of waste and its suitability for landfilling in a particular location should be

---

[1] See Appendix A for definition of wastes.
[2] See WMP26F Landfill Co-disposal.

determined as part of an initial feasibility study prior to commencing landfill design. This will include

- assessment of alternative waste management options prior to choosing the landfill option

- site selection and consideration of alternative locations

- pre-treatment of wastes prior to landfilling

- consideration of afteruse.

1.7   The position of landfilling within the waste hierarchy as discussed in paragraph 1.20 should be taken into account when assessing the need for a new landfill site. The reader should refer to other published guidance on this matter[3]

1.8   Although guidance on site selection is not included in this Paper, it is a process often intimately associated with the risk assessment approach to landfilling. If risks are unacceptably high in a locality a site may need to be rejected, particularly if there are other, lower risk options available.

1.9   Guidance on the pre-treatment of wastes is not within the scope of this Paper, but consideration of pre-treatment forms part of the Government's Waste Strategy and may become more important as further research is undertaken[4]. The designer and operator should be aware of the implications of pre-treatment for site selection and in determining the methods for construction and operation of the landfill.

1.10   Consideration of the afteruse of the site should be carried out at the inception of the project. Detailed guidance on the restoration, afteruse and aftercare of landfill sites will be given in WMP26E.[5]

1.11   This Paper should be useful to all those who may play a part in the design, construction and operation of landfill sites. The guidance is intended to assist skilled practitioners, such as engineers, operators and regulators of landfill sites, to achieve a consistent approach to landfill design, construction, operation and regulation. It provides an *overview* of the technical considerations and professional skills required, and refers to detailed guidance elsewhere on specific topics.

1.12   This Paper's guidance to WRAs is **non-statutory**[6]: a WRA is thus not obliged to have regard to it. In substituting its own view, however, the WRA should ensure that it informs licensees, applicants and intending applicants what its intentions

---

[3] *Sustainable Waste Management – A Waste Strategy for England and Wales*, DoE/Welsh Office (in preparation) provides an appropriate starting point.

[4] The pre-treatment of wastes prior to landfilling may include
- separation of recoverables, such as glass, plastics, paper, soils, aggregates and green waste for compost
- crushing, screening, shredding or pulverisation
- composting to treat putrescibles
- anaerobic digestion
- incineration
- solidification with cementitious materials or vitrification.

[5] DoE: Waste Management Paper No 26E (in preparation 1995).

[6] Some WMPs provide waste regulation authorities with statutory guidance; that is, the authority is obliged by statute (specifically, ss35(8) and 74(5) of the Environmental Protection Act 1990) to have regard to the guidance. The papers on licensing, WMP4 and WMP4A, are of this kind, as is the paper on landfill completion, WMP26A. For a comprehensive treatment of statutory guidance, see DoE Circular 11/94 (Welsh Office 26/94; Scottish Office Environment Department 10/94), London, HMSO. 1994: ISBN 0 11 752975 3 of 19 April 1994, at paragraph 19 on page 7.

and requirements are. To do otherwise might be to disregard the **statutory** guidance in WMP4[7].

General principles and definition of terms

1.13 **The overall philosophy described in this Paper is that of a construction project, carried out over an extended period, to build a desired landform using waste materials and incorporating appropriate measures for environmental protection.** These will inevitably change during the life of the site and the design should be flexible to allow for the implementation of enhanced environmental standards.

1.14 This concept combines the following two elements in ways which are appropriate for a particular site and its waste inputs

    i)   Established engineering practices for construction, based on a pre-determined design, with appropriate performance standards for the materials used.

    ii)   Process engineering to accommodate biological, chemical and physical changes which will take place within bioreactive wastes during the active life of the site.

1.15 All landfills should have regard to the requirements for environmental protection in order to ensure that they do not cause pollution of the environment or harm to human health or become seriously detrimental to the amenities of the locality, in accordance with current legislation and the aims of sustainable development. The guidance embodied in subsequent chapters of this Paper is based on

- a *holistic* approach to landfill design and operation, utilising scientific and engineering skills as an integrated process from initial conception through to final capping, restoration and aftercare

- use of a site-specific *risk assessment*, rather than a prescriptive approach to environmental protection, for each element and at each stage in the project, in order to determine the overall design and operational practices appropriate to the environmental setting of each individual landfill site.

1.16 The guidance also emphasises that designers and operators should

- recognise the effects of the different nature of wastes and their degradation processes on landfill gas and leachate generation and the potential of these to change during the course of design and operation of the site

- adopt methods, standards and operational systems based on best current practice which reflect progress in techniques and improving standards

- underpin all actions by a quality approach to ensure that the required quality is achieved in implementation and that landfill standards match rising public expectations

- ensure that the appropriate level of environmental protection is required in order that the operator is not burdened with unnecessary costs.

[7] For example, paragraph 2.8 of WMP4.

1.17   Further explanation of these general principles is given in Chapter 3, and the reader should also have particular regard to WMP26E on landfill restoration in respect of the holistic approach to landfill design. Guidance on the quality approach is given in Chapter 4.

1.18   The approach described is that of a single project carried out in a number of stages over an extended period. Terms appropriate to each stage are used throughout the Paper and include

Design   The formulation of the plan for the landfill project, including all the details and drawings for the particular site.

Construction The actions to build the landform, incorporating all parts of the facility. The engineering works associated specifically with the base, lining, monitoring, environmental control and infrastructure items of the facility prior to emplacing waste are referred to as *preparation*.

Operation   The process of emplacing waste, and the associated management activities, for the prepared facility.

The need for new guidance

1.19   The Department last published guidance on landfill design in WMP26[8]. Significant developments since then have led to the need for revised guidance.

> The legislative framework for waste management control and regulation has been significantly revised in the Environmental Protection Act 1990 and planning legislation has been updated and consolidated within the Town and Country Planning Act 1990 and the Planning and Compensation Act 1991[9]. The implications of these are discussed in Chapter 2.

> There is a greater emphasis on groundwater protection which is promoted in the NRA's Policy and Practice for the Protection of Groundwater[10] and Regulation 15 of the Waste Management Licensing Regulations 1994. This is reflected in the risk assessment approach to landfill design and construction which forms the basis of guidance throughout this Paper.

> Techniques, practices and quality control available for landfill construction and operation have advanced considerably in the last decade, as indicated in Table 1.1.

> There has been increasing public awareness of environmental issues associated with landfill sites, demanding higher standards of landfill construction, operation and restoration.

> The sustainability debate following the Earth Summit in 1992 has focused attention on the longevity of waste degradation processes.

---

[8] Waste Management Paper 26, *Landfilling Wastes*. HMSO, 1986: ISBN 0 11 751891 3.
[9] In Scotland, The Town and Country Planning (Scotland) Act 1972, as amended.
[10] National Rivers Authority 1992; in Scotland, the *Groundwater Protection Strategy for Scotland* (in preparation 1995).

Table 1.1

Developments in landfill practices since 1986

Item	Development
Capping	Alternative construction materials and increasing use of synthetic membranes
	Increased understanding of contribution of soils, restoration layers and vegetation to cap protection and performance
Contract management	CQA and use of formalised contract procedures
Design tools	Advances in computer technology and wide availability of computer aided design
Environmental assessment	Regulations requiring formal environmental assessment of many landfill proposals at the planning stage
Landfill gas	Recognition of potential hazards and opportunities leading to high specification management systems and increased utilisation
Landfill science	Improved understanding of processes, plant and equipment
Leachate	Frequent use of leachate management systems and new technologies for leachate treatment
Liners	Use of artificial and composite liner systems
	Liner protection and leakage detection systems
	Application of CQA
Operational technology	Use of computerised weighbridges and checking systems
	Introduction of alternative daily cover materials
	Wider availability of equipment and survey techniques to assist site management
Restoration and aftercare	Now an integral part of the site development programme and a key interface with planning controls over landfills
Settlement and stability	Research data on settlement and assessment of stability
Waste decomposition	Improved understanding of microbiological aspects and recognition of the very long timescales required for degradation and leaching

UK position on landfilling

1.20   Landfill offers one of a series of options for waste management. The waste management hierarchy is a central element of the EC 5th Programme of Policy and Action[11] in relation to the environment and sustainable development. It encourages, in order of priority, the following alternatives to disposal

- prevention or reduction of waste

- re-use

- recovery, recycling, or reclamation, including the use of waste as a source of energy.

1.21   This is an important philosophy which will cause profound changes to patterns of manufacture and consumption, and to the nature of wastes. Where these options are not feasible, wastes should be disposed of without using processes or methods which could harm the environment.

1.22   The UK and many other countries are parties to the 1992 agreement on sustainable development at the Earth Summit[12]. The UK's strategy for sustainable development was published in 1994[13]. In the field of waste management, the strategy requires that the present generation should deal with wastes it produces and not leave problems to be dealt with by future generations[14]. For the purposes of this Paper a generation is regarded as 30–50 years after completion of the landfill operation for each separate phase of a site.

1.23   In the UK, waste disposal by landfilling remains an integral part of our approach to waste management. Approximately 70% of controlled wastes in the UK are currently disposed of to landfill sites and it is recognised that landfill will remain the Best Practicable Environmental Option (BPEO) for certain types of waste for the foreseeable future. In order to apply the principles of sustainable development to waste management the Government has prepared a waste strategy. The waste strategy policy on landfill is to promote landfill practices which will achieve stabilisation of landfill sites within one generation. This policy will be implemented through guidance set out in the revised series of waste management papers on landfill.

1.24   Many of the wastes currently disposed of to landfills are bioreactive, and many existing landfills already act as sub-optimal bioreactors. However, to enable the bioreactive landfill to continue as an acceptable method of disposal in the longer term, the emphasis must change from one of uncontrolled biodegradation towards that of controlled bioreaction, in order to reflect the aims of sustainable development.

1.25   **A key issue for landfilling is therefore how to optimise the design and operation of every site in order to achieve the overall objectives of environmental protection and beneficial afteruse, compatible with the aims of sustainable development.**

---

[11] Towards Sustainability, A European Community Programme of Policy and Action in Relation to the Environment and Sustainable Development, published by the Office for Publications of the European Communities, 1992.

[12] The United Nations Conference on Environmental Development: Rio de Janeiro, 1992.

[13] *Sustainable Development – the UK Strategy*, Summary Report: HMSO, London 1994.

[14] *Landfilling in the UK and Landfill Containment.* DoE Waste Technical Division Note June 1994.

Approach to landfilling in this Paper

1.26   The objective of this guidance is to return the products of stabilisation of a landfill to the environment in a controlled manner, at a rate which the environment can accept without harm. To be compatible with the Government's policy towards sustainable development, this must be carried out in a manner which minimises pollution control burdens for future generations. Ways in which this can be achieved include

- selection of inert wastes for landfill disposal

- pre-treatment to a quality which will not cause unacceptable harm

- management of bioreactive wastes in such a way that the system degrades to approach a stable, non-polluting state.

1.27   For *inert wastes and wastes of low reactivity*, pollution of the environment should be prevented by appropriate design incorporating passive or simple control measures. Any leachate and gas generation from the landfill will need to be managed proactively to ensure that the site will stabilise according to sustainability criteria.

1.28   *Pre-treatment of wastes* should either result in a less bioreactive waste, or a more predictable material for which it is easier to design appropriate environmental controls. Pre-treatment may also considerably reduce the quantity of waste requiring disposal.

1.29   For *bioreactive wastes*, the achievable rate of stabilisation will dictate the requirements for environmental protection. Achieving a timescale of a generation for the stabilisation of wastes currently presents a number of difficulties, arising from limitations in our current understanding of the rates of many landfill processes, and the ability to achieve rapid flushing of wastes within a bioreactive landfill. The landfill designer must therefore select the approach at the time of design consistent with the BPEO.

1.30   The practical design approach for bioreactive wastes will depend on the waste types and properties proposed for disposal, the characteristics of the site and the proposed afteruse. In selecting the most appropriate approach for landfilling in a particular situation the designer should consider the following approaches in descending order of priority, as illustrated by the decision tree in Figure 1.1.

    i)   In accordance with the strategy for sustainable development, the designer should first examine the potential for *accelerated stabilisation* of the landfill to achieve degradation of wastes to a stable form within a generation of cessation of tipping.

        >   To achieve this objective, the landfill will have to be designed and operated to maintain as high a rate of activity as necessary within a *biological reactor*, together with a sufficient degree of flushing to remove the products of decomposition. Fail-safe control measures and a very high degree of management will be needed during the active period of waste degradation. The degree of control required raises issues for the designer and operator which are highlighted throughout this Paper.

        >   The state of knowledge at the time of the design must be sufficient to give confidence that a particular design objective can be achieved. A summary of the considerations for accelerated

stabilisation is given in Appendix D. For sites which will accept hazardous wastes for co-disposal, reference should also be made to WMP26F.

ii) It may not be possible to predict confidently the achievement of stabilisation within a specific period at the time of design. As part of the risk assessment approach and iterative design process, the designer should examine whether accelerated stabilisation should be encouraged, by considering the impact on the environmental controls should stabilisation be only partly successful within the intended timescale.

> Design models will need to either incorporate the ability to install appropriate passive control measures retrospectively or utilise attenuation to minimise the long term burden for future generations. This approach is likely to be the practical option in the majority of situations for the foreseeable future.

iii) Where accelerated stabilisation is not possible but landfill is nevertheless acceptable in a particular location, the design approach should consider the degree of containment required and the incorporation of very long term passive controls.

> In such situations the landfill cap may need to be of high quality and durability, such that the environmental impact should be very low even if the liner failed, and the maintenance obligation, though long-term, should be small and of low technological requirement. Isolation of waste from the environment is not compatible with the aim of sustainable development in the long term because the potential hazards do not diminish with time, even if the risk is low.

1.31   Where the risks are unacceptably high or place too high a burden on future generations, the designer will need to reconsider whether the particular wastes should be landfilled, and may need to seek alternatives for the wastes, site and afteruse under consideration. **In all cases, the suitability and mechanism of the approach to landfilling is site specific and should be determined by risk assessment.**

Figure 1.1 Approach to landfilling

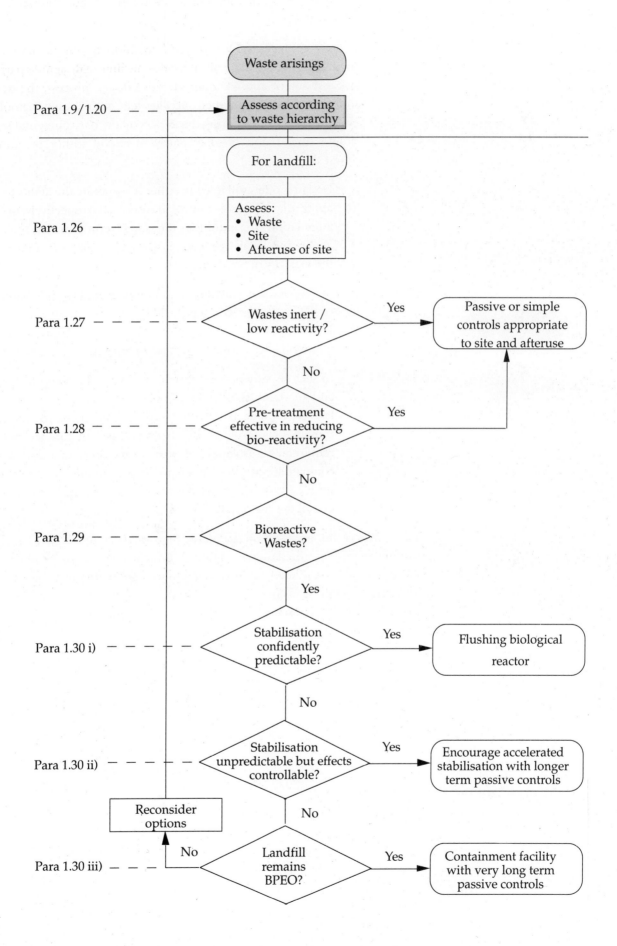

2 An Overview of the Legislative Framework

Introduction

2.1   All landfill sites in the UK are subject to legislative controls. A landfill development cannot proceed without the necessary consents. Therefore designers and operators of landfill sites should be aware of the general provisions for regulating landfill and the relevance of these to each stage of design, construction, operation and restoration.

2.2   This chapter summarises the main legislation regulating landfill development (paragraphs 2.3 to 2.7) and the main consultees for the planning and operation of landfill sites (paragraphs 2.8 to 2.11).

Legislation and guidance affecting landfill development

2.3   There are three main areas of legislative control relating to landfill developments

    i)   The planning system, which controls the development and use of land in the public interest, and affects the choice of site location.

    ii)   Pollution control legislation, incorporating waste management licensing and measures for environmental protection.

    iii)   Regulations and statutory controls to protect health and safety and ensure minimum standards for engineering construction.

2.4   Legislation and guidance on its application are found in a range of documents. Central government implements its objectives through primary and secondary legislation. Primary legislation takes the form of Acts of Parliament, whilst subordinate legislation in the form of Regulations or Orders aids the implementation of these Acts. There is usually separate primary and secondary legislation for England and Wales, Scotland and Northern Ireland.

    >   A directive of the European Union is a legally binding instrument addressed to the Member States of the European Union. It prescribes the aims to be achieved, but gives discretion to the Member States on how such aims can be attained. Implementation of a directive within the UK requires its adoption into national legislation.

2.5   Advice and guidance on government policy and procedural matters, which can be statutory or non-statutory, are provided in a variety of documents including

- Circulars (DoE, Welsh and Scottish Offices)

- Guidance Notes (DoE Planning Policy Guidance Notes and Minerals Planning Guidance Notes; Scottish Office National Planning Policy Guidelines and Planning Advice Notes)

- Waste Management Papers (DoE)

- Health and Safety Guidance Notes (HSE)

- NRA and WRA Guidance Notes

- Government and industry Codes of Practice.

Table 2.1

Main legislation and guidance relating to landfill design, construction and operation (England, Wales and Scotland)

Planning

Acts and Regulations	*Guidance*
Town and Country Planning Act 1990/Town and Country Planning (Scotland) Act 1972	DoE Circular 15/88 Environmental Assessment 1988/SDD Circular 13/1988 Environmental Assessment
Planning and Compensation Act 1991	
Town and Country Planning (General Permitted Development) Order 1995/Town and Country Planning (General Development Procedure) Order 1995/Town and Country Planning (General Development Procedure)(Scotland) Order 1992/Town and Country Planning (General Permitted Development)(Scotland) Order 1992, as amended	PPG23 Planning and Pollution Control 1994/NPPG Land for Waste Disposal (Draft 1994)
	MPG7 The Reclamation of Mineral Workings
Town and Country Planning (Assessment of Environmental Effects) Regulations 1988/The Environmental Assessment (Scotland) Regulations 1988 (as amended)	

Pollution control, water quality and waste management licensing

Acts and Regulations	*Guidance*
Environmental Protection Act 1990	WMP4 Licensing of Waste Management Facilities
Water Resources Act 1991	
Water Industry Act 1991	WMP26A Landfill Completion
Controlled Waste Regulations 1992	WMP26B Landfill Design, Construction and Operation
Environmental Protection (Duty of Care) Regulations 1991	WMP26D Landfill Monitoring
Waste Management Licensing Regulations 1994	WMP26E Landfill Restoration and Post Closure Management
Controlled Waste (Registration and Carriers and Seizure of Vehicles) Regulations 1991	WMP26F Landfill Co-disposal
The Special Waste Regulations 1995	WMP27 Landfill Gas
Control of Pollution (Amendment) Act 1989	DoE Circular 11/94 Waste Management Licensing 1994/Welsh Office Circular 26/94 Waste Management Licensing/Scottish Office Circular 10/94 Waste Management Licensing
	NRA Policy and Practice for the Protection of Groundwater 1992/Groundwater Protection Strategy for Scotland (in press 1995)
	Landfill and the Water Environment, NRA Position Statement 1995

Health and safety

Acts and Regulations	*Guidance*
Health and Safety at Work etc Act 1974	HSE Occupational Exposure Limits Guidance Note EH40 (current edition)
Management of Health and Safety at Work Regulations 1992	
Work Place Health, Safety and Welfare Regulations 1992	HSE COSHH Assessments: A step by step guide to assessment and the skills needed for it: COSHH Regulations 1988
Control of Substances Hazardous to Health Regulations 1994	
The Construction (Design and Management) Regulations 1994	

2.6   Table 2.1 summarises the main legislation that is relevant to landfill development in general. Appendix B expands on those aspects of the planning system, waste management licensing and pollution control which are central to the design, construction and operational processes. Appendix B also makes reference to health and safety provisions, construction standards and the regulation of nuisance.

2.7   **For further guidance the practitioner should refer to current legislation and associated interpretative guidance documents appropriate to a specific matter.**

Consultations

2.8   Planning control is exercised through the local authorities, whilst waste management licensing is the responsibility of the waste regulatory body, at present the Waste Regulation Authority (WRA)[1]. Water pollution control is a function of the National Rivers Authority (NRA) in England and Wales and the River Purification Authorities (RPA) in Scotland. The Health and Safety Executive (HSE) is concerned with construction and operational standards. The relationship between the planning system and pollution control legislation is explained in Planning Policy Guidance Note No 23 *Planning and Pollution Control* (PPG 23) (England only)[2]

> The planning system focuses on whether the development itself is an acceptable use of land, rather than the control of the processes or substances themselves.

> The function of pollution control is to control processes and substances which can have potentially harmful effects on the environment.

2.9   During the decision process for a planning application for a new landfill, or an extension to an existing site, planning authorities are statutorily required to consult a range of other interested bodies about the application. Consultations are also required at the licensing stage. **The prospective landfill developer should discuss proposals at an early stage with the relevant planning authority, WRA and the NRA (RPA).** WRAs must also be consulted on planning applications in the vicinity of closed landfill sites and the HSE must be consulted by the WRA in respect of licence applications. Table 2.2 summarises the main subject areas and appropriate consultees pertinent to landfill developments.

2.10   The relevant matters to be considered in a planning application for a landfill site include

- adjacent development and population

- agricultural land quality

- air quality

- archaeological interests

- duration of the development

- ecology and nature conservation interests

---

[1] In Scotland, the District and Islands Councils are the WRA. From 1996, the functions of the WRA and NRA (RPA) will be combined in the Environment Agency (England and Wales) and Scottish Environmental Protection Agency (Scotland).
[2] In Scotland, the National Planning Policy Guideline *Land for Waste Disposal* (Draft October 1994) gives policy guidance for waste disposal.

Table 2.2

Statutory and non statutory consultees

Subject	Consultee
Agriculture	MAFF/Welsh Office Agriculture Department /Scottish Office Agriculture and Fisheries
Environmentally Sensitive Areas (ESA)	MAFF/Welsh Office Agriculture Department Countryside Commission/Countryside Council for Wales
Hazardous materials	HSE HMIP/HMIPI Local authority environmental health department
Landscape Areas of Outstanding Natural Beauty (AONB) National Parks	Countryside Commission/Countryside Council for Wales/Scottish Natural Heritage Local authority
Local amenities	Local amenity and environmental groups Parish Councils
Nature conservation Local Nature Reserves (LNR)	English Nature/Countryside Council for Wales/Scottish Natural Heritage Local authority Local Wildlife Trusts Royal Society for the Protection of Birds (RSPB)
Nuisance (noise, odours, smoke, fumes)	Local Authority environmental health department WRA
Pipelines Overhead cables	Water companies/Regional and Islands Councils Oil pipeline operators Electricity companies Gas companies Telecommunications companies
Protection of water resources	NRA/RPA Water plcs
Public rights of way	Local authority Ramblers Association
Safeguarding zones (airports, special installations etc)	Civil Aviation Authority Ministry of Defence (MoD) Relevant establishments
Scheduled Monuments Listed Buildings Archaeological sites Historic buildings and gardens	English Heritage/CADW: Welsh Historic Monuments/ Historic Scotland Royal Commission on the Historic Monuments of England/Royal Commission on the Ancient and Historical Monuments of Wales/Royal Commission on the Ancient and Historical Monuments of Scotland County archaeologist National Trust
Sites of Special Scientific Interest (SSSI) National Nature Reserves (NNR)	English Nature/Countryside Council for Wales/ Scottish Natural Heritage
Traffic	Local authority highways department
Trees and woodlands Tree Preservation Orders (TPO)	Local authority

- landscape and visual amenity

- local amenity (noise, dust, odour, litter)

- minerals and other material assets

- nature and amounts of wastes

- other designated areas or buildings of importance in the vicinity

- restoration to an appropriate afteruse

- road and transport networks

- services (gas, electricity, water)

- surface and groundwater.

2.11   For waste management licence applications, reference should be made to guidance in WMP4.

Part 2
Principles and Approach to Landfill Design

3 Design Objectives and Considerations

Introduction

3.1 **All landfill designs and changes to design should start with a review of this chapter**. It is essential that the designer has a clear understanding of the approaches to landfilling and defined objectives before commencing design, in accordance with the overall aims and approach set out in Chapter 1.

3.2 The principles considered at the design stage must also be embodied in and carried through the construction and operational stages of the development. This chapter describes the fundamental principles to be followed in preparing a landfill design and provides guidance on design objectives, considerations and standards which should be applied.

> The overall approach is based on **risk assessment** rather than **prescription**. It is neither possible nor desirable for all guidance to be prescriptive and **users should not attempt to take recommendations for individual aspects of design out of context.**

> Discussion of design considerations highlights some of the limitations of current knowledge. Understanding and knowledge will develop during the currency of this Paper. **The designer should be guided by the state of knowledge at the time of design taking into account the life of the landfill and its aftercare.**

> The sections on objectives and standards set out clear guidance on design methodology, which is considered in more detail in subsequent chapters.

3.3 The chapter is arranged in the following order

- key principles for the designer, which reiterate the overall concept for the design described in Chapter 1 (paragraph 3.4)

- stages in the design process (paragraphs 3.5 to 3.9)

- design considerations for the overall approach, with reference to the issues for the landfilling of bioreactive wastes in accordance with the aims of sustainable development (paragraphs 3.10 to 3.26)

- risk assessment as applied to landfill design and determination of the acceptability of impacts (paragraphs 3.27 to 3.34)

- design objectives which must be applied consistently throughout the design, preparation, operation, restoration, aftercare and afteruse of the site (paragraphs 3.35 to 3.55)

- design standards including absolute standards, performance standards and guidelines (paragraphs 3.56 to 3.61).

Key principles for the designer

3.4 The following key principles for the designer should be considered at the outset of the design process.

- **The overall concept is the construction of a landform with waste as an engineering project which is appropriate for a particular site and its waste input.**

> This requires consistency in approach to preparation works and environmental controls, operation, restoration and aftercare. All stages must be taken into account by the designer and the design must be understood by the operator.

• **The design model for the site must have regard to the objectives of sustainable development for future landfills.**

> A decision tree for assessing the approach is given in Figure 1.1 and the design considerations discussed further in paragraphs 3.10 to 3.26.

• **The overall approach to design and the design of each element of the landfill appropriate to its environmental setting are determined through risk assessment.**

> The risk assessment approach and methodology are described further in paragraphs 3.27 to 3.34.

• **The nature of the wastes that will be used to build the new landform and the processes of degradation and leaching during the life of the landfill are important factors in the overall design approach and methods of operation for a particular site.**

> A detailed description of the processes of waste decomposition that occur within a landfill is included as Appendix C. This indicates the complexity of the processes and the range of composition of the ensuing leachate and landfill gas. For any given types of waste proposed for use in construction of the landform, the designer should consider its probable decomposition processes and products of decomposition over the whole timescale.

• **Design is an iterative process which should be reviewed both at its inception and before making any changes.**

> Any amendments to a design should be considered against all aspects of the design, construction and operational processes according to the cycle illustrated in Figure 3.1, and cross-reference made to other sections of this Paper and parts of the WMP26 series as appropriate.

• **Landfill practice is a dynamic science.**

> Landfill designers must consider probable changes in landfill practice and waste input that may occur over the whole lifetime of the landfill from conception to completion of aftercare and should, where possible, make provision for these changes, or allow for them to be incorporated at a later stage. A process of periodic review should be used throughout the life of the site and prior to the design of later phases[1].

---

[1] See Chapter 6 for explanation of phases.

Figure 3.1 Design, construction and operation cycle

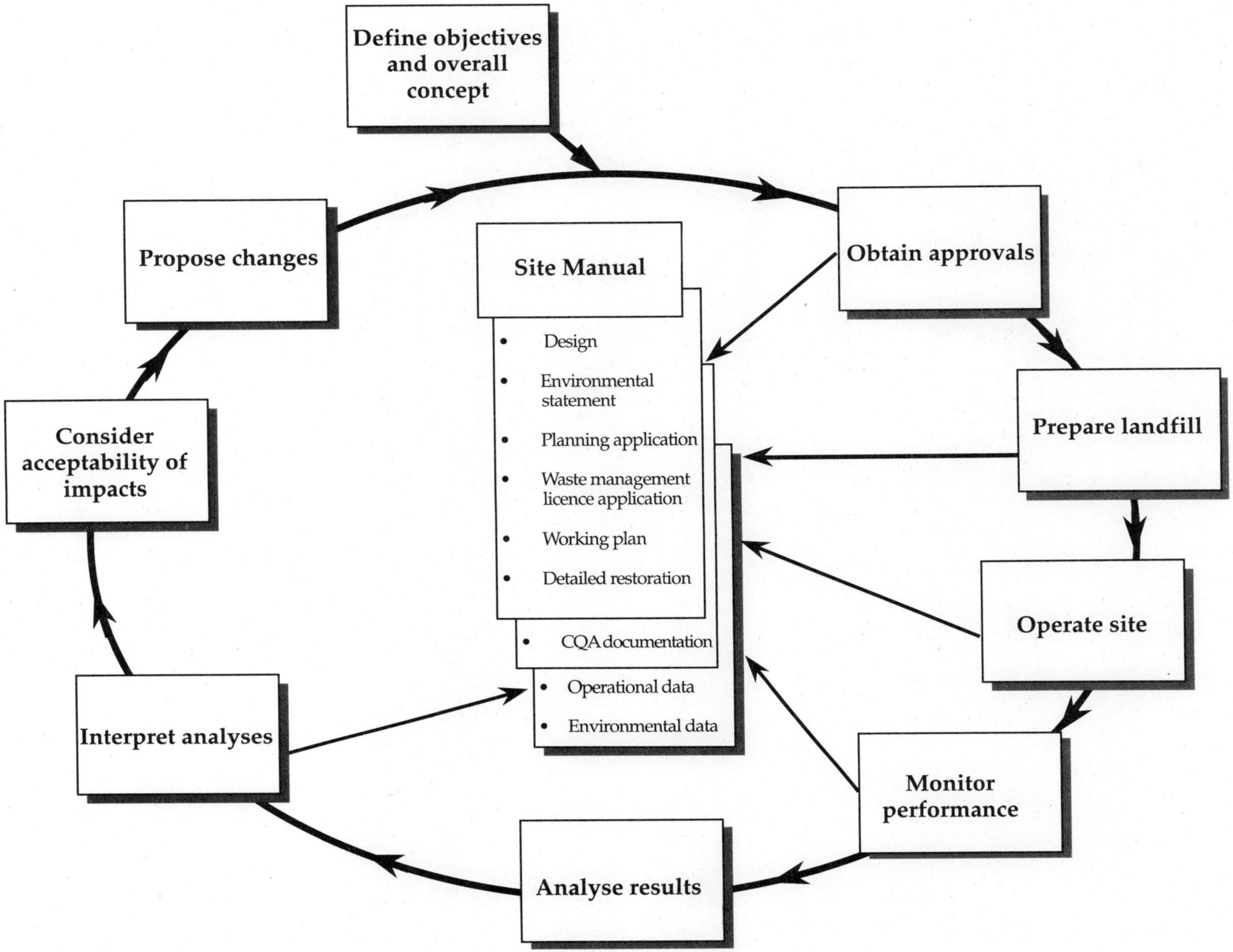

Define objectives and overall concept

Obtain approvals

Prepare landfill

Operate site

Monitor performance

Site Manual
- Design
- Environmental statement
- Planning application
- Waste management licence application
- Working plan
- Detailed restoration
- CQA documentation
- Operational data
- Environmental data

Analyse results

Propose changes

Consider acceptability of impacts

Interpret analyses

Stages in the design process

3.5 The landfill design process should be the same as that used in other engineering projects where the objectives for proposed use and design of a project are clearly stated at the outset of the design.

3.6 Landfill design should follow a staged approach which can be broadly divided into three key stages, referred to here as *conceptual, main* and *construction* design. In each of these stages the holistic principles for the site should be adopted with an appropriate level of detail for each stage.

3.7 At the *conceptual* stage the designer will be principally concerned with the overall feasibility and viability of the site, using experience to determine any fundamental constraints or items of major expenditure. This will result in a notional model for the development of a site, giving approximate volumes, possible design features and proposals for afteruse and setting out the principal aspects for clarification or investigation in subsequent phases.

3.8 At the *main design* stage a detailed site investigation[2] and assessment of environmental issues should be carried out, which will lead to a fully reasoned design for the overall construction, operation and restoration of the site. The main design forms the basis of the planning application for the development and of the working plan for the waste management licence application[3].

> The main design should consider all aspects required for the satisfactory development of the site, including the cost of the development. If formal environmental assessment[4] is required, the level of detail should be suitable for inclusion in an environmental statement.

> The main design is an essential part of the Site Manual[5], which provides a means of transferring information between the design, construction and operation process, and is vital for the attainment of the holistic approach to landfilling.

3.9 When the site progresses to construction, the main design should be developed into a fully documented *construction design* with sufficient detail, specification and contract documentation to permit construction. The construction design should include comprehensive calculations to confirm or qualify the outline calculations and assumptions in the main design, but should not require significant changes in concept. The construction design is likely to be carried out on a number of occasions during the site's life, and should be periodically reviewed.

Design considerations

3.10 The overall approach to landfilling described in Chapter 1 is defined by three key elements

- the nature of the waste and prediction of the degradation processes

- site characteristics

- proposed afteruse.

3.11 These should be assessed applying a risk assessment approach at the beginning of the design process to establish a conceptual design and method of

---

[2] See paragraphs 5.26 to 5.28 and Figure 5.1.
[3] See WMP4 for guidance on the licensing of waste management facilities.
[4] See Chapter 2 and Appendix B.
[5] See paragraphs 8.19 to 8.21 for further details of the contents of the Site Manual.

operation for a particular site. For bioreactive wastes, the designer should examine the overall approach in accordance with the strategy set out in paragraph 1.30 and illustrated on Figure 1.1 and consider in order of priority

- whether stabilisation within a relatively short timescale can be predicted with confidence, and the site designed and operated fully as a process engineering activity for accelerated stabilisation

- whether accelerated stabilisation can be encouraged even where stabilisation within a generation cannot be predicted with confidence, because provision can be made for longer term passive controls

- where accelerated stabilisation is not feasible, whether a long term containment facility is environmentally acceptable.

3.12   In assessing the nature of the wastes and site characteristics, the designer should also consider whether attenuation or passive control measures will provide the required environmental protection for low reactivity wastes or for bioreactive wastes in a particular location. The environmental suitability of such control measures will have to be demonstrated by the risk assessment.

3.13   In determining the optimum approach, the designer will need to consider

i)   The prediction of degradation times under different circumstances, taking into account the physical constraints of the waste and how changes in waste composition due to waste minimisation and recycling will affect predictions.

ii)   The acceptability of release rates over the life of the site.

iii)   The potential mobilisation of residues should the landfill eventually become aerobic.

3.14   These considerations are discussed in turn in paragraphs 3.15 to 3.26 and apply to all sites. Additional details summarising the overall issues for developing the site design and operation as a process engineering activity for accelerated stabilisation are provided in Appendix D.

Prediction of waste degradation

3.15   **The landfill designer must clarify at the time of the design the nature of the wastes used to construct the landfill and give consideration to how these are likely to change over the active life of the landfill.** From this, the preparation works and operational methods should be designed appropriately.

> As wastes are progressively minimised, reused, recycled, processed and recovered, the characteristics of waste arriving at a landfill site may change. As it is not possible to predict at the outset the effect that these changes will have on wastes arriving at a particular site, periodic review of the design and operating methods should be carried out as the site is developed.

3.16   Typical untreated household waste is a highly heterogeneous material with variable permeability and water retention properties, which limit access for biodegradation by micro-organisms. The micro-organisms are active at the surfaces of the waste and rely on leachate movement for colonisation and for nutrient supply. The ability to achieve flushing of leachate uniformly throughout the waste is thus a key factor in the prediction of waste degradation rates.

3.17   The hydraulics of landfilled wastes are poorly characterised but often appear to be affected by short-circuiting and by barriers to flow[6]. There is a need for better knowledge of the hydraulic characteristics of wastes under different conditions and the development of engineered techniques for leachate recirculation at high rates in order for landfills to be operated effectively as flushing reactors.

> It seems likely that pre-treatment may be required (see Chapters 1 and 8) prior to landfilling to produce a more uniform waste mass, and placement of the waste carried out with an appropriate degree of compaction, in order to optimise permeability and achieve the required flushing rate.

3.18   Our knowledge of landfill processes will continue to improve with time, such that the potential burden on future generations due to the risk of our not achieving stabilisation within a generation will gradually reduce to less than the burden of long term maintenance. **At the present time we only have the knowledge of factors which might accelerate decomposition, but cannot predict with confidence, and supported by experience, how long it will then take.**

The concept of acceptable release rates

3.19   In the broadest terms, a landfill which fulfils the aims of sustainable development is one in equilibrium with its environment 30–50 years after cessation of filling. This implies that at certain levels of quality and flow rate, leachate and gas may be returned safely to the local environment. These rates will be determined by the risk assessment process.

3.20   Landfill design philosophy in the early 1990s had tended towards the objective of total containment and isolation of wastes. It is now recognised that this is unattainable and that it may be more responsible to design for controlled release than to attempt indefinite isolation, depending upon the nature of the wastes.

3.21   **All liner materials will allow the passage of liquids to an extent determined by their permeability.**   Risk assessment methodologies[7] can quantify the probability distribution for a derived seepage rate for a given liner/landfill situation. This should be used either to assess the probable impact on the receiving environment or to determine the performance specification for the liner and landfill operational methods. In this way an appropriate liner specification can be derived incorporating a suitable safety margin. Although the provision of any safety margin implies a degree of deliberate over-design, going beyond an appropriate degree of protection requires an unnecessary use of material resources. *Excessive* **over-engineering should be avoided as this can itself contravene the principles of sustainable development**.

3.22   Any landfill liner is part of a landfill's leachate management system. Systems may need to be designed for a range of seepage rates from very low (the best containment that can be achieved) to high (a controlled form of disperse and attenuate) depending on the degree of environmental protection needed at that

---

[6] Technical Overview of Co-disposal, Appendix A in WMP26F.

[7] A summary of a methodology for probabilistic risk assessment for landfill leachate migration is given in Appendix E. This methodology will be published in 1996. The methodology has been developed by the DoE in association with the NRA. It is intended to be simple to apply as a first pass for the early stages of design, with progression to more complex methods where detailed risk assessment is required.

site. Many guidance documents or statutory assessment methods use absolute terms such as total containment, prevention of leachate and landfill gas migration, or impermeable. These terms can lead to the belief that such concepts are achievable, and that failure to do so is indicative of poor materials or workmanship. Consideration of material properties demonstrates that, as all materials have a finite permeability, some finite seepage is inevitable.

> For example, the frequently quoted requirements for one metre of clay with a maximum permeability coefficient of 1×10^{-9} m/s and a maximum leachate head of 1m implies, using Darcy's law, a seepage rate of 1.7 m^3/d/ha, and yet it is commonly referred to as the provision of total containment. Actual flow rates are affected by a range of ameliorating and aggravating factors. A range of indicative seepage rates, for the purposes of illustration only, is shown in Figure 3.2. Calculation of actual seepage rates is complex and should be carried out using agreed risk assessment methodology.

> For gases, viscosity and diffusion characteristics must be taken into account. In general, natural clay liners[8] on their own are not usually effective barriers against gas migration, though they can be useful components of a multi-barrier system. Measurements of hydraulic conductivity are of little relevance as gas is able to pass through a barrier at a rate several orders of magnitude greater than that which may be measured for water.

3.23   The effects of changing conditions with time on the acceptability of a release is illustrated in Figure 3.3.

3.24   The EC Groundwater Directive prohibits the direct discharge of List I substances to groundwater and requires prior investigation before licensing List I disposals which might lead to indirect discharge. Licensing of potential direct and indirect discharges of List II substances must also be subject to prior investigation. In this it is recognised that landfill sites release leachate. The concept of acceptable seepage as described is not therefore in conflict with the Directive. For waste facilities the Directive is implemented by Regulation 15 of the Waste Management Licensing Regulations. The standards to apply for the discharge or disposal of List I and List II substances are set out in WMPs 4 and 26A and the circular accompanying the Waste Management Licensing Regulations[9]. The Commission has recently agreed with member states the information that is to be provided on the implementation of the directive. The first report is to be made in September 1996 and is to cover the three years 1993–1995. In order for the UK to comply with these requirements, WRAs should keep a record of the following

• all existing licences where Regulation 15(1)(a) or (d) of the Waste Management Licensing Regulations (1994) applies, together with the details of those licences, required in Regulation 15(6) or (7)

• all existing licences where Regulation 15(4)(a) applies, together with the location and the date of each licence

---

[8] See paragraphs 7.35 to 7.39 and Table 7.2 for use of natural clay liners.
[9] EC: Directive 80/68/EEC: *Council Directive of 17 December 1979 on the protection of groundwater against pollution from certain dangerous substances.* Official Journal of the European Communities L 020, January 1980. Waste Management Licensing Regulations 1994 and DoE Circular on Waste Management Licensing 11/94 (Scottish Office Circular 10/94, and Welsh Office Circular 26/94).

Figure 3.2 Typical comparative seepage rates

FOR ILLUSTRATION ONLY

*Calculation of actual seepages rates is complex and dependent upon many variables,
and should be carried out using an agreed risk assessment methodology (see text).*

A - Rates derived from theoretical studies (based on 1m head)

Case	Material	Thickness (metre)	Conductivity (metre/sec)	Defects	Seepage (l/ha/day)	Source
1	Clay	1	1×10^{-9}	None	1720	Darcy
2	Clay	1	1×10^{-8}	None	17200	Darcy
3	Clay	1	1×10^{-9}	1% of area at 1×10^{-6}	17200	Darcy
4	BES	0.3	1×10^{-10}	None	370	Darcy
5	GCL	0.006	1×10^{-12}	None	145	Darcy
6	HDPE	0.001*		None	3	Gross et al, 1990
7	HDPE	0.001*		5 x 3mm holes/ha	3000	Gross et al, 1990
8	HDPE over mineral	0.001* not stated	1×10^{-10}	5 x 3mm holes/ha	1	Gross et al, 1990
9	HDPE over mineral	0.001* not stated	1×10^{-8}	5 x 3mm holes/ha	30	Gross et al, 1990

* US reference: HDPE used in UK is more usually 2mm thick

B - Rates obtained by measurement

10	HDPE/mineral	CQA, 50% probability level	40	Aiken &
11	HDPE/mineral	No CQA, 50% probability level	75	Roberts, 1994

Notes:
1. Examples 1-9 are based on permeability alone.
2. HDPE is quoted for illustration only. Other materials may also be considered.

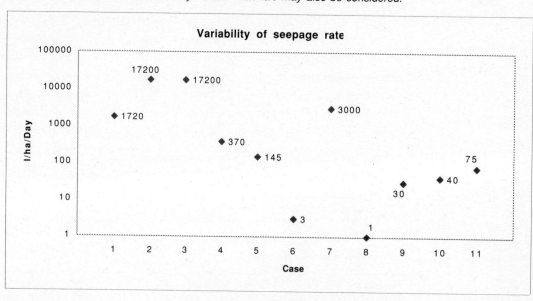

Figure 3.3 Accelerated stabilisation followed by residual low activity

A: Initially –

Highly active, accelerated decomposition
Landfill contained, leachate recirculated and treated
High quality capping
Very low seepage
Acceptable or no impact at monitoring and supply boreholes

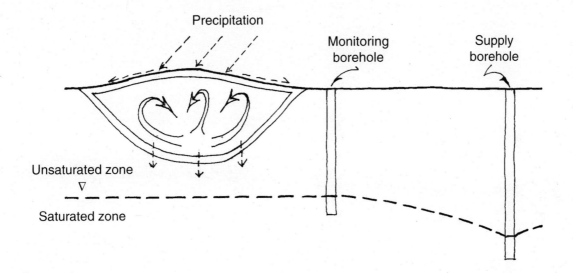

B: 50 years plus later –

Landfill decomposition rate low
Containment breached
Capping maintained intact
Low flow rate, low strength leachate
Acceptable or no impact at monitoring and supply borehole

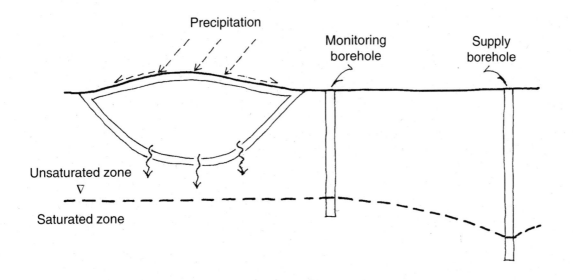

- the number of existing licences where Regulation 15(1)(b) applies.

3.25   In the NRA's Policy and Practice for the Protection of Groundwater[10], landfill acceptability is classified by type within zones of travel time to a water source and within resource protection areas. Landfills are defined as acceptable when subject to engineered containment and operational safeguards. If the nature of the waste and the hydrogeological conditions are such that the pollution control authorities in consultation with the WRA judge that its deposit does not pose an unacceptable threat to groundwater, then they may agree to a site being operated on non-containment principles. Acceptable operational safeguards must then be implemented.

Mobilisation of residue

3.26   When the rate of decomposition slows sufficiently, the rate of gas production may be insufficient to prevent the ingress of air to the main body of the waste. Eventually this could change the decomposition processes from anaerobic to aerobic[11]. The previously reducing conditions which maintained many contaminants in an insoluble state would then disappear, allowing for the mobilisation of many inorganic compounds. This would apply to all landfills containing bioreactive wastes. The designer should consider the possible effects of such a change in source term when carrying out the risk assessment for the site. However it is probable that the diffusion of air into a typical lined and capped modern landfill will be very slow, such that any release rates would be exceptionally slow.

Risk assessment

3.27   Landfill design has historically been based on a selection of design features from a menu of alternative measures to achieve an absolute goal. For example, containment has been perceived as an objective which can be achieved either absolutely, or to an equivalent degree, by one of a range of techniques according to availability of materials. It is now understood that all liners will allow some leakage. A probability distribution can be applied to each of the factors governing the rate of leakage for a given liner design, such that its probable leakage rate and consequent impact can be modelled.

3.28   The acceptability of a landfill design in the environment should therefore be assessed by a process which quantifies the probable impact, or the probability distribution of an impact, for each source term on each relevant receptor, that being the persons or features affected by it. This process is known as *risk assessment* and should be used in an iterative way to produce an acceptable design.

3.29   The process of risk assessment leading to an acceptable quantified impact and thereby to an appropriate design is outlined below. An example of a risk assessment process applied to a quantifiable element of the design, and the source/pathway/receptor relationship, are illustrated in Figure 3.4 and Table 3.1. The risk assessment process and a summary of a methodology with an illustration of its application to leachate seepage is given in Appendix E[12].

---

[10] NRA: *Policy and Practice for the Protection of Groundwater*. Bristol, National Rivers Authority, 1992. In Scotland, the *Groundwater Protection Strategy for Scotland* is the equivalent document.
[11] See Appendix C.
[12] Further general guidance on risk assessment is given in DoE (1995): *A Guide to Risk Assessment and Risk Management for Environmental Protection*, London, HMSO. ISBN 0 11 753091 3.

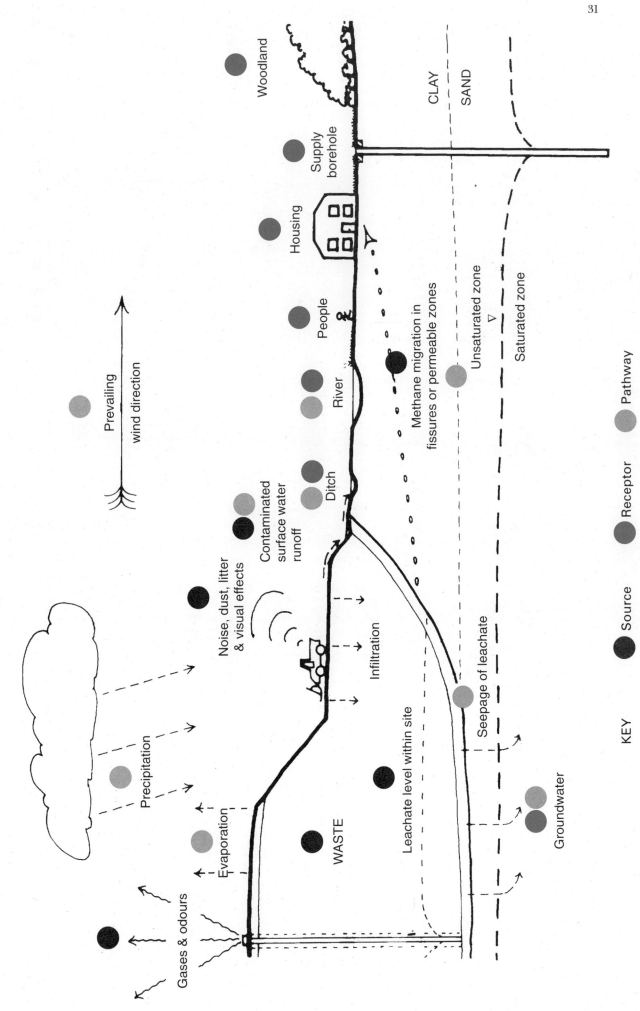

Figure 3.4 Environmental protection – illustrations of source/receptor/pathway

31

Prevailing wind direction

Woodland

Supply borehole

Housing

People

River

Ditch

Methane migration in fissures or permeable zones

Unsaturated zone

Saturated zone

CLAY

SAND

Contaminated surface water runoff

Noise, dust, litter & visual effects

Precipitation

Evaporation

Gases & odours

Infiltration

WASTE

Leachate level within site

Seepage of leachate

Groundwater

KEY

Source

Receptor

Pathway

32

Table 3.1

Example of a risk assessment approach for a quantifiable impact of landfilling

Potential impact	Water pollution
Source	Leachate
Receptor	Groundwater
Pathway	Leakage through liner system, movement through unsaturated zone and groundwater

Establish:

Sensitivity	Determine water quality objectives
Source term	Quality and volume of leachate

Evaluate

Relationship between landfill and receptor	Prediction of leakage rates against impact (using agreed methodology)
Adjust design accordingly	Improver liner quality Reduce leachate generation rate Reduce leachate head Improve leachate quality

3.30   The approach may be summarised as

- **identify all potential impacts**

- **for each potential impact identify the *source*, the *receptors* or *targets*, and the *pathway***

- **establish the source term** by geotechnical and other investigations

- **derive a relationship between the landfill and the receptor** using an agreed methodology and probability distribution for the source term and for each element of the pathway[13]

- **establish the sensitivity of the receptor** by consideration of background levels, statutory limits or policy

- **consider the impact on the receptor** and its acceptability

- **repeat this process to obtain a satisfactory design for the landfill** consistent with an acceptable impact.

3.31   **The process should be repeated iteratively** for each potential impact until both an acceptable overall impact and an appropriate design for environmental protection is produced. A risk assessment process should be applied to any quantifiable impact including, for example, leachate, landfill gas, traffic and noise, providing that the effects of mitigation can also be quantified.

---

[13] A summary of a methodology for probabilistic risk assessment for landfill leachate migration is given in Appendix E. This methodology will be published in 1996. The methodology has been developed by the DoE in association with the NRA. It is intended to be simple to apply as a first pass for the early stages of design, with progression to more complex methods where detailed risk assessment is required.

3.32   **The concept of derivation of design performance standards, through the use of probabilistic risk assessment to estimate an acceptable impact on the surrounding environment, underpins the approach to site design and operation described in this Paper.**

3.33   Inherent in the use of probability-based risk assessment is the possibility that improbable events might occur. Consideration should be given to possible responses to extreme events, and whether contingency measures need to be built-in from the start (for example, a leakage detection/interception system) or could be installed subsequently in sufficient time should the need arise (for example, a cut-off wall). This can be a practical option offering reduced initial costs, but may require acquisition and reservation of the necessary land.

3.34   For landfill extensions, the risk assessment must take into account the effect of the existing waste. In some instances more stringent controls may be required for the new area, whereas in others it may be appropriate to consider the impact of the site as a whole.

Design objectives   3.35   The design objectives must run consistently through the design, preparation, operation, restoration and aftercare stages of the construction of the landform. Designers must be clear about their objectives and should record their methods of achieving them for the design. This information should be incorporated in the Site Manual, as described in paragraphs 8.19 to 8.21, to enable the exchange of information from the designer to the operator[14].

3.36   Key objectives for all sites include

- environmental protection

- physical acceptability

- longevity

- appropriateness

- cost effectiveness.

These are discussed in paragraphs 3.37 to 3.54 below.

Environmental protection   3.37   A landfill should be designed in conjunction with its intended mode of operation and restoration to be acceptable in its environment. The requirements for environmental protection should be determined by risk assessment, the process of which is described in paragraphs 3.27 to 3.34.

Physical acceptability   3.38   Consideration must be given within the landfill design to the physical acceptability of a landfill in its surroundings. The factors to be considered in the development of the landform, whether a quarry infill or landraising, are listed in Table 3.2. These matters are considered by the planning authority in determining whether to grant planning permission for a proposed development[15].

---

[14] This is part of the holistic quality approach to landfills. See Chapters 4 and 8 for further details.
[15] See also paragraph 2.10.

Table 3.2

Considerations for physical acceptability

Factor	Considerations
Stability	Settlement or sliding within the foundation (subgrade) beneath the base or side wall liner
	Sliding within the liner system on base or side walls
	Sliding at the waste/liner interface
	Rotational failure within the waste, or through the whole cross-section
	Sliding failure of the cap or of its components
	See Chapters 6 and 7
Visual appearance and landscape	Setting of the site in its surroundings
	Impacts on views from sensitive locations
	Sympathy of the landform with its surroundings, particularly in terms of gradients, heights and overall form
	Appropriateness of the planting, in terms of the restoration soils, the afteruse, local climatic and ecological conditions, visual screening requirements, stability and access
	Use of CAD and DTM computer techniques, which can be of considerable assistance
	See Chapter 6 and WMP26E
Settlement	The difference in the landform between completion of filling and after settlement has occurred
	Predictions of settlement should be provided (see Chapter 6)
Maximum level	Planning policy guidance for the particular location
	Aircraft flight paths
Afteruse	Compatibility with performance criteria for engineering cap, particularly stability, gradients and drainage
	Suitability in the context of various other parameters, such as predicted settlement, gas evolution, and foundations

3.39   Sensitive landfill design incorporating a raised profile may lead to an improvement in the existing conditions, for example, where a site is poorly drained, has been used for mineral extraction, or is contaminated by former uses. For land currently in agricultural use or which is of ecological interest, both the existing quality and the feasibility of achieving an adequate standard for the intended afteruse should be assessed[16]. The site must be acceptable not only in relation to its former use, but also in the context of the surrounding land use, and must not be designed in isolation.

Landraising

3.40   Landraising can offer significant technical advantages for landfill design and operation[17]. Amongst the advantages of landraising are

- it can facilitate gravity drainage of leachate to the outside of the site

- leachate drainage systems can be made more accessible for inspection and maintenance outside the site

- it can be easier to provide a substantial thickness of unsaturated zone beneath the site

- sites can be chosen on their technical merits rather than by the location of former mineral workings

- a sudden change of depth (as in a quarry site) can be avoided, reducing problems due to differential edge settlement[18]

- gas migration control is facilitated

- poor surface drainage due to settlement beneath relatively flat restoration contours can be avoided

- it can be technically more straightforward, for example, landraising avoids problems of lining vertical quarry walls.

3.41   Potential disadvantages of landraising for accelerated stabilisation include possible difficulties in reaching high enough temperatures, air ingress control and gas emission control.

Other considerations

3.42   Land use planning considerations will initially influence the location and therefore the physical acceptability of a landfill. These include matters such as the relationship of the landfill to other development, the transport network and local population, and the effects on areas of acknowledged importance in the locality[19].

3.43   The presentation of the proposed landform should be managed sensitively. The planning, waste regulation, and pollution control authorities should be invited to comment on proposals and the presentation of a reasoned outline proposal may assist the progress of a development. **Whatever approval or encouragement is given by statutory authorities, the liability for a design remains with the landfill developer.**

Longevity

3.44   The whole process of landfill design, construction, operation, restoration,

---

[16] Restoration is discussed in WMP26E.
[17] Harris R C, Knox K and Walker N (1994): "A strategy for the development of sustainable landfill design and operation". 1994 Harwell Conference proceedings. Also in Proc IWM, January 1994, Vol 6. ISBN 0968-7068. See also NRA (1995): Position Statement on *Landfill and the Water Environment*.
[18] See paragraphs 10.21 to 10.24 and Figure 10.2.
[19] See PPG23 for further guidance (England). In Scotland, refer to NPPG on *Land for Waste Disposal* (Draft 1995).

aftercare and afteruse should be considered as a single entity, where proposed changes to any one part are considered in the context of the whole. This is particularly so in terms of the required life of each element of the construction. The overall considerations for design and operation as determined by the predicted rate of stabilisation will indicate whether the design features should last for decades or for centuries, and whether their function is static or dynamic.

> Where fluid flow or waste movement is to be accommodated, means should be provided to maintain, repair or replace the facilities for the duration of their intended service life. Where this period is long, consideration should be given to the possibility of replacement or the use of low or zero maintenance alternatives to avoid reliance on attention by future generations.

3.45   If materials are deemed to be required to last for very long periods, it may be difficult to be confident in the prediction of their serviceable life. Flexible synthetic membranes, for example, have only existed for some 50 years, and in their present form for even less. Extensive testing has, however, provided much information on the factors affecting their ageing, leading to the prediction by some that **if properly installed and protected** there is no reason why they should not last for 'hundreds of years'[20]. Nevertheless, manufacturers are reluctant to commit themselves to long term guarantees or warranty.

> It is never possible to be confident of a material's performance with time simply because it appears to have a long history of use. A thorough understanding of the material in the context of its intended use is essential.

3.46   **The landfill designer should consider the specified performance of all materials used in the landfill's construction over its anticipated life, and document those considerations for inclusion in the Site Manual.** Aspects to be considered include

- the location of materials within the landfill and susceptibility to changes in physical loads or chemical attack

- the effects of variations in operational or maintenance practice on landfill materials

- the manner and effects of deterioration in performance.

These considerations will necessarily be constrained by the limitations of knowledge at the time.

---

[20] Landreth R E (1990): "Service life of geomembranes in hazardous waste management facilities" in *Geosynthetics: Microstructure and Performance.* ASTM STP 1076, ed I Peggs, pp 26-33.

Table 3.3

Interrelationship between design and operation

Operational aspect	Design aspect affected
Waste reception	Site entrance, roads and tipping face
Type of plant	Haul roads; daily cover excavation and placement; direction of phasing
Traffic control/total vehicle movements	Site road layout; reception area capacity
Litter control	Edge bunds; daily cover; suitable thickness of liner protection to accept litter fencing; perimeter litter catchment areas; phasing of filling
Leachate management	Collection system; hydraulic head on liner; access for maintenance; need for treatment; direction of phasing; capping specification
Gas control	Installation of wells during or after waste emplacement; direction of phasing
Visual screening	Whether edge bunds are required; direction of phasing; size of phases; tree and shrub planting and protection of retained vegetation
Staffing	(Interacts with the above aspects)
Accelerated stabilisation (if adopted)	Waste processing/pretreatment facilities; access roads; waste emplacement; increased capacity of leachate collection system; capping design (including insulation); edge seals; ability to cope with rapid settlement; leachate recirculation system; gas collection system
Recycling/materials recovery	Site entrance, infrastructure; leachate and gas formation

Appropriateness

3.47 The landfill designer must ensure that each design is appropriate to the

- site location
- type of waste
- receptors at risk
- intended method of operation
- proposed restoration and afteruse.

3.48 The landfill designer should ensure that the design is suitable for the intended mode of operation of the landfill, and that the operation is organised to reflect the design. The Site Manual will record the intentions and assumptions of the designer, whilst feedback from the operator may amend the design[21]. The interrelationship between operational practices and the design is given in Table 3.3. Operational matters are discussed in Chapters 8 and 9.

[21] See Figure 3.1.

38

Cost-effectiveness

3.49   The designer should be aware of the cost of each element of the works and of the landform as a whole. This should include the costs of site assessment, operations, environmental control and monitoring, restoration and aftercare, as well as of the preparation and development works. Costs should be assessed in terms of the total costs, the costs expressed per tonne of waste, and costs against time over the history of the landfill.

>   Without a demonstration of the cost of a landfill project, and from that its cost-effectiveness, even the most technically advanced landfill design may remain just a design. Even if submission of costs is not required, failure to determine the financial viability of a project may lead to financial difficulties and environmental problems if funds run short before its completion.

3.50   A consistent basis for cost assessment should be defined to allow a valid comparison of alternative designs or design elements. Appendix F incorporates tables of overall costs applicable to landfill which provide a convenient method of assessment of each aspect of landfill costs[22].

3.51   In expressing costs as unit ($£/m^3$ or $£/t$) amounts it can be useful to extend this expression from a simple total to a calculation for each item. This will enable the effects of significant variable items to be rapidly assessed. Consideration should also be given to the distribution of development, restoration and aftercare costs across a landfill. In this way the cost for areas such as perimeter areas where the waste is particularly thin, or those areas requiring difficult engineering works, can be assessed and the site's boundaries and profile adjusted accordingly.

3.52   A financial model will be of value in comparing the cost-effectiveness of differing designs, for example, of liner and cap. Similar sensitivity analyses can be made of different parameters to assess their impact on profitability.

>   For example, two liners of equal performance in terms of environmental protection and durability might be of different thicknesses and costs. The thicker liner (for example, clay) may be of lower construction cost than the thinner liner (such as a multi-composite construction), but would occupy more airspace. The thicker liner may, however, be partially formed from materials excavated from elsewhere on-site, thereby releasing airspace not available were the thinner liner to be used. A financial appraisal may indicate which of these alternatives is overall the more cost-effective.

3.53   Any assessment of cost-effectiveness must take into account prevailing (and potential future) gate prices at alternative facilities. This in turn requires consideration of the location of the landfill and the costs of transport to it from the areas of waste origin, particularly where transport distances are significantly in excess of normal. Some of this information may be confidential and hard to obtain. In these circumstances appropriate estimates should be made.

---

[22] Reference should also be made to the current edition of standard civil engineering references which provide detailed current cost rates, for example Spon's Civil Engineering and Highway Works Price Book and Spon's Landscape and External Works Price Book, both published by E & F N Spon, London. Also current edition of CESMM3 Price Database, published by Thomas Telford Services Ltd, London.

3.54 Adequate provision must be made for post-closure aftercare, as referred to in WMP4. Consideration must be given to the investment requirement to yield an adequate annual sum in real terms for what is likely to be a considerable period.

3.55 An appraisal of cost-effectiveness can provide guidance on the value of initial investment compared with future aftercare costs, which will include insurance premiums. Examples include

> improving the liner specification to greater than that indicated by the risk assessment in return for lower premiums

> in the case of accelerated stabilisation, comparing the extra costs of waste processing and possible reductions in tonnage input with enhanced gas production and the potentially reduced costs of operation and period of aftercare.

Design standards

3.56 The design, construction, operation and restoration of a landfill as an engineering project requires the use of engineering standards. Because of the evolutionary nature of landfill design and the lack of historical models, absolute standards may not be available for all aspects of design. Standards therefore fall into the categories of

- absolute standards
- performance standards
- guidelines.

Absolute standards

3.57 Where quantification is possible, relevant British or International Standards published by recognised bodies should be used as appropriate in the design of landfills. Table 3.4 gives references for a number of different aspects. These standards may change over time and current standards should always be consulted.

Performance standards

3.58 In many aspects of landfill construction, advantage can be taken of contractors' experience and proprietary methods and equipment. In these circumstances, a **performance specification** (where the required output is specified together with minimum standards for materials and workmanship) may be appropriate, rather than conventional highly detailed design, drawings and bills of quantities.

> Examples of successful applications of performance standards include landfill gas equipment, cut-off walls, structural walls and leachate treatment control equipment.

3.59 The performance specification should be drawn up by designers experienced in the topic and who have carried out a conceptual or main design in some detail. The performance specification must be comprehensive enough to provide a complete construction with the features and long term performance required without unreasonably constraining the contractor's freedom.

3.60 The choice of specification type and form of contract may vary with each contract.[23] It will be influenced by many factors including

- the employer's preferences for certainty in price, willingness to pay for reduction in risk, and willingness to yield some control in design detail

---

[23] See paragraphs 4.10 to 4.15 and Table 4.2 for further details.

- • the degree of complexity of the appropriate design.

Guidelines 3.61   Where quantification is not possible, designers should document their reasons for design selection from reference sources current at the time of design. Table 3.5 gives examples of reference sources for some key elements of the design.

Table 3.4

Standards applicable to landfill design

Feature	Aspect	Standard	Comment
Earthworks	Stability/general	BS 6031 : 1981 Code of practice for earthworks	Earthworks should be designed by a geotechnical engineer based upon site specific information
	Foundation	BS 8004 : 1986 Code of practice for foundations	Method specification should be proven by trial testing
	Preparation	DTp manual of contract documents for highway works, Volume 1 : Specification for Highway Works Earthworks, Series 600	Suitable for subgrade preparation prior to liner construction (see also Chapter 7)
Pipe strength	Deflection	Dependent upon pipe material	Pipe strength calculations should be carried out to give a safety factor of 1.5 against unacceptable deformation, written confirmations of suitability shall be obtained from the pipe supplier/manufacturer
	Collapse	BS 8010 : — Code of practice for pipelines	
Structural	Steelwork	BS 5950: — Structural use of steelwork in building DD ENV 1993 : — Eurocode 3 : Design of steel structures	
	Reinforced and mass concrete	BS 5328 : — Concrete	
		BS 8110 : — Structural use of concrete DD ENV 1992 : — Eurocode 2 : Design of concrete structures	
	Brickwork	BS 5628 : — Code of practice for use of masonry	
Site investigation	Design and statistical interpretation	BS 5930 : 1981 Code of practice for site investigations	See also Chapter 5
		Site Investigation Steering Group - Site investigation in construction series, parts 1 to 4, Thomas Telford, London	
	Testing	BS 1377 : — Methods of test for soils for civil engineering purposes	
Geotextiles	Testing	BS 6906 : — Methods of test for geotextiles	

Notes: 1. *Different standards may apply in Scotland, and the equivalent should be sought.*
  2. *Reference should always be made to current standards and editions.*

Table 3.5

Guidelines on standards for landfill design

Feature	Aspect	Guidelines	Comment
Leachate collection	Pipework	NWWDO 1991[1]	NWWDO is a useful collation of other references but is not a recommendation in itself
	Blankets	NRA 1995[2]	
	Base slope		
	Manholes		
Settlement of waste	Rate and duration	Wallis 1991[3]	Check against current practice (see Chapter 6)
Stress cracking of liners	Material degradation	Peggs et al 1990[4]	
Membrane protection materials	Adequacy		German guidelines due for publication 1995
Leachate composition	Waste types and leachate quality	NWWDO 1991[1] DoE leachate review[5] NRA consent limits	
Landfill engineering	General	DoE : GGP[6] NWWRO 1995[7]	In press 1995
	Liners	NWWRO 1995[7] NRA 1995[8]	

Notes: 1. *Different guidelines may apply in Scotland, and the equivalent should be sought.*

   2. *Reference should always be made to current guidelines and editions.*

1   NWWDO (1991): *Leachate Management Report.* Lancashire Waste Disposal Authority, Preston. (98 pp inc Appendices).

2   NRA (1995): *Leachate Management.* Internal Guidance Note No 8.

3   Wallis, S (1991): Factors affecting settlement at landfill sites. *The Planning and Engineering of Landfills,* Midland Geotechnical Society, 1991, pp 183-186.

4   Peggs I D, Carlson D S and Peggs S J (1990): *Understanding and preventing shattering failures of polyethylene geomembranes.* Proceedings of the 4th International Conference on Geotextiles, Geomembranes and Related Products. A A Balkema Rotterdam, Vol 2, p 549.

5   DoE: *A Review of the Composition of Leachates from Domestic Wastes in Landfill Sites.* DoE Research Report No CWM 072/94 (in preparation 1995).

6   DoE: *Guidance on Good Practice for Landfill Engineering.* DoE Research Report No CWM 106/94 (in press 1995).

7   NWWRO Technical Sub-group (1995): *Pollution Control Objectives for Landfill Design, Development and Operation.* Available from North West Waste Regulation Officers.

8   NRA (1994): *Landfill Liners.* Internal Guidance Note No 7.

4 Quality and Contracts

Introduction

4.1   A quality approach is vital to the successful implementation of a landfill development. The site selection, design, construction, operation, restoration and aftercare stages are an integrated and comprehensive process that requires clear direction and effective management. Achieving quality requires the understanding and involvement of everyone. One of the essential elements of a quality approach is effective contract management.

Purpose and scope of this chapter

4.2   This chapter explains the basis of a quality approach and provides guidance on

- the objectives and general principles of a quality approach to landfill design, construction and operation

- contractual arrangements, including the parties involved and types of contract

- construction quality assurance (CQA).

The quality approach

Definitions

4.3   The following terms are used in this chapter[1]

Quality	the totality of features and characteristics of a product or service that bear on its ability to satisfy stated or implied needs
Quality assurance	all those planned and systematic actions necessary to provide adequate confidence that a product or service will satisfy given requirements for quality
Quality control	the operational techniques and activities that are used to fulfil requirements for quality.

Objectives of a quality approach

4.4   As shown in the definitions above, the main objective of a quality approach is *to give confidence* that a product or service will satisfy defined requirements for quality. Another objective should also be *'getting it right first time, and every time'*, in order that economic benefits can be gained through improved efficiency of working methods and communications, and to achieve completion on time and to budget.

4.5   **The quality approach should not be considered as an absolute guarantee of quality (for example, that there will be no faults in a liner) but, when applied specifically to landfill developments, should give confidence that the following requirements are met**

- The landfill design is competent and of a high standard, conforming to the objectives set out in Chapter 3.

- Effective mechanisms are in place to ensure that construction and operation will not fail the design.

- The approach and actions undertaken, at each stage of the development, are well documented for the purposes of regulation, insurance and legal liability.

---

[1] BS 4778 : Part 1 : 1987 (1993) : Quality vocabulary - international terms; also ISO 8402 : 1986: Quality - vocabulary.

> The keeping of auditable records will also assist learning and future improvements in landfill techniques.

• The public can be assured about the acceptability of landfilling throughout design, construction, operation, restoration and aftercare.

Principles of a quality approach

4.6   The principles of a quality approach are embodied in a series of British Standards on quality systems[2]. Guidance notes on quality assurance are also produced by various professional and trade organisations[3]. It is not mandatory for companies involved in landfill developments to become registered but these standards provide a comprehensive model for the development of a quality approach to landfill.

4.7   The quality approach should be applied to the entire process of landfill development. The principles of the quality approach are similar for each stage of the development and include the following

• Requirements must be adequately defined, documented and agreed.

> The requirements of the design team should be agreed in the client contract.

> The requirements of the construction phase should be well defined in the contract documents (see section on contractual arrangements below). These must also reflect agreed requirements in conditions attached to planning permission for the development.

> Statutory requirements for the control of operations include the waste management licence and the working plan. These, and associated documentation incorporated in the Site Manual[4], will give comprehensive guidance on the operational requirements.

• Personnel should have the appropriate skills, expertise and qualifications.

> At the design phase, the principal qualifications are those of the chartered engineer, as the development is essentially an engineering project. However, designing a landfill involves a multi-disciplinary approach and planners, geotechnical engineers, geologists, hydrogeologists, landscape architects, soil scientists, ecologists, chemists, leachate treatment and waste disposal specialists should also contribute to the design process.

> Training is available to update the landfill operator on procedures, legislation, methods and technology. These include WAMITAB

---

[2] The British Standards for quality assurance are the BS EN ISO 9000 series (formerly BS 5750). Designers can be registered to BS EN ISO 9001:1994 and contractors to BS EN ISO 9002:1994. Registration is carried out by a NACCB (National Accreditation Council for Certification Bodies) accredited body.

[3] The Association of Consulting Engineers has produced a quality assurance guidance note which includes a draft quality manual and a draft project quality plan (ACE QA Guidance Note 1993). The Construction Industry Research and Information Association (CIRIA) have produced a series of special publications giving guidance on quality systems for the construction industry.

[4] See paragraphs 8.19 to 8.21.

courses leading to certificates of technical competence[5] and other courses such as those organised by the National Association of Waste Disposal Contractors (NAWDC) and Institute of Wastes Management (IWM)[6].

- Communication channels should be agreed and procedures established to ensure that information is circulated.

  > The Site Manual[7] is an effective vehicle for the transfer of information from the design team, to the contractors and finally to the operators and should be maintained for every site. Operators should be instructed on the implications of their actions (or inactions) upon the landfill, for example, accidental damage to the liner.

  > The accumulated experience of operators should also be fed back to the designers and contractors as part of the holistic approach to landfill design, construction and operation.

- Recognised standards, procedures, methodologies and proven techniques should be applied. Procedures should be documented, regularly reviewed and implemented.

  > Guidance on standards for specific aspects of landfill design, construction and operation is provided on a topic basis throughout this Paper.

- Actions should be planned, documented and communicated to all involved.

  > This is best achieved in the form of a project quality plan which describes the 'who, what, where, why, when and how' of each planned action.

- Records should be kept at an appropriate level of detail to monitor the implementation and results of the planned actions.

  > The Waste Management Licensing Regulations 1994 make record keeping mandatory. The records that the operator is required to keep are defined by the WRA in the waste management licence. Planning conditions may further require records to be kept of particular actions and data. An operator should also consider recording additional relevant information. Chapter 8 gives further guidance.

- Inspection, measuring and test equipment should be well maintained and where appropriate calibrated.

---

[5] Under the Waste Management Licensing Regulations 1994, the site must be managed by someone who is technically competent. The Waste Management Industry Training and Advisory Board (WAMITAB) issues a range of certificates for the managers of most types of waste management sites and a person who has a full WAMITAB certificate for the type of site is technically competent under the Regulations.

[6] The Institute of Wastes Management, 9 Saxon Court, St Peter's Gardens, Northampton NN1 1SX organise a series of courses covering subjects such as landfill, site licensing, landfill gas monitoring and duty of care.

[7] See paragraphs 8.19 to 8.21.

> This includes computer software, surveying, investigation and monitoring equipment.

- Checking and review of outputs should be undertaken to ensure adherence to planned actions and requirements.

> This should be a clearly defined responsibility of a member or members of the design team and adequate time allowed for in the project programme (part of the quality plan).

- Independent verification may be required to ensure that the outputs meet the requirements.

> Designs should be comprehensively checked and verified by competent persons, independent of the design team. This may be in-house or external to the company preparing the design.

> Independent verification of the construction stage should be carried out as part of Construction Quality Assurance (CQA)[8].

Management of health and safety

4.8   The quality approach to landfill development will require the effective management of health and safety throughout the design, construction, operation and restoration of the site. In approaching landfill as an engineering project to build a desired landform using waste materials, the parties involved should where appropriate comply with the Construction (Design and Management) Regulations 1994[9]. These Regulations place formal health and safety obligations on all parties within the building process and include the appointment of a *planning supervisor*. The planning supervisor is responsible for co-ordinating the health and safety aspects of the project. In accordance with the Regulations, a satisfactory health and safety plan should be provided prior to the commencement of construction, and a health and safety file prepared. These documents should form part of the comprehensive information within the Site Manual.

Contractual arrangements

The parties involved

4.9   The parties involved in the design, construction and operation of a landfill may be categorised according to their role in the process. Table 4.1 lists these parties and their responsibilities, and gives guidance on considerations for contract management. Their titles may vary from those listed in Table 4.1, but their roles, which have a formal basis in a contractual sense, should not significantly change.

---

[8] See paragraphs 4.16-4.19.

[9] DoE: *The Construction (Design and Management) Regulations 1994.* SI 1994 No 3140. For further information, the reader should consult the HSE document Approved Code of Practice L54, Managing Construction for Health and Safety (1995).

Table 4.1

Parties involved in contract management		
Title	**Responsibility/function**	**Considerations**
Employer (owner/ landfill operator) who may be an individual or a corporate body	Requires the facility to be designed and constructed	A large company acting as the employer may encompass, in-house, some of the other roles given below (for example designer, contractor, project manager, engineer) Smaller companies will tend to enter into contracts with other parties to provide the design and construction services
Designer	Design of the landfill to fulfil the design objectives and considerations described in Chapter 3	A single design company can integrate all elements of the landfill The designer should have adequate experience of the work in question The designer may sub-contract or prepare performance specifications for specialist elements of the works The designer should operate quality assurance to a recognised standard
Contractor(s)	Construction of the works to the design	May also be the designer in design and construct forms of contract The Employer may award a single contract for the construction, with the main contractor engaging sub-contractors, nominated sub-contractors, suppliers, designers, and quality engineers as appropriate Alternatively a series of contracts may be awarded, though the use of several different contractors on-site at any one time should be avoided to limit the division of responsibilities
Project manager/ engineer who may be an individual or a company	Management and supervision of the works	Depends on the type of contract arrangement Could also be the designer or the quality engineer
Quality engineer	Independent certification of CQA	Should be engaged by the employer, not the contractor for the construction Independence is a key factor Should be a chartered engineer (or engineering company with chartered engineers) with experience of the type of work being constructed
Regulators	Checking that the landfill is constructed in accordance with the conditions of any permissions, licences, consents and other legal obligations	Include the following: Planning authority Waste regulatory body NRA/RPA HMIP/HMIPI EHOs Building inspectors HSE

4.10   Employers' options for types of contract for landfill design, construction and operation include

- in-house management

- construct only contracts

- design and construct contracts

- design, construct and operate contracts

- management contracts.

The first three options are illustrated in the flowchart in Figure 4.1. Design, construct and operate contracts and management contracts may be organised in a number of ways between the employer and different contractors for the design, construction and operation elements of the process. In all cases, the quality engineer should be independent of the design and construction teams[10].

4.11   The choice of contract and model conditions should depend upon an assessment by the employer (or designer or project manager) of technical, economic and contractual factors. Some merits and typical applications for the various model conditions are given in Table 4.2, which gives guidance on industry model conditions of contract that an employer may consider for the above types of contract. This table is provided for information and is not exhaustive. In particular

> site investigation model conditions are not included, these are discussed in Chapter 5

> the model forms listed are for projects funded by the employer, special contract conditions may be required for joint venture contracts

> there are no model conditions for design, construct and operate contracts, although the model conditions listed in Table 4.2 may be extended for operations

> there are no model conditions for management contracts where the employer engages a contractor to manage the works and the contractor employs other contractors and consultants to design and construct the works, for which he is paid a fee.

4.12   In addition to the conditions of contract for construction, there should be agreed conditions of engagement for the designer, project manager/engineer, and quality engineer. Typically, these are the parties' standard terms of work or the Association of Consulting Engineers conditions of engagement.

4.13   The employer should be aware of the basis for liability of the designer and the contractor. The test for liability for the designer is one of having taken all *'reasonable care and skill'* in the performance of the design task. The test of liability for the contractor for construction is to provide the works that are reasonably *'fit for the purpose intended'*.

---

[10] See also paragraph 4.16.

Figure 4.1   Types of contract

In-house management

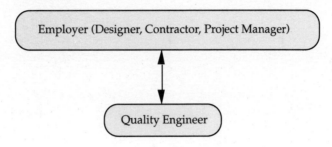

Construct only contracts *(for example ICE 6th edition)*

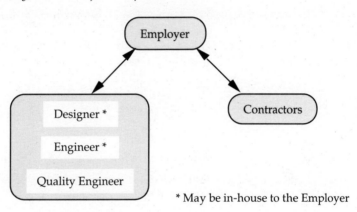

* May be in-house to the Employer

Design and construct contracts *(for example ICE New Engineering Contract)*

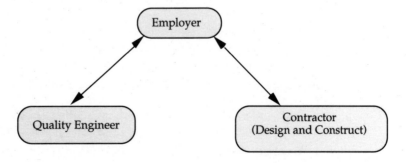

Table 4.2

Conditions of contract

Model conditions of contract	Type of contract	Merits	Method of payment	Applications
ICE, 6th Edition	Construct (does have design clauses, but not widely used for design)	Technically suited to most landfill works Familiar to the construction industry Proven and tested Requires an impartial engineer	Priced contract (admeasurement) with cost reimbursable element (dayworks)	General civil engineering works with employer-contractor-engineer relationship
ICE, Conditions of Contract for Minor Works	Construct Maintenance/service contracts	Suitable for low risk, low value (<£100 000) works Simplified conditions Requires an impartial engineer	Priced contract (admeasurement, lump sum) Cost reimbursable	Low risk, low value contract work of straightforward nature
ICE, Design and Construct	Design and construct	Optimises use of contractors' knowledge in design May provide cost savings May reduce period to completion of works Simplified responsibilities and relationships	Priced contract Target contract Cost reimbursable	General and specialist engineering works where the employer requires integrated design and construction

Table 4.2 *continued*

Model conditions of contract	Type of contract	Merits	Method of payment	Applications
ICE, New Engineering Contract	Construct Design and construct Management contracts	Flexible Suitable for multidiscipline projects Written in simple language Designed for co-operation between the parties, rather than adversary	Priced contract Target contract Cost reimbursable	Management oriented system of contract conditions which may be selected for any size of project and combination of disciplines
I Chem E, Conditions of Contract for Process Plant - Lump Sum	Design and construct	Flexible Performance based, with requirement for 'fitness for purpose' Handles complex contractual interfaces Suitable for multidiscipline projects Fast programme	Priced contract Target contract	Projects involving processes with performance requirements, for example treatment works
I Chem E, Conditions of Contract for Process Plant - Reimbursable Contracts	Design and construct	Flexible Suitable for wide range of projects	Cost reimbursable (target cost)	Projects with high degree of uncertainty, such as remedial works and fast track projects
Institutions of Electrical and Mechanical Engineers, Model Forms	Design and construct	Performance based, with requirement for 'fitness for purpose'	Priced contract Target contract Cost reimbursable	For the supply of mechanical and electrical plant

4.14   The employer should ensure that

- the designer, project manager/engineer, and quality engineer have appropriate professional indemnity insurance

- any contractors have an appropriate level of insurance for the works, and for third parties.

4.15   It is increasingly unlikely that the designers or contractors will be able to arrange insurance to cover the cost of any long term environmental damage.

Construction quality assurance

4.16   Construction quality assurance (CQA) is applicable specifically to construction activities and is an essential tool for the assurance of quality in landfill developments. CQA should be certified by an independent quality engineer.

- The independent quality engineer should be either

  > an independent third party quality assurance company
  > **or**

  > a resident chartered engineer with appropriate geotechnical experience[11] who is independent from the contractor carrying out the works and who is working to an approved design and specification.

  > In either case, the independent quality engineer should be acceptable to the waste regulatory body.

4.17   The CQA Certificate should state that the works have been constructed in accordance with the CQA plan and comply with the design[12]. Table 4.3 lists the headers of a typical CQA plan for a geomembrane liner.

4.18   Whatever the level of involvement, it is important that the quality engineer liaises with the contractor and takes a proactive approach by seeking to identify potential problems before they arise. The quality engineer should contribute positively to the maximum achievable quality within the framework of the design. **A reactive adversarial approach is not in keeping with the principles of quality management.**

4.19   Where CQA is undertaken by the contractor and audited by the independent quality engineer, it is important that

- the contractor is involved in the project as early as possible (design and construct contracts)

- the CQA offered is not just checking procedures (quality control)

- the contractor's quality plan is available at the start of the contract.

4.20   The cost of quality assurance should be incorporated into the overall landfill development costs[13].

---

[11] Appropriate experience might be regarded as a minimum of 3 years experience in the field of landfill engineering, specifically the installation of clay liners and flexible membrane liners.

[12] Note that independent certification of *designers* is not usual.

[13] For CQA for liner systems, typically 2.5 to 5% of the construction cost of the liner system is often quoted.

Table 4.3

Typical headers for a CQA plan for a geomembrane liner

Introduction

Definitions

Parties and responsibilities

Duties of CQA manager

Geomembrane materials

- manufacture
- conformance
- delivery
- storage

Protective layer materials

- manufacture
- conformance
- delivery
- storage

Geomembrane installation

- earthworks
- geomembrane placement
- field seaming
- defects and repairs
- anchor trenches
- materials in contact with HDPE
- protection of geomembrane

Documentation

- site
- final report

54

Summary

4.21   A quality approach should be adopted for all aspects of the landfill development. Quality assurance incorporating procedures for design and CQA for construction should be applied to the design and construction of all engineered works.

4.22   Site specific *quality plans* should be drawn up for design, construction and operation of the landfill. The quality plan should

>   describe the objectives

>   provide definitions of terms

>   define the parties to the plan, their roles and communication procedures

>   specify quality procedures.

4.23   Mechanisms should be agreed and implemented for the transfer of information between the designer, the engineer and the operator. This should include

>   records in the form of a Site Manual, which documents all the aspects of the site development.

>   consideration of the contractual arrangements for the landfill project.

4.24   The cost of a quality approach should be considered in the overall budget for landfill development.

5 Site Investigation

Introduction

5.1   A site investigation is required to provide the information and data necessary to design an acceptable landfill and monitoring system[1] for a particular site. As indicated in Chapter 2, this information is also required by the planning, waste regulation and other statutory authorities in order to assess the potential effects of the development proposals on the environment before necessary consents can be issued. Under the Groundwater Directive, a site investigation must be carried out before a discharge of a List II substance direct to groundwater is permitted, or disposal of a List I or List II substance that may lead to the indirect discharge of that substance to groundwater is permitted[2].

5.2   Many landfill proposals will fall within the scope of developments requiring an environmental assessment (EA) before planning can be determined[3]. Investigations must fulfil all of the requirements of a formal EA in such cases, including not only the geological, hydrogeological and hydrological issues, but also the assessment of the traffic implications of a proposed development, amenity aspects, ecology, soils, agriculture, landscape and cultural heritage. Comprehensive guidance on all these aspects is not within the scope of this Paper, although the principles of data collection, collation, appraisal and monitoring described in this chapter are applicable to each of these elements in the design and EA process. Further guidance in relation to assessments for restoration is given in WMP26E and for monitoring in WMP26D.

5.3   This chapter describes the organisation and process of site investigation as it relates to the geological and hydrogeological controls on emissions of leachate and gas from the site and the geotechnical, engineering, hydrological and hydrogeological aspects of the landfill design. The chapter is arranged in the following order

- objectives of site investigation (paragraphs 5.6 to 5.7)

- scope of investigations, including the details to be provided and the scale and extent of investigations (paragraphs 5.8 to 5.11)

- organisation of site investigation (paragraphs 5.12 to 5.14)

- overall approach including the initial appraisal, field investigations and monitoring (paragraphs 5.15 to 5.35)

- requirements and standards for site investigation work, including legislative requirements, quality and contractual issues, specifications, supervision and safety (paragraphs 5.36 to 5.43).

---

[1] For a more detailed account of monitoring, the reader should refer to WMP26D (in preparation 1995) which incorporates monitoring to assess the potential environmental impacts of groundwater and surface water pollution, landfill gas migration, noise, dust and odour.

[2] EC: Directive 80/68/EEC: *Council Directive of 17 December 1979 on the protection of groundwater against pollution from certain dangerous substances.* Official Journal of the European Communities L 020, January 1980. Implemented in respect of discharge of substances to groundwater from landfills by Waste Management Licensing Regulations 1994. See also DoE Circular on Waste Management Licensing 11/94 (Scottish Office Circular 10/94, and Welsh Office Circular 26/94).

[3] See Appendix B for further explanation.

5.4   The chapter concentrates on the requirements for site investigation for a site and does not include guidance on the information for site selection or assessment of alternative sites, which should be part of an initial feasibility study for landfill development.

Requirements of the statutory authorities

5.5   The general site investigation requirements to satisfy the planning authority in respect of planning permission and the waste regulatory body in respect of waste management licensing are similar, although different levels of detail will be appropriate in each case[4].

> The planning authority is concerned with environmental matters as they relate to land use. The planning application must be able to demonstrate that the development is feasible, and sufficient site investigation is required to provide assurance regarding statements on potential environmental impacts.

> The waste regulatory body, in consultation with the NRA (RPA Scotland) must be satisfied that the site will neither endanger human health nor cause harm to the environment. This may require more detailed site investigation information than that required at the planning stage. The waste regulatory body will be primarily responsible for using the information provided from the site investigation to assess the risk of pollution from a particular site.

Objectives of site investigation

5.6   The objectives of site investigation are to identify and provide sufficient information

- to establish that the site is suitable for its intended purpose
- to establish baseline conditions for the site
- to enable an assessment of the impact of the development on human health and the environment
- to enable a monitoring programme for the environmental impacts from the release of gas and leachate to be developed and implemented
- for the engineering design of the site.

5.7   It must also be sufficiently detailed to allow the design of measures to mitigate any adverse impacts.

Scope of investigations

5.8   An adequate appraisal of the soil, geological, hydrogeological and hydrological conditions at the site will be necessary and should provide details of the following

- extent of any historical mining or quarrying at the site
- extent of any contamination resulting from historical uses of the site
- presence/absence of topsoil and subsoil capable of supporting plant growth and its quantity, type and spatial distribution for use in restoration
- presence/absence and spatial distribution of other superficial drift deposits and their suitability for use as cover and as an engineering material

---

[4] See Planning Policy Guidance Note PPG23 (England). In Scotland, advice is given in the NPPG on Land for Waste Disposal (Draft 1994).

- depth to, and nature of, the strata underlying drift deposits

- depth and characteristics of the unsaturated zone and variations in the water table including long term trends and identification of any confined or perched water-bearing strata

- groundwater flow and quality

- geotechnical properties of materials at the site in order to assess foundation conditions

- geotechnical and hydraulic properties of materials at the site or to be imported (for example clay) in order to assess suitability for use in landfill earthworks and slope stability

- flow rate and quality data for surface streams, springs and areas of standing water

- background soil gas concentrations, taking into account possible sources of soil gas

- potential flowpaths for leachate and gas.

5.9   The scale and extent of the investigations will relate to the size and nature of the proposed landfill (types of waste), the complexity and sensitivity of the geological and hydrogeological environment, and the proximity of potential receptors which may be affected. Since knowledge of many of these aspects will only be revealed as the investigation unfolds, any investigation should be phased with clear identifiable objectives and should be reappraised during and between each phase.

5.10   This Paper does not give guidance on the minimum requirements of an investigation. The minimum requirements for site investigation are project specific, but should be sufficient for the information required at the particular stage of the design, construction or operation of a site[5]. If employing statistical methods in assessment, the minimum requirements for site investigation will need to be adequate to demonstrate the statistical validity of the findings. The use of statistical methods is dealt with in more detail in WMP26D.

5.11   **The requirements of the planning authority and the pollution control authorities should be an integral part of the site investigation strategy and as such consultation at the earliest stage should be undertaken[6].**

Organisation of site investigation

5.12   An overall strategy with clear objectives should be developed before commencing site investigation to ensure that it is efficient, comprehensive and cost-effective. There is generally a need for a multidisciplinary team and, where the site investigation forms part of an EA, skill areas will be required to cover all aspects of the local environment. The range of specialisms and skill areas for landfill site investigations is given in Table 5.1.

5.13   The multidisciplinary design team will determine the scope of the investigation to meet the needs of the particular project.

[5] The design process may be divided into *conceptual, main* and *construction* stages as described in Chapter 3.
[6] See paragraph 2.8 and Table 2.2.

Table 5.1

Specialisms and skill areas for site investigation

Specialism	Skill area
Acoustician	Baseline noise assessment and prediction
Archaeologist	Archaeological survey and interpretation
Chemist/geochemist	Waste/rock/materials compatibility
Ecologist	Vegetation mapping, habitat surveys, flora and fauna surveys, assessment of nature conservation interest
Engineer (landfill)	Drainage works, site structures, site construction methods and risk assessment
Geologist	3-D geological mapping, stratigraphy and mineralogy
Geotechnical engineer/engineering geologist	Strength of materials, foundation design, slope stability, risk assessment
Hydrogeologist	Groundwater flow directions, hydraulic and contaminant plume modelling, monitoring, risk assessment, statistical methods
Hydrologist	Surface water assessment, catchment modelling, drainage and water quality assessment
Land surveyor	Topographic survey and digital terrain model preparation
Landscape architect	Landscape and visual assessment, landform design, restoration and afteruse requirements
Planner	Overall planning and environmental issues
Public health engineer	Airborne emissions, monitoring systems, risk assessment
Soil scientist	Materials handling and assessment of suitability for restoration
Traffic engineer	Highways and traffic assessment, access and road design
Water treatment engineer	Design of leachate treatment systems

Figure 5.1 The site investigation process

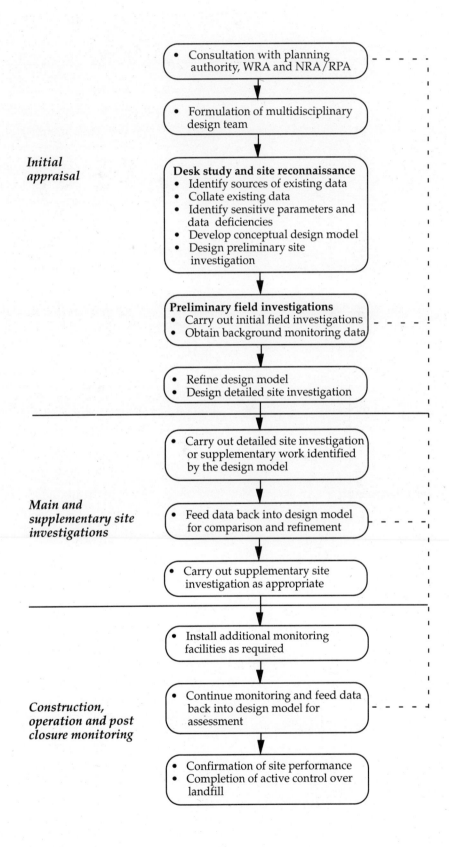

Initial appraisal

- Consultation with planning authority, WRA and NRA/RPA

- Formulation of multidisciplinary design team

Desk study and site reconnaissance
- Identify sources of existing data
- Collate existing data
- Identify sensitive parameters and data deficiencies
- Develop conceptual design model
- Design preliminary site investigation

Preliminary field investigations
- Carry out initial field investigations
- Obtain background monitoring data

- Refine design model
- Design detailed site investigation

Main and supplementary site investigations

- Carry out detailed site investigation or supplementary work identified by the design model

- Feed data back into design model for comparison and refinement

- Carry out supplementary site investigation as appropriate

Construction, operation and post closure monitoring

- Install additional monitoring facilities as required

- Continue monitoring and feed data back into design model for assessment

- Confirmation of site performance
- Completion of active control over landfill

5.14   A wide range of techniques is available for site investigation and the choice of techniques to be used should be made by the design team to meet the needs of the proposed development. General guidance on a number of more commonly used techniques is given in Appendix G. The reader should also refer to BS 5930: Code of Practice for Site Investigation[7].

Approach

5.15   It is recommended that all site investigation studies are undertaken in a phased approach as illustrated in Figure 5.1. This can be related to the stages in the design process described in paragraphs 3.5 to 3.9 as follows

- An *initial appraisal* is required to formulate a *conceptual design* model for the landfill, determine any fundamental constraints and items of major expenditure, design the main field investigations and determine the needs of the subsequent phases. These needs should relate both to the assessment of risk and the design of mitigating measures (for example liners, capping and gas and leachate control measures). This is undertaken at the *conceptual* stage of the design.

- The *main site investigation* incorporates detailed site investigation field work to refine the design model. The site investigation information will need to be in sufficient detail to enable a fully reasoned design for the construction, operation and monitoring of the site to be prepared, in accordance with the requirements of planning and waste management licensing authorities.

- *Supplementary site investigations* may be required at either the *main* or *construction* stages of the design to further refine the design model and monitoring programme, to provide detailed information to confirm or qualify calculations, and to satisfy the regulatory authorities with respect to environmental protection. Guidance on the monitoring of the landfill to provide a measure of performance of the site design is given in WMP26D.

Initial appraisal

5.16   The initial appraisal is divided into three stages; desk study and site reconnaissance; preliminary field investigation to obtain background monitoring data and provide basic data on which to assess landfill viability; and design of field work.

Desk study and site reconnaissance

5.17   The desk study should include[8]

- site history and previous uses including details of any existing licences or permissions and historical map data

- aerial photograph interpretation

- existing site investigation data

- examination of geological records

- evidence of voids, natural and artificial

- hydrological and hydrogeological data

---

[7] Additional guidance is given in the Site Investigation in Construction Series, Volumes 1 to 4, prepared by the Site Investigation Steering Group and published by Thomas Telford, London.
[8] Refer to BS 5930 : 1981 : Code of Practice for Site Investigations, and Appendices A to C for further details of the information required for desk studies and site reconnaissance.

- meteorological data.

Data collection and collation should also take account of the requirements for restoration design described in WMP26E.

5.18   Any study must include not only the site but also surrounding areas, as these will influence and be influenced by the landfill[9]. The extent of the study will be determined by the particular circumstances of the site and proposed development, and will emerge as part of the initial appraisal programme. At the fieldwork stage legal difficulties may impede access to these surrounding areas and this problem must be balanced against the sensitivity of the risk assessment to the desired investigation data.

5.19   The use of aerial survey can provide cost-effective information to facilitate site planning and design. Aerial photographs provide a useful means for communicating the context of the site and recording development throughout its life.

5.20   A site reconnaissance visit should be undertaken to provide both a visual confirmation of the desk study findings, and to confirm the scale of the site and any potential problems. Again it should extend beyond the immediate site boundaries if access permits.

Preliminary field investigations

5.21   Field investigations carried out as part of the initial appraisal should contain a limited number of exploratory boreholes, trial pits or probes (for example, static cone or dynamic ranging rods are useful in peat deposits) to confirm the findings of the desk study and provide sufficient information to define the conceptual design model and background monitoring requirements[10]. In practice, initial field investigations may be combined with the main site investigation if extensive data exists, or if there are time, cost or access constraints.

5.22   Good quality photographs should be taken at this stage for reference during the design work, and to provide evidence of the condition of the site and its environs before construction works commence.

Design of fieldwork

5.23   The desk study and site reconnaissance will enable the conceptual design model to be formulated. From this, the design team should determine the scope of a tailored programme of investigation which enables all the key features identified in the desk study and site reconnaissance to be thoroughly investigated.

5.24   Details of commonly used site investigation techniques are given in Appendix G. For details concerning monitoring methods, frequencies and parameters, WMPs 4, 26A and 26D should be consulted.

Field investigations

5.25   Following the initial appraisal, field investigations should be undertaken, again in accordance with a staged approach comprising main and supplementary investigations. A staged approach will ensure the effective planning of each stage to obtain the required information and may lead to cost savings by avoiding

---

[9] Where the site includes existing landfill or contamination the recommendations of CIRIA Special Publication 78 and DD 175:1988 should be consulted. Arup Geotechnics (1991) and Applied Geology (1993) have carried out studies which provide useful information on both artificial and natural cavities which may exist beneath a site (see bibliography).

[10] Where the site contains an existing landfill or contaminated land, or is in the zone of influence of such land, the scope of the investigation may have to be extended to assess the degree of existing contamination. In these cases the recommendations of DD 175:1988, CIRIA Special Publication 78 and WMP27 should be consulted.

unnecessary investigations and duplication. Regardless of the approach, it is essential that sufficient information is gained to provide a robust landfill design and a full understanding of the environmental issues associated with the development.

Main site investigation

5.26   The main site investigation should be designed to provide sufficient geotechnical and hydrogeological data for the design of the proposed works and should be carried out at an early stage in the main design process. It should also include the initial design of the monitoring programme and installation of groundwater and soil gas monitoring points to allow collection of background/base readings over a maximum period of time, for example, taking into account seasonal fluctuations in water levels.

> Opportunities should be taken to maximise the efficiency of data collection for all aspects of site investigation by co-ordinating field activities; for example, obtaining soil information from trial pits to feed into the restoration design when carrying out geotechnical investigations. The particular requirements for restoration design are described in WMP26E.

5.27   The site investigation must include identification of all significant pathways and targets (receptors) relevant to migration of gas and leachate. The work may comprise exploratory boreholes and trial pits, and in-situ and laboratory testing as appropriate. Advantage should be taken of boreholes to obtain measurements of the soil atmosphere. The scope of the work should be determined by the design team, in consultation with the regulatory authorities. It is likely that the detailed investigation will concentrate on specific sensitive areas or areas where data is scarce.

5.28   The monitoring points installed during the investigation should be reviewed and consideration given to their upgrading to reflect the design proposals.

Supplementary site investigations

5.29   As the design progresses or during construction, inconsistencies or shortfalls in data may become evident. Depending on the magnitude of the problem and the implication on the design and operation of the landfill, it may be necessary to carry out further site investigations. Further investigations are often brought about by changes in the design or monitoring results which do not conform with the predictions of the design model.

5.30   For extensions to existing sites, a high level of detailed information may already exist and in such circumstances a supplementary site investigation may be appropriate.

Topographic survey

5.31   An accurate topographic survey should be undertaken for both site design purposes and for the calculation of void space. All borehole positions and other site features such as streambeds, springs, outcrops and exposures should be surveyed. Wherever possible, the survey data should be in an electronic format that can be easily used as part of the design process; for example, a CAD drawing file with the capability to produce an output format which can be universally read by other systems. The use of aerial survey may be advantageous in areas where access is difficult.

Monitoring

5.32   The requirements of any monitoring programme must be considered at the initial appraisal stage. Detailed monitoring should commence at this stage to obtain background base level readings. There may be existing monitoring records or installations which can provide valuable information but it is essential to check the construction of existing installations to ensure that they are suitable for the proposed use. Monitoring of base levels is essential in order to assess the environmental impacts associated with the proposed development, and will be valuable throughout the life of the site. The monitoring points should be reviewed during the design of the main and any supplementary site investigations, and if necessary upgraded to reflect the design proposals.

5.33   The effectiveness of any monitoring programme relies on regular data supplemented by extra readings as and when appropriate. Installations must therefore be read after completion of the site investigation and during the construction phase. The data must then be continually fed back into the design model to determine inconsistencies or abnormalities as indicated in the flowchart in Figure 5.2. Further guidance on monitoring is given in WMP 26D and WMP 27.

5.34   Monitoring is an essential and integral part of the risk assessment approach to landfill management. The risk assessment will have identified receptors and pathways for which mitigation measures will have been incorporated in the landfill design[11]. The objective of monitoring is to determine whether the assumptions used for the risk assessment were correct and whether the mitigation measures are performing to specification. Most of the landfill impacts, particularly leachate and gas migration, are more difficult and expensive to remedy the longer they remain undetected. **It is, therefore, in the interests of all parties, operators, and regulators, to detect any variance from the performance criteria at the earliest opportunity**.

Reporting

5.35   Factual and interpretative site investigation reports should be produced which document the methodologies used, data collected and implications for the landfill design. The factual report should be included with any tender documentation for the construction contract. Site investigation reports should be incorporated into the Site Manual.

>   A *factual report* covers the scope of work carried out, the methodologies used, borehole construction, borehole and trial pit logs and results of in-situ and laboratory tests. It is usually prepared by the site investigation contractor.

>   An *interpretative report* covers items such as the interpretation of site ground conditions, and geotechnical, groundwater and landfill gas design parameters, based on factual data obtained during the site investigation.

---

[11] See paragraphs 3.27 to 3.34 and Appendix E.

64

Figure 5.2 Outline process map for landfill monitoring

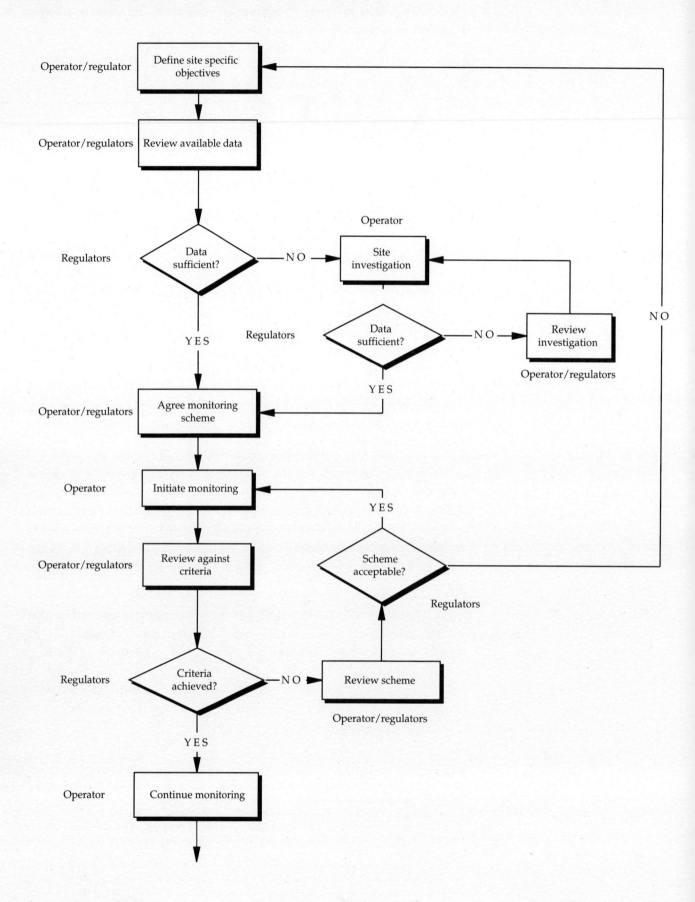

Requirements and standards
Legal requirements

5.36   Field investigations and the installation of monitoring boreholes and combined equipment may constitute development for which planning permission is required[12].

5.37   As site investigation activities are likely to precede any application for full development of a landfill site, the need for separate permission should be established before undertaking fieldwork. Consent will be required if investigation activities are likely to affect national or internationally designated sites such as Sites of Special Scientific Interest and Scheduled Ancient Monuments[13].

Services

5.38   The location of any services should be checked before commencing site investigation work, and appropriate precautions or protection measures adopted to avoid damage to pipelines and overhead cables, and for the safety of operators. Particular care should be taken when working in road verges around sites as these often contain live electrical cables, gas mains, water services or telephone cables.

Quality issues and contractual arrangements

5.39   A quality approach should be adopted for all site investigation activities, as part of the overall quality approach to landfill design, construction and operation. Further guidance is given in Chapter 4[14].

5.40   Contractual arrangements should be clearly defined[15], including

- use of competent and experienced contractors to undertake site investigation work

- preparation of a clear brief for contractors.

Standards

5.41   Within the United Kingdom the standards most commonly used are BS 1377:1990 and BS 5930:1981 for laboratory testing and site investigation respectively. While these are primarily aimed at site investigations for more conventional construction projects, they are equally applicable to investigations for landfills. For work directly related to landfills, DD 175:1988 may be useful in designing desk studies and ground investigations. Guidelines for drilling investigation of landfills are also given in the Site Investigation in Construction series[16].

Supervision

5.42   Any site investigation is an iterative process requiring continual feedback into the design model for comparison with the anticipated conditions or the design requirements. It is therefore important that a representative of the design team is present on-site throughout the fieldwork programme to monitor the results and modify the works as required. Such a person must have a detailed knowledge of the design requirements and have sufficient experience and expertise to make rapid decisions as the works proceed[17].

---

[12] See Appendix B. Development is defined in Section 55 of the Town and Country Planning Act 1990 as the *'carrying out of building, engineering, mining or other operations in, on, over or under land, or the making of any material change in the use of buildings or other land'*.
[13] See Table 2.1. The relevant authorities for consultation are shown in Table 2.2.
[14] A useful source of advice for site investigation is the Site Investigation Steering Group 1993, *Planning, Procurement and Quality Management*, Site Investigation in Construction Series No 2, Thomas Telford, London.
[15] The ICE *Conditions of Contract for Ground Investigations (1st Edition) 1983* provide guidance on standard contract documents which may be used. See also Site Investigation Steering Group 1993, *Specification for Ground Investigation*, Site Investigation in Construction Series No 3, Thomas Telford, London.
[16] Site Investigation Steering Group 1993, *Guidelines for the Safe Investigation by Drilling of Landfills and Contaminated Land*, Site Investigation in Construction Series No 4, Thomas Telford, London.
[17] See Site Investigation in Construction Series No 2, *Planning, Procurement and Quality Management*.

Safety

5.43   All site investigations must be carried out in a safe and proper manner. The British Drilling Association and HSE have documented the appropriate safety issues which must be followed[18]. Under the CDM Regulations[19], a health and safety plan is legally required for site investigation fieldwork involving more than five persons at work; the HSE must be notified of the project by the Planning Supervisor if the construction phase is longer than 30 days or involves more than 500 person days of construction work.

[18] British Drilling Association (Operations) Limited (1992): *Guidance notes for the safe drilling of landfills and contaminated land.*
[19] DoE: *The Construction (Design and Management) Regulations 1994.* SI 1994 No 3140; see also paragraphs 4.8 for further application.

6 Engineering Design and Construction

Introduction

6.1   This chapter gives guidance on the principal elements of the engineering and development works required to achieve the objectives set out in Chapter 3, based on the overall concept of construction of a landform using waste. These include

- profile of the final landform, including consideration of slopes, void capacity, settlement and waste density (paragraphs 6.3 to 6.17)

- phasing of the development (paragraphs 6.18 to 6.23)

- site infrastructure, incorporating safe traffic access and haul routes, all the facilities for reception and handling of waste and administration of the landfill site (paragraphs 6.24 to 6.31)

- materials requirements and materials balance, to enable the construction of the landform (paragraphs 6.32 to 6.40)

- groundwater and surface water management (paragraphs 6.41 to 6.47)

- leachate management (paragraphs 6.48 to 6.63)

- landfill gas management (paragraphs 6.64 to 6.74)

- preparatory works required prior to filling with waste in the first phase (paragraph 6.75)

- monitoring requirements (paragraphs 6.76 to 6.78).

6.2   The design of a landfill is an interactive process incorporating the conceptual design proposals, the findings of the initial scoping of environmental issues, the results of the risk assessment and findings of the site investigation. It is also an iterative process requiring regular feedback and amendment during progress towards achieving the final design, including during the filling (operational) stages as shown on Figure 3.1. The planning of site operations and the proposed operational practices for the site, as described in Chapters 8 and 9, should feed into the engineering design process.

Profile of final landform

6.3   The design of the landform is the starting point of the design of a landfill at a given location. The landform is a key factor in determining the standard of restoration achievable, afteruse and the waste capacity of the site, and its design needs to take into account the likely waste input to the facility and the landscaping requirements in the context of the surrounding land[1]. The key factors affecting the landform are

- maximum and minimum surface gradients

- capacity

- settlement

---

[1] See paragraphs 3.38 to 3.43 and Table 3.2.

• waste density.

Maximum and minimum
surface gradients

6.4   The surface gradients should not compromise the overall stability of the landfilled wastes and the capping layers, as referred to in paragraphs 6.5 to 6.7, 7.16 and 9.69. They should provide adequate drainage of surface water and be appropriate for the proposed afteruse. Where the objectives for stability cannot be met in the basic design, specific remedial design measures may be required to ensure their achievement.

> Guidance on the suitability of slopes for various afteruses is given in WMP26E and Table 2 of MPG7[2].

6.5   In all cases, geotechnical checks must be carried out on the foundation and liner system materials underlying the waste to ensure their stability.

> For household, general industrial and commercial wastes a slope of 1 in 4 will generally provide an acceptable factor of safety[3]. For wastes whose geotechnical properties are known, different slopes may be justifiable, provided that adequate factors of safety can be demonstrated.

> Steep slopes (between 1 in 4 and 1 in 6) can lead to instability in the capping layers and problems of erosion, and may limit the use of agricultural machinery[4], as described in paragraphs 7.6 and 9.69.

> In general, final gradients after settlement no flatter than 1 in 25 will ensure adequate drainage and will minimise ponding problems created by local differential settlement[5]. Further guidance on the construction of the capping system is given in Chapter 10 and afteruse considerations are examined in WMP26E.

6.6   Consideration should also be given to the stability of temporary slopes during landfilling. The designer should pay particular attention to engineering cap gradients at the edge of a landform, especially where this overlies an area of significant change in depth[6].

6.7   Afteruse considerations may require that a complex landform is produced. However, the fundamental objectives and performance criteria of the engineering cap[7] must not be compromised, and the designer should overcome such additional constraints by specific measures. These may include locally strengthening the engineering cap, or creating the required surface undulations within the restoration layer above a more uniformly sloping capping membrane. **The engineering designer should work with the landscape architect/afteruse designer to produce a landform appropriate to both its engineering and projected afteruse functions.**

Capacity

6.8   A crucial element in any landfill design is its *capacity*[8]. At the conceptual

---

[2] Minerals Planning Guidance Note MPG7: *The Reclamation of Mineral Workings.* DoE/Welsh Office, 1989.

[3] Golder & Associates (1984): *Geotechnical Engineering and Refuse Landfills.* 6th National Conference on Waste Management in Canada, Vancouver, BC.

[4] RPS Clouston and Wye College: *Reclamation of Landfill Workings to Agriculture: Phase 2 Report to DoE* : DoE Research Report (in preparation 1995) and Minerals Planning Guidance (MPG7 1989) *The Reclamation of Mineral Workings* DoE/Welsh Office.

[5] Oweis I S and Khera R P (1990): *Geotechnology of Waste Management.* Cambridge University Press, 1990.

[6] See paragraphs 10.21 to 10.24.

[7] See paragraph 10.14 and Figure 10.1 for description of the capping system.

[8] This may also be referred to as the *site volume, the airspace* or *site size* (see Glossary).

design stage, an indication of gross air space can be calculated by comparing the existing landform with the proposed restoration profile.

> Where a detailed site survey is not available, initial estimates can be obtained using large scale (1: 2,500 or 1: 10,000) Ordnance Survey Plans. Care should be taken where the site levels may have changed since the last survey date.

> Aerial survey offers a rapid method of topographic survey and void space calculation, particularly of large areas, and can provide accurate and cost-effective survey information to facilitate site planning and design. The accuracy and sensitivity of information vary with the height flown. The Global Positioning System can contribute to a rapid survey.

> To obtain an accurate estimate of waste capacity a *materials balance* is also required but this will only be possible later in the design process[9].

6.9   The calculation of usable waste capacity, that is, net capacity available for waste, measured in tonnes, will depend on the

- density of the wastes

- amount of intermediate and daily cover

- amount of settlement that the waste will undergo following tipping

- thickness of the capping system

- construction of the lining and drainage layers (see Chapter 7).

6.10   A given landform's maximum volume for waste will be achieved if all of the earth materials for lining, drainage, cover, bunds, capping and restoration can be obtained from excavation within the boundary of the landform. A potential advantage of landraising is that the landform is more likely to be located above accessible materials.

Settlement

6.11   Settlement[10] of the completed waste mass beneath the capping layers will inevitably occur as a result of the consolidation of waste within a landfill site resulting from the complex interplay of physical, biological and chemical processes. Initial settlement occurs predominantly because of the physical rearrangement of the waste material after it is first placed in the landfill. Later settlement mainly results from biochemical degradation of the waste, which in turn leads to further physical settlement. Inert or low reactivity waste sites will be affected less than sites taking bioreactive wastes in this respect. Inevitably there is an overlap in timing in these two processes which makes them impossible to separate. These factors make prediction of settlement highly complex.

6.12   Accurate prediction of settlement is difficult because time related settlement data are rarely available from surface data. Those data which are available indicate that long term settlement can be approximated to an exponential curve which could result in most settlement taking place over 30 years with the majority occurring in an initial 5 year period.

6.13   Initial settlement values of between 12 and 17% have been reported for household waste sites in the UK with long term (30 year) values of approximately

---

[9] See paragraphs 6.32-6.40.
[10] See Glossary for definitions of settlement and surcharge.

20%[11]. Values of 15-20% are accepted as being typical of the surcharge allowance that may need to be made when considering the void capacity and final pre-settlement contours of a household waste landfill. The effects of settlement need to be considered in quarry landfills or in landfills whose base is non uniform (or stepped) and measures taken to avoid problems due to differential settlement which can lead to stresses and breaks in the engineering cap, and possible drainage problems.

> The precise effect that controlled bioreactor landfilling techniques may have on settlement is unknown. It is likely that there will be no overall increase in total settlement resulting from loss of mass; however, the rate of settlement is likely to be accelerated. Further guidance is given in Appendix D.

6.14 An example of a detailed analysis of settlement is given in Figure 6.1. This considers the composition of the waste as received, by origin, and sub-divided by degradation rate. Each component is then considered against an individual pattern of degradation and aggregated to give an overall settlement curve. Much of the settlement is manifested as a loss of mass of carbon, hydrogen and oxygen, through gas generation. The results in Figure 6.1 are derived from a mathematical model of a small landfill, but the approach is valid generally and can be used with either measured parameters, or assumed data based on current published research.

Waste density

6.15 The density of waste in a landfill varies widely because of the large variations in waste constituents, the degree of compaction, the state of decomposition, the amount of daily cover, the total depth of waste and the depth from which a sample is taken. Reported densities range from lows of 0.4 tonnes/m³ recorded in the United States[12] to highs of 1.23 tonnes/m³ recorded in the UK[13], with more generally recorded values of 0.65 to 0.85 tonnes/m³[14] For planning purposes, a density range of between 0.65 to 1.0 tonnes/m³ for bioreactive wastes should be assumed unless there are overriding reasons for departing from these values. Inert wastes may have higher densities[15]. Waste density may change with age as significant mass may be lost by the formation of landfill gas and leachate.

[11] RPS Clouston and Wye College (1993): *Reclamation of Landfill Workings to Agriculture.* Phase 2 DoE. Other reports have suggested settlement values in excess of 25%: see Bjarngard A and Edgers L (1990): "Settlement of Municipal Solid Waste Landfills". Thirteenth Annual Madison Waste Conference, pp 192-205; Di Stefano, A B (1993): "Settlement of Beddingham Landfill" in pre-prints of papers for the 29th Annual Conference of the Engineering Group of the Geological Society of London, ed S P Bentley; Wall D K and Zeiss C (1995): "Municipal Landfill Biodegradation and Settlement". J Environmental Engineering, Vol 121 No 3, pp 214-224.
[12] Oweis I S and Khera R P (1990): *Geotechnology of Waste Management.* Cambridge, University Press, 1990.
[13] Biddle A (1985): *Evaluating Landfill Compactors.*
[14] Harrison N H (1985): "Compaction and effective densities in landfill sites." Proc Inst WM. North West Centre Meeting, Leyland, February 1985.
[15] The South East Waste Regulation Advisory Committee (SEWRAC) use conversion factors of 1.5 tonnes/m³ for Type A (inert/low reactivity) wastes and 0.8 tonnes/m³ for Types B and C (non inert) wastes. See SEWRAC (1994): *Waste Disposal in the South East Region: Results of the 1993 Waste Monitoring Survey,* page 2.

71

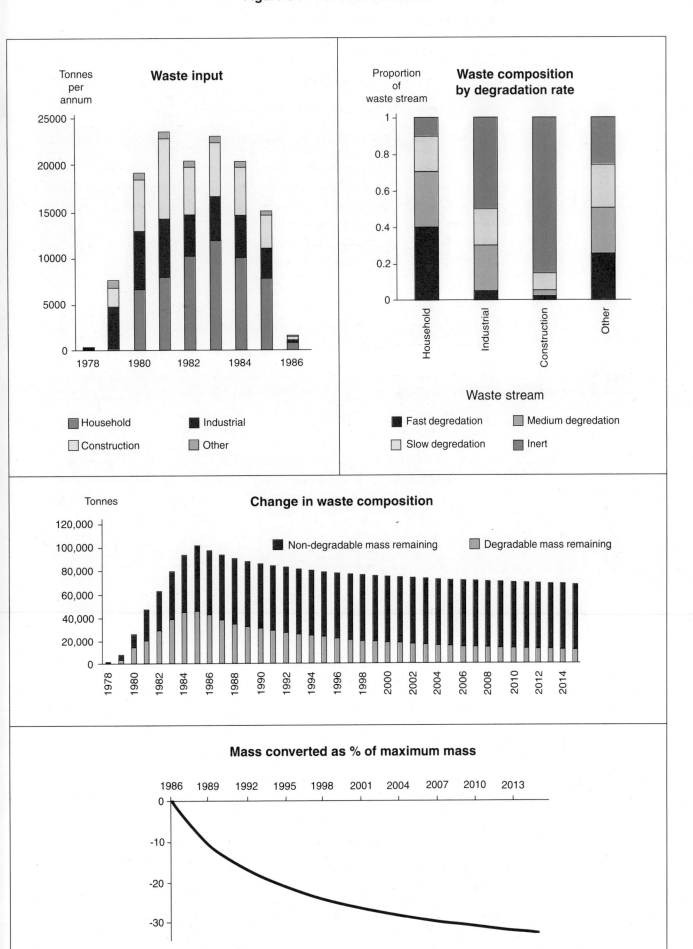

Figure 6.1 Landfill settlement

6.16   The landfill designer should consider carefully the implications of the density assumed. The density assumed will affect, or be affected by the

- depth of the site

- type of compaction to be used

- absorptive capacity and field capacity[16]

- permeability of the waste, where leachate recirculation is intended.

6.17   The designer should clarify whether the density assumed is of waste only, or of waste and daily cover. The use of frequent surveys of the waste surface and comparative measurement of void consumed, facilitated by CAD or DTM techniques, is a valuable management tool. Regular aerial mapping in conjunction with computerised volume calculation provides an effective means of recording the changing capacity of a landfill site.

The operator should clarify whether the tonnage of waste recorded at reception or the estimated volume change in airspace includes or deducts daily cover. The calculation of density will be further affected by the settlement that has occurred between placing the waste and the date of survey.

Phasing

6.18   It is good practice to develop, operate and restore landfills in a series of phases of sufficient size. This will facilitate the planned sequential filling of the site. In deciding on an appropriate sequence the designer should consider the following objectives of phasing

- to allow the progressive use of the landfill area, such that at any given time part of the site may be capped and restored, part being capped, part being prepared to receive waste, and part undisturbed, with only a small area being actively filled

- to enable progressive excavation of on-site fill materials and minimisation of double handling

- to provide adequate storage and protection of materials required for subsequent restoration

- to minimise the area required for landfill operations at any one time and to concentrate waste disposal activities within a sequence of defined and prepared areas

- to reduce leachate generation by keeping areas of active and unrestored tipping to a minimum[17]

- to enable progressive installation of leachate and gas controls

- to enable progressive restoration

- to co-ordinate haul roads and access routes

- to segregate clean surface water run-off both within and outside the site

---

[16] NRA Internal Guidance Note No 8 *Management of Landfill Leachate*, December 1994.

[17] The control of leachate generation is important even where recirculation is an objective of the design. For leachate recirculation in a flushing bioreactor, the rate and quality of leachate recirculated is a fundamental process control. Uncontrolled input of water will affect this and must therefore be minimised.

- to phase development and restoration expenditure

- to protect local amenity.

Phase size

6.19   A *phase* is a sub-area of a landfill site which has been identified at the planning stage as being able to meet the objectives identified above. *Cells* are generally sub-divisions of phases and are planned and set out by site staff for operational requirements.

> In order to avoid frequent and disruptive preparatory works, it is advisable to provide each phase with a life of between 12 and 18 months. This period allows adequate time for the design and preparation of subsequent stages and allows experience gained from the current operating phase to be incorporated in the new design. Phases with an operational period greater than 18 months can lead to excessive volumes of leachate production in wet areas.

> Operational considerations are likely to impose a minimum size for manoeuvring of vehicles. It may also be possible to restrict leachate generation by restricting the cell area such that the consequent rate of vertical filling is more than (rainfall ÷ absorptive capacity). This is a very simplistic approach, however, and in all situations it will be necessary, having minimised the cell area, to calculate and make provision for the probable rate of leachate generation.

6.20   Phases are generally filled from base to engineering cap in a continuous operation, then capped and restored, leaving a temporary unrestored face sloping to the landfill base.

> These faces should be considered according to stability requirements in each case but are generally specified as being between 1 in 2 and 1 in 3[18].

> In some instances, a temporary cap is placed prior to restoration, for example where rapid settlement is anticipated, such that additional waste can be placed prior to final capping and restoration. The designer should balance the advantages of this with the costs of double handling the engineering cap materials, possible increased leachate production and the inability to restore more quickly.

> In deep landfills, such as those located in disused quarries, constraints on plan area may require vertically tiered phases in addition to the full height phases described above. A temporary cap is usually placed over the upper surface of such phases to reduce rainwater infiltration and cover the underlying waste. The temporary cap need only be a layer (say 600 mm) of soil cover, but should be removed before the surface is covered with waste in the next vertical phase. Careful consideration will need to be given to the layout of haul roads and to the relationship between the various tiers of phases.

> The phased restoration of the site should take account of the afteruse requirements. Further details are given in WMP26E.

---

[18] The slope adopted will depend on the nature of the waste, its moisture content, the height of the slope, the nature of the slope foundations, including the lining system, and the consequences of any possible failure. The chosen slope should be appraised by a geotechnical engineer.

Sequence

6.21   Factors which affect the phasing sequence include

- leachate drainage layout

  > Commencement of filling from the low point or collection sump is preferred, to reduce the risk of any leachate overflow into unfilled areas, particularly where these may be used for the collection of surface water.

- materials excavation

  > Limited initial excavation reduces the need for stockpile areas.

- haul roads

  > It is preferable to retain a high standard haul road for as long a period as possible rather than having to move it frequently. The phases will need to be designed so that haul roads to upper levels are constructed at a gradient acceptable to all vehicles using the landfill. 1:10 has been regarded as an acceptable slope for most vehicles; however, higher gross vehicle weights and greater use of automatic gear boxes on refuse collection vehicles have led to a need for slacker gradients. 1:15 is now a typical slope.

- screening and restoration

  > Early development, infilling and restoration along sensitive boundaries of the site may screen the remaining site operations from adjacent properties.

6.22   For any given site, the landfill designer should consider the best sequence against each of these factors to produce an appropriate overall filling sequence. A simplified example is shown in Figure 6.2.

Phase boundaries

6.23   The boundary between phases is generally delineated by a separation bund, approximately 2 m high, located on the proposed base of the phase. The designer and site operator will need to consider the relationship between the bund and the base liner and leachate drainage systems to ensure that design requirements do not conflict with operational requirements, particularly where leachate recirculation for flushing is required. Specific designed interconnections between cells and phases may be required. Unless careful attention is given to their design and construction, the use of high 'Christmas tree' bunds to define an exposed phase face is not recommended as such bunds are prone to instability.

Site infrastructure

6.24   The general objectives of the design for the site reception and administration facilities are

- to provide efficient reception of all wastes delivered to the site

- to ensure compliance with waste management licence requirements for the receipt, inspection and recording of wastes and other materials delivered to the site

- to provide an appropriate standard of accommodation and facilities for all personnel employed at the site

- to present a good image to the general public.

6.25   As with any major engineering project, a landfill will require a variety of infrastructure provision. The landfill designer will need to consider the

Figure 6.2   Phasing

A: Phasing plan

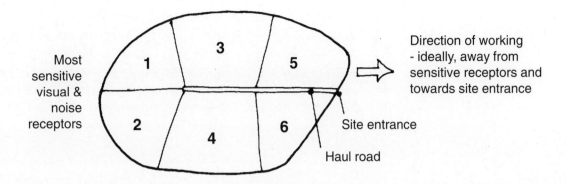

Most sensitive visual & noise receptors

Direction of working - ideally, away from sensitive receptors and towards site entrance

Site entrance

Haul road

B: Phase 2 in operation

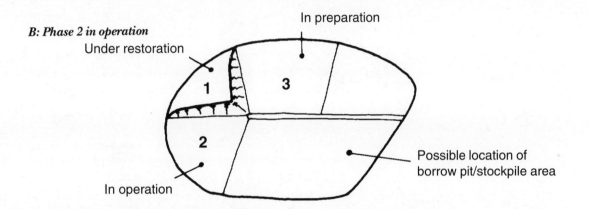

In preparation

Under restoration

In operation

Possible location of borrow pit/stockpile area

C: Phase 4 in operation

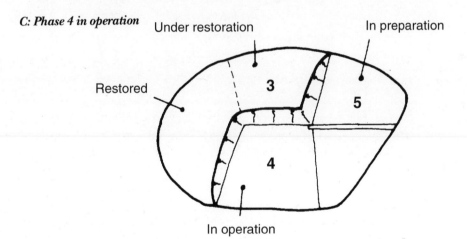

Under restoration

In preparation

Restored

In operation

D: Phase 6 in operation

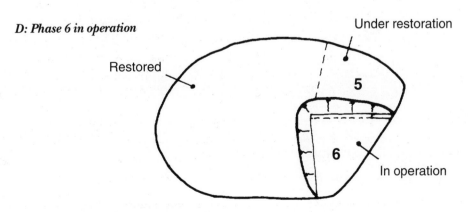

Under restoration

Restored

In operation

infrastructure provision in liaison with the site operator. Key considerations for the designer are set out below, and further details of the provisions are given in paragraphs 9.4 to 9.51.

Access

6.26   Landfill sites may be accessed by road, rail or water and the design of the access must accommodate the mode of transport of the waste. Where there is road access the design of the site entrance should be undertaken in consultation with the local Highways Authority, who will advise the developer of the appropriate design parameters required for the proposed entrance. The authority will also set out any requirements for improvements to the public highway. No vehicles should be required to queue back onto the public road.

6.27   The impact that the proposed development will have on the local highway network must be considered at the planning stage. The proposed traffic movements may be such that substantial provisions are required, such as the construction of dedicated link roads or improvements to the public highway. Any improvements to the network required must be carried out in consultation with the Highways Authority.

6.28   An important consideration for both the site access and site reception areas is their aesthetic design, particularly as they provide the interface between the development and the public. It should reflect the technical quality of the landfill design and be appropriate to the surrounding area. The landscape designers advising on the landform may also provide advice on appropriate site entrance design.

6.29   The specifications for site accommodation, waste reception, wheel cleaning and maintenance facilities should be agreed in discussion with the landfill operator. However, the designer should consider the location of these facilities so that there is sufficient space within the allocated areas for vehicle movement and queuing, if appropriate.

6.30   Temporary structures (for example, portable offices) are frequently employed on landfill sites. Where temporary or permanent structures are to be provided the designer should consider carefully the appropriate location and may be required to supply full details for planning and building regulations approval. Where offices are required to last for active filling periods of 20 years or more, consideration should be given to the cost/benefit of permanent structures, particularly if they could be used for another purpose following completion of landfilling.

6.31   The design of site fencing should be appropriate to the degrees of security and safety that are required[19], and should be compatible with adjoining land uses. A post and wire or stock proof fence may be sufficient to indicate the boundary of non-operational parts of a large landfill, while security fencing is required around the active tipping and reception areas. The appearance of the fencing should also be considered, in order to satisfy planning authority requirements on visual impact. Fencing may need to be moved or upgraded during the site life.

Materials requirements and materials balance

6.32   One of the commercial objectives of successful landfill development and operation is for the proposed site to be, so far as possible, self sufficient in the large amounts of different soil materials that will be required through its working life.

---

[19] Appropriate specifications may be found in British Standard BS 1722 and the Manual of Contract Documents for Highway Works: Volume 3 *Highway Construction Details*, HMSO.

> Void space will be maximised if all the necessary materials are available on-site.

> Total self sufficiency in all materials requirements is rarely possible, and for sites such as worked out quarries there is sometimes very little material available for use for the landfill.

> If materials are not available they will need to be imported and may occupy air space that would otherwise be available for waste. Imported materials will use up void space and may have to be purchased or charged at sub-economic rates. The vehicles used to deliver materials to site will need to be considered in the traffic and noise assessments.

6.33 The designer should estimate the likely materials requirements for the site engineering, as appropriate to the level of containment required for environmental protection, and consider what proportion is available on-site. This is termed a materials balance.

Materials requirements

6.34 Materials may be required for

> groundwater drainage - granular material

> lining - clay, sand (also as protection layer to membrane liner)

> leachate drainage blankets - granular material (non carbonate)

> internal and external bunds - suitable fill

> gas venting and collection - granular material

> haul roads - hardcore

> daily cover - suitable material during site operations (unless plastic or other synthetic alternatives are to be used[20])

> cap barrier layer - clay or synthetic membrane

> pipework zone, drainage and protection layers above the barrier layer[21] - suitable soils, granular or screened material

> restoration layers - subsoil and topsoil

> bulk fill of uneconomic areas that will not be landfilled with waste materials.

6.35 The designer should consider what construction, operational and restoration materials are required for the site against each of the indicative uses and types listed above. The designer should consider the overall cost effectiveness of materials use and whether any particular features of the design require additional quantities of a particular material, or whether replacement or substitute materials are available.

> For example, enhanced cap design will require additional material; manufactured drainage nets may be used for side slope drainage instead of granular drainage blankets; artificial or no daily cover may be used.

---

[20] See paragraphs 9.86 to 9.90.
[21] See Figure 10.1 and paragraphs 10.14 to 10.20.

> The afteruse requirements will determine the thickness of the restoration layers (see WMP26E).

Materials balance

6.36   The site investigation should identify the quantities and types of materials available on-site. The assessment of materials available may require estimation of materials *cut* and *fill*, and should consider the sequence of operations, stockpile locations and the desired shape of the base of the site once the earthworks are complete[22]. The results of this assessment can then be used to prepare a materials balance, an example of which is provided in Table 6.1.

6.37   The overall materials balance should also be prepared on a phase by phase basis. This will indicate clearly which phases are located over the largest reserves, or have the largest shortfall, and of which material.

> Within the other constraints on phasing sequence the designer should avoid locating early phases on major borrow areas, as this will increase the need for stockpiles and double handling, or the establishment of stockpiles in the wrong place. The objective should be for appropriate materials to be obtained as required for earlier phases from borrow areas, such that the borrow areas are then available for preparation as later filling phases without further excavation.

> In planning the number and sequence of phases the seasonal implications for earth moving conditions should be assessed. The excavation and placement of granular materials such as sand and gravel can be carried out at most times of year, but it is common practice for clay to be worked only during the spring, summer and early autumn months.

> The movement of soils is similarly limited by suitable weather conditions and soils for the restoration layers should be carefully handled and stored. WMP26E provides further guidance.

> Similar constraints apply to the welding of flexible membrane liners (which cannot be carried out on a wet membrane) and to the laying of bentonite and its derivatives. Major clay excavations and liner preparation should therefore be programmed for the summer months if possible, which may require additional forethought if, for example, a phase is due to commence filling in April.

Other sources of materials

6.38   In addition to materials available within the site, it may be possible to obtain additional material by segregation of the incoming waste stream so that the need to import material such as daily cover, hardcore, granular drainage material or some soils is reduced. This may require planning permission and licensing as an on-site operation, and should be considered at the planning application stage of the landfill.

> Processing may require expenditure on the hire of crushing and/or screening plant, and storage areas may also be required. It also requires careful planning and site control so that the segregated material does not become contaminated by unsuitable waste. The operator's intentions should be clarified by the designer at the outset, and recorded in the Site Manual.

---

[22] The base of the site will be of importance to leachate management, as discussed in paragraphs 6.48 to 6.63.

Table 6.1

Example of a materials balance calculation

a)	Difference between existing ground level and proposed final contours					3,000,000
b)	Landfill area					120,000 m^2
c)	Development materials **required**:					

Material use	Basis	Natural soils	Clay	Inert	Granular	Total
Clay component of liner	1.0 m		120,000			120,000
Gas venting well surround					5,000	5,000
Leachate drainage blanket	0.3 m				36,000	36,000
Internal bunds (length)	600 m			3,000		3,000
Cap: engineering layers (*inc pipework zone*)	1.5 m		120,000	60,000		180,000
Cap: restoration layers	1.0 m	120,000				120,000
Replace alluvium/soft spots (*: if suitable)			*10,000			10,000
Groundwater drainage					1,000	1,000
Total materials required		120,000	250,000	63,000	42,000	**475,000**

d)	Materials **available** on-site	120,000	200,000	70,000	11,000	401,000
e)	Shortfall *(c - d)* *(-ve = surplus)*	0	50,000	- 7,000	31,000	**74,000**
f)	Volume available for waste and daily cover *(a - e)*					2,926,000
g)	Volume available for waste *(assuming daily cover @ 10% waste volume, and excluding 5% cover material obtained from waste stream)*					2,660,000
h)	Volume of waste *(including additional 15% for settlement surcharge, ie g x 1.15)*					3,059,000
i)	Tonnage of waste *(assuming 0.8 t/m^3, ie h x 0.8)*					2,447,000 tonnes
j)	Daily cover requirements @ 10% of waste volume *(off-site material, and excluding cover material obtained from waste stream, ie h x 0.1)*					306,000
k)	Materials importation requirements *(e + j)*					380,000
l)	Materials exportation					Nil
m)	Life of site at input rate of 150,000 t/yr					16.3 years

Notes: 1.   *All quantities in m^3 unless otherwise stated.*

           2.   *All items to nearest 1,000 m^3.*

> Guidance on the selection and use of alternative materials to natural topsoil, including the screening of granular waste materials, is provided in BS 3882:1994.

> Despite the operational cost implication in segregation and processing, it should be seriously considered by the designer because of the airspace potentially conserved and the beneficial use of otherwise waste materials.

6.39 The export of any excess (or surplus) of soil materials identified on a site for use or sale elsewhere will need planning permission.

Storage of materials

6.40 Different types of materials will need to be stored separately and adequate provision must be made within the site for storage requirements during the course of the development. Topsoil and subsoil should be excavated carefully and stored such that these remain in good condition until required for restoration. They should not be used as daily cover or lost within the landfill. Further details on storage are given in WMP26E.

Groundwater and surface water management

Groundwater management

6.41 The protection of groundwater from unacceptable impact from landfill leachates is one of the principal objectives of modern landfills, and is increasingly satisfied by the provision of high specification low permeability liners which assist the management of landfill leachate[23]. Of equal importance is the management of the groundwater such that its normal flow is not adversely affected by the landfill, and the groundwater itself does not adversely affect the landfill, in particular the liner system.

6.42 In most cases the landfill site and the liner system will be located above the groundwater table such that there is an unsaturated zone immediately below the site. Landfills located in excavations may encounter groundwater seepages from either the base or sides which will require management.

6.43 In those sites which are located below the water table, it will be necessary to relieve hydrostatic pressures which might otherwise give rise to uplifting forces on the site liner and lead to potential instability. In such cases an under drainage system will be required. Pumping of groundwater following completion of the landfill is not compatible with the aims of sustainable development and gravity drainage is preferred for all long term requirements.

• Landfills constructed below the groundwater table can cause direct discharge to groundwater if the liner or leachate management system fails: see paragraph 3.24. Annual analysis of leachate for List I and II substances at the point of discharge should be undertaken in such situations.

Groundwater drainage systems

6.44 Considerations include[24]

• choosing the correct size of filter stone or fabric to avoid problems from clogging of drainage layers by fine material[25]

---

[23] Further guidance on liners is given in Chapter 7. Risk assessment is described in paragraphs 3.27 to 3.34.
[24] Groundwater drainage systems are described in CIRIA Report No. 113 (CIRIA 1986), and the principles of leachate collection drains are described in NWWRO document *Pollution Control Objectives for Landfill Design, Development and Operation* and in NRA Internal Guidance Note No. 8 *Leachate Management* (1995).
[25] Guidance is given in *Guidance on Good Practice for Landfill Engineering*, DoE Research Report (in preparation 1995); also in NRA (1994) Internal Guidance Note No 7 *Lining of Landfills*.

- incorporating specific drainage requirements to accommodate discrete spring flows

- ensuring that the risk of damage to pipes is negligible where the use of drain pipes or culverts is unavoidable

- designing pipes for inspection and maintenance, and to accept the maximum probable flow

  > Maintenance of self-cleansing velocities is less important as the inflow will be self-filtering. However, an initial flush of fines will occur, and provision should be made for cleaning this out. Closed circuit television (CCTV) and remote control hydro-jetting may be used for the inspection and cleaning of pipework.

  > The designer will need to demonstrate through calculation that the proposed design is sufficiently robust. The design of groundwater drainage is complex and may require specialist assistance. It is recommended that drainage layers are over-designed to account for possible future deterioration and clogging.

  > Monitoring of groundwater flow rate and quality will be necessary, for further details see WMP26D.

Surface water management 6.45 Surface water management is required to ensure that

- rainwater run-off does not drain into the waste from surrounding areas

- rainfall does not generate excessive and unnecessary quantities of leachate

- contaminated surface run-off from the operational area does not enter water courses

- slopes on the landfill are protected from infiltration and erosion

- the drainage system is safe and unobtrusive

- restored soils are not subject to ponding or waterlogging.

6.46 These objectives should be achieved by the following

  > Rainwater running off slopes above and outside the landfill area should be intercepted and channelled to watercourses without entering the operational area of the site. This channel may require a low permeability lining to prevent leakage into the landfill.

  > Rain falling on active tipping areas should be collected separately and managed as leachate, via the leachate collection drain and leachate collection sumps to the leachate treatment and disposal system.

  > Rainfall on areas within the landfill site which are not actively being used for waste disposal should be diverted away from active tipping areas, and directed through a settling pond to remove suspended silt, prior to discharge.

  > Any drainage channels or drains constructed on the restored landfill surface should be able to accommodate settlement, resist erosion and cope with localised storm conditions.

82

Surface water discharges

6.47   Water discharged from any of the above sources to surface water courses must be disposed of in accordance with a discharge consent issued by the NRA. The consent will stipulate both quality and quantity limits, and to a large extent will be based on data provided by the designer. The consent should reflect the anticipated conditions that will apply to surface water management on the site. Surface water discharge design should be undertaken in accordance with design criteria as agreed with the regulatory authority.

> Flow attenuation ponds or tanks may be required to store peak flows and limit discharges to an agreed flow rate.

> Culverts should not normally be constructed beneath landfills. However, should such a provision be unavoidable particular care should be taken to provide

- structural stability for the intended loads, generally ignoring any narrow trench conditions

- measures to prevent drainage of any liner leakage along the culvert bedding

- duplicate culverts to permit maintenance

- adequate peak flow capacity

- monitoring for effective performance for the design life of the site.

Leachate management

6.48   A landfill will need an efficient leachate collection and removal system to enable leachate to be removed from the site for disposal or recirculation. A good leachate management system is the prime requirement for accelerated stabilisation. The primary objectives for a leachate management system are to

- remove leachate contained within the site by the liner system for treatment and disposal according to the site's objectives

- control and usually minimise leachate heads within the site

- avoid damage to the liner system.

These objectives are determined by the risk assessment process described in paragraphs 3.27 to 3.34 and Appendix E.

Water balance and leachate production

6.49   A knowledge of the likely leachate generation of a landfill is a pre-requisite to the planning of a leachate management strategy. An assessment of leachate generation rate cannot be prepared in the absence of a phasing sequence plan.

6.50   An understanding of the likely potential for leachate generation at the site is essential at the conceptual design stage. A water balance calculation is used to assess likely leachate generation volumes and considers waste volumes, input rates and absorptive capacity, effective and total rainfall, infiltration and other site parameters. As the landfill design progresses and is refined, the calculation should be refined accordingly. The calculation should be of the form[26]

$$Lo = [ER + LIW + IRA] - [LTP + aW + DL]$$

where: Lo = free leachate retained

---

[26] For guidance in water balance techniques see also WMP26F and *Water Balance Methods and their Applications to Landfill in the UK*: DoE Research Report No CWM031/91.

ER = effective rainfall (or actual on active surface area); this may need to be modified to account for run-off, especially after capping

LIW = liquid industrial waste (including any surplus water from sludges with a high moisture content)

IRA = infiltration through restored and capped area

LTP = discharge of leachate off-site

a = unit absorptive capacity of wastes

W = weight of absorptive waste

DL = designed seepage (if appropriate).

6.51   The output of a typical water balance assessment is given in Figures 6.3(a) and (b). The table in Figure 6.3(a) is based on annual figures for the whole site and the calculation can be refined by using data for monthly or storm rainfall, or based on phases rather than years. Figure 6.3(b) shows the findings plotted as a graph, and also shows the output of other computations based on varied input values. The leachate generation calculation will assist in predicting the likely scale of leachate generation from the site and will provide reasonable volume predictions for design purposes.

> Site conditions will influence the actual rate of generation and a worst case approach using a daily peak flow of up to 3 times the predicted average flow rate for consideration in the detail design should be taken when sizing plant or negotiating discharge consents.

> It is necessary to undertake a series of calculations using varied parameters to formulate a sensitivity envelope for estimated leachate generation volumes, possibly on a time or phase basis.

> Where leachate generation assessments are undertaken on sites being developed as extensions to existing sites, whose original design and subsequent operation may be unknown, a high degree of caution must be exercised when using the estimates in sizing any leachate management proposals.

> Where a site is to be operated as a flushing bioreactor for accelerated stabilisation, the capacity of the leachate management system should be substantially greater than the generation rate, to allow for the designed rate of recirculation.

Leachate drainage

6.52   All liquids, including rain and surface water, which enter waste become leachate. In order to avoid an unacceptable build up of leachate on the site lining system, leachate should be drained to collection sumps located at low points from where it can be removed from the landfill for disposal or recycling. Given the variability of leachate flows through waste it is necessary to provide drainage paths to conduct the leachate by gravity to the sumps.

Figure 6.3a Prediction of leachate generation
Example calculation for a single set of assumptions

Actual rainfall	619	mm/yr	Effective rainfall - grass 260 mm/yr
Infiltration	20	mm (capped and restored areas)	
	619	mm (waste - active and unrestored areas) - assumes all of total rainfall infiltrates into the waste	
Density	1.0	t/m³	
Estimated waste input	30,000	t/yr	increasing to 70,000 t/yr
Liquid waste input	0	m³/yr	
Absorptive capacity	0.010	m³ per m³	
Site life	21	years	

Year	Active Phase No.	Active Area (m²)	Waste Input t/yr	Active Infiltration (m³)	Restored Phase No.	Restored Area (m³)	Restored Infiltration (m³)	Liquid waste Input (m³)	Total Water (m³)	Cumulative Water (m³)	Absorptive Capacity (m³)	Cumulative abs. capacity (m³)	Cum. available abs. capacity (m³)	Cumulative generation (m³)	Annual generation (m³/yr)
1	1	17,000	30,000	10,523		0	0	0	10,523	10,523	300	300	0	10,223	10,223
2	2	28,000	40,000	17,332	1	12,000	240	0	17,572	28,095	400	700	0	27,395	17,172
3	2	28,000	50,000	17,332	1	12,000	240	0	17,572	45,667	500	1,200	0	44,467	17,072
4	3	27,000	60,000	16,713	1,2	34,000	680	0	17,393	63,060	600	1,800	0	61,260	16,793
5	3	27,000	70,000	16,713	1,2	34,000	680	0	17,393	80,453	700	2,500	0	77,953	16,693
6	4	28,000	70,000	17,332	1,2,3	55,000	1,100	0	18,432	98,885	700	3,200	0	95,685	17,732
7	4	28,000	70,000	17,332	1,2,3	55,000	1,100	0	18,432	117,317	700	3,900	0	113,417	17,732
8	5	30,000	70,000	18,570	1,2,3,4	76,000	1,520	0	20,090	137,407	700	4,600	0	132,807	19,390
9	5	30,000	70,000	18,570	1,2,3,4	76,000	1,520	0	20,090	157,497	700	5,300	0	152,197	19,390
10	5	30,000	70,000	18,570	1,2,3,4	76,000	1,520	0	20,090	177,587	700	6,000	0	171,587	19,390
11	6	28,000	70,000	17,332	1,2,3,4,5	98,000	1,960	0	19,292	196,879	700	6,700	0	190,179	18,592
12	6	28,000	70,000	17,332	1,2,3,4,5	98,000	1,960	0	19,292	216,171	700	7,400	0	208,771	18,592
13	6	28,000	70,000	17,332	1,2,3,4,5	98,000	1,960	0	19,292	235,463	700	8,100	0	227,363	18,592
14	6	28,000	70,000	17,332	1,2,3,4,5	98,000	1,960	0	19,292	254,755	700	8,800	0	245,955	18,592
15	7	22,000	70,000	13,618	1,2,3,4,5,6	118,000	2,360	0	15,978	270,733	700	9,500	0	261,233	15,278
16	7	22,000	70,000	13,618	1,2,3,4,5,6	118,000	2,360	0	15,978	286,711	700	10,200	0	276,511	15,278
17	7	22,000	70,000	13,618	1,2,3,4,5,6	118,000	2,360	0	15,978	302,689	700	10,900	0	291,789	15,278
18	8	27,000	70,000	16,713	1,2,3,4,5,6,7	133,000	2,660	0	19,373	322,062	700	11,600	0	310,462	18,673
19	8	27,000	70,000	16,713	1,2,3,4,5,6,7	133,000	2,660	0	19,373	341,435	700	12,300	0	329,135	18,673
20	8	27,000	70,000	16,713	1,2,3,4,5,6,7	133,000	2,660	0	19,373	360,808	700	13,000	0	347,808	18,673
21	8	27,000	70,000	16,713	1,2,3,4,5,6,7	133,000	2,660	0	19,373	380,181	700	13,700	0	366,481	18,673
22	Restored	0	0	0	1,2,3,4,5,6,7,8	160,000	3,200	0	3,200	383,381	0	13,700	0	369,681	3,200
23	Restored	0	0	0	1,2,3,4,5,6,7,8	160,000	3,200	0	3,200	386,581	0	13,700	0	372,881	3,200
24	Restored	0	0	0	1,2,3,4,5,6,7,8	160,000	3,200	0	3,200	389,781	0	13,700	0	376,081	3,200
25	Restored	0	0	0	1,2,3,4,5,6,7,8	160,000	3,200	0	3,200	392,981	0	13,700	0	379,281	3,200
26	Restored	0	0	0	1,2,3,4,5,6,7,8	160,000	3,200	0	3,200	396,181	0	13,700	0	382,481	3,200
27	Restored	0	0	0	1,2,3,4,5,6,7,8	160,000	3,200	0	3,200	399,381	0	13,700	0	385,681	3,200
28	Restored	0	0	0	1,2,3,4,5,6,7,8	160,000	3,200	0	3,200	402,581	0	13,700	0	388,881	3,200
29	Restored	0	0	0	1,2,3,4,5,6,7,8	160,000	3,200	0	3,200	405,781	0	13,700	0	392,081	3,200
30	Restored	0	0	0	1,2,3,4,5,6,7,8	160,000	3,200	0	3,200	408,981	0	13,700	0	395,281	3,200

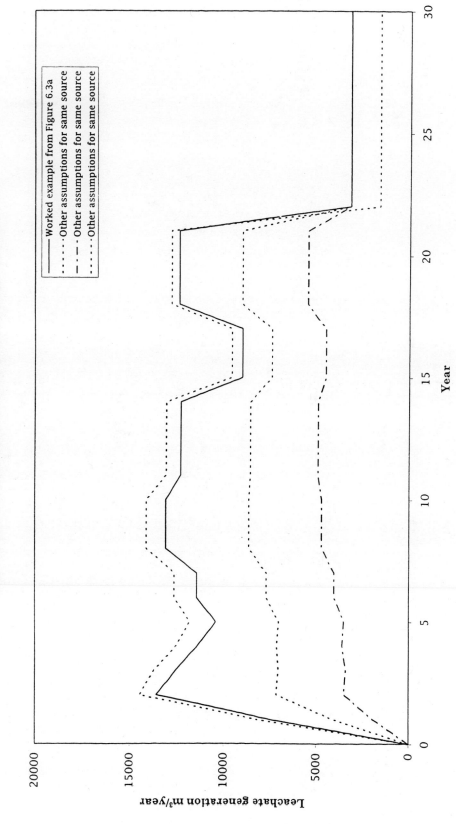

Figure 6.3b   Summary of leachate generation predictions

6.53   The risk assessment will have determined the nature of any leachate drainage system to be provided in conjunction with the required performance of the leachate collection system[27].

> Where a landfill requires a drainage system to drain leachate to the removal sumps this will usually take the form of an all-over granular blanket with perforated pipes included in the blanket. Should leachate recirculation be an objective of the design, the drainage blanket may need to be modified in the upper parts of the side slopes to avoid short-circuiting.

> In less sensitive settings lower specification drainage, such as herringbone drains, may suffice.

6.54   The shape of the site base and hence the drainage gradients will have a bearing on the amounts of earthworks that will be required[28]. Figure 6.4 shows drainage gradients for leachate management.

6.55   There are several methods of calculating the efficiencies of drainage blankets and collection systems[29]. There are also research data and operational experience which show that drainage layers, drain pipes and geotextile separation layers are potentially susceptible to silting and to blockage by biomass growth and chemical accretions. The removal system should be accessible for CCTV and jetting so that any blockage in the collection pipework can be investigated and removed. All the relevant factors must be taken into consideration in the risk assessment, so that the proposed drainage system is sufficiently robust to provide a means of removing leachate from the site which is appropriate to its hydrogeological sensitivity.

Leachate removal

6.56   Leachate is removed from collection sumps by the following means, which may be used in combination on a particular site

• pumping in vertical wells or chimneys

• side slope risers located on the site perimeter

• by gravity drains through, say, an end bund of a valley site[30].

6.57   Where discharge is by *gravity drains*, a freeboard should nevertheless be provided to contain leachate in the event that the discharge becomes blocked, or is closed temporarily, or for peak storm flows.

6.58   There is an increasing awareness of a possible fall off in the efficiency of drainage removal systems through clogging of drainage blankets and pipes with solid deposits and microbial growths associated with leachate. In order to counter this and facilitate maintenance the designer should consider whether, for instance, up slope risers or gravity drainage is preferable to deep manholes.

[27] The NRA (1995) Internal Guidance Note No 8 *Leachate Management* suggests the following standards for construction of leachate collection systems:
• base slope 2%
• drainage blanket 300 mm Type B filter drainage media
• 200 mm perforated smooth bore pipes
• possible geotextile or geonet at waste/drainage blanket interface.
[28] See also materials balance calculations in Table 6.1.
[29] Koerner, R M (1993): *Collection and Removal Systems*. Chapter 9 in *Geotechnical Practice for Waste Disposal*, ed David E Daniel, pp 187-213.
[30] See DoE: *Guidance on Good Practice for Landfill Engineering* (in preparation 1995)

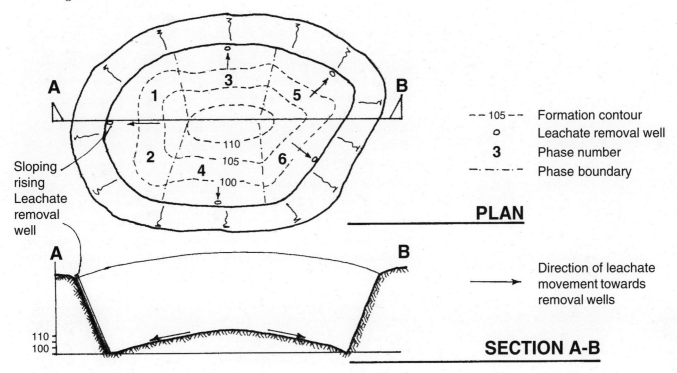

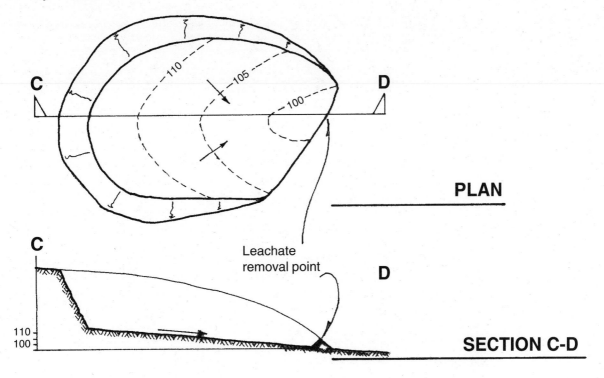

Figure 6.4   Leachate management – drainage gradients

A: Below ground excavation

Sloping rising Leachate removal well

- - 105 - - Formation contour
  o Leachate removal well
  3 Phase number
- · - · - Phase boundary

PLAN

→ Direction of leachate movement towards removal wells

SECTION A-B

B: Valley or hillside site

Leachate removal point

PLAN

SECTION C-D

88

6.59   The preferred means of *pumping* will be determined on a site specific basis. Submersible pumps have been used satisfactorily for many years. Eductor pumps are increasingly used, particularly where there is a large number of leachate removal points.

6.60   Temporary pipework is acceptable during site operations but is prone to damage and is unsightly. The design should allow for the use of permanent pipework as soon as is practicable to carry leachate from the removal manholes to the treatment or disposal facility.

6.61   *Manholes* should be classified as permitting or not permitting entry.

> Manholes and wells may be constructed of many materials. Pre-cast concrete is convenient but prone to physical damage. HDPE is also commonly used. The minimum size should be c. 300 mm to facilitate pump insertion if necessary. Manholes, including temporary pumping chambers, should be fitted with heavy lockable covers which cannot be removed by one person. Entry to any manholes or chambers should only be undertaken where it is unavoidable, and in accordance with appropriate written safety procedures which are incorporated into the site safety plan.

> The discharge pipe/manhole function at any pumping manhole should accommodate settlement of the waste around the manhole. The manhole should itself accommodate potential down-drag effects. With all manholes care must be taken to ensure that any foundation loads do not cause damage to the liner system.

6.62   The management of collected leachate is considered in detail in paragraphs 9.118 to 9.156. At the design stage, the designer should consider with the site operator whether treatment of leachate will be required, and if so, should ensure that sufficient area is available at a suitable location. The designer should also consider whether or not easements or agreements are necessary for the routing of pipelines connecting the site to a discharge point.

Accelerated stabilisation

6.63   Recirculation of collected and possibly treated leachate is likely to be a key consideration where accelerated stabilisation is to be achieved. It will only be possible where there is an effective leachate collection system. There will be a need to consider the means of distributing the recirculated liquids through the waste to ensure that there is overall wetting of the wastes and flushing of the leachable contaminants, that preferential pathways are not established, and that downward flowing leachate does not impair the landfill gas collection system. Accelerated stabilisation is discussed further in Appendix D.

Landfill gas management

6.64   The primary objectives of the landfill gas management system are

• to minimise the risk of migration of landfill gas beyond the perimeter of the site such that risk of explosion, combustion, asphyxiation, odours or vegetation damage on adjoining property are eliminated as far as possible

• to avoid unnecessary air ingress into the landfill and minimise the risk of underground fires

• to minimise damage to soils and vegetation within the restored landfill area

- to minimise the impact on air quality and the effect of greenhouse gases on the global climate.

6.65 The risk assessment will determine the appropriate level of landfill gas management. All aspects of design, construction and operation of any landfill gas control system should be to the highest standards, and commensurate with the requirements of the risk assessment and WMP27. This assessment should include harm to the global climate and air quality. The design should also take account of the planned afteruse for the site (see WMP26E).

Features of a landfill gas management system

6.66 The following features should generally be incorporated in a landfill gas management system to meet these objectives, as indicated by the risk assessment:

- a containment system which will retain gas within the site and prevent off site migration

- a system for landfill gas collection and utilisation or flaring with adequate back-up facilities (see paragraphs 9.169 to 9.184)

- a separate system to control gas migration at the site perimeter which can operate independently of gas collection from within the body of the waste

- gas monitoring boreholes outside the waste boundary

- use of safe practices to avoid hazardous concentrations of gases within temporary or permanent working areas of the site.

> These features are illustrated in Figure 6.5.

6.67 As the control and management of landfill gas is rapidly evolving, the designer and site operator should ensure that full advantage is taken of changing theory and design. The designer should assess the likely landfill gas generation pattern having regard to the waste types and the rate of filling, and the intended mode of operation.

> Where accelerated stabilisation is an objective, a substantially greater rate of gas production is likely. This may necessitate larger plant and provision of a high degree of standby plant facilities. This will enable the control system to be sized and appropriate collection and flaring or utilisation equipment to be specified.

> The designer should ensure that an appropriate location is available for gas plant, generally one that is screened or hidden from view with minimal visual and noise impact. The impact of flare and exhaust emissions from landfill gas plant should be assessed.

Gas wells

6.68 Gas wells may be either vertical boreholes passing through the waste or horizontal pipes laid in the waste lifts as landfilling progresses. Horizontal wells constructed in deep landfills can suffer blockage and dislocation due to differential settlement. Their use is generally restricted to shallow landfills (less than about 10m deep) or to existing landfills with high water (leachate) tables where there is little dry waste between the surface and the leachate table. Where vertical wells are to be used the potential effects of settlement on the well should be assessed, including the possibility of damage to the lining system.

Figure 6.5   Landfill gas management

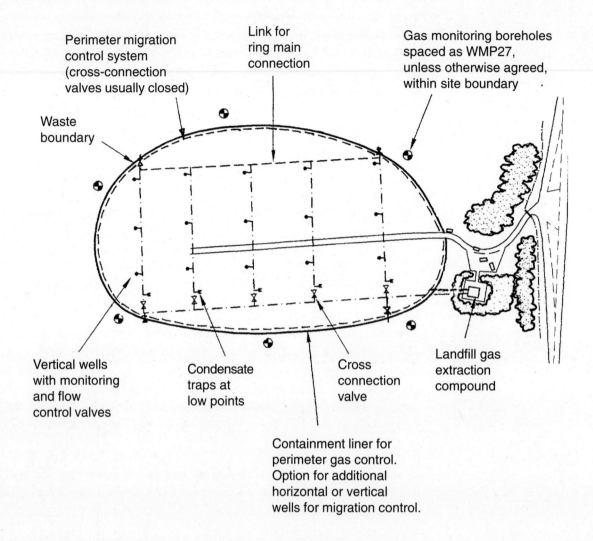

Perimeter migration control system (cross-connection valves usually closed)

Link for ring main connection

Gas monitoring boreholes spaced as WMP27, unless otherwise agreed, within site boundary

Waste boundary

Vertical wells with monitoring and flow control valves

Condensate traps at low points

Cross connection valve

Landfill gas extraction compound

Containment liner for perimeter gas control. Option for additional horizontal or vertical wells for migration control.

Three tier landfill gas management system:

1. Gas extraction

2. Liner barrier (plus migration extraction if necessary)

3. Monitoring wells

6.69   It is most probable that the gas extraction systems will comprise vertical extraction wells in the waste linked by pipework in the capping system to a gas pumping and flaring compound. The wells may either be constructed as waste filling progresses or drilled retrospectively - this will be determined in consultation with the site operator. Possible damage to the lining system must also be considered if wells are drilled after waste filling is completed. The layout of the collection wells should be considered at the design stage using best current practice, and the design should also consider the positioning of any perimeter migration control system. The layout of the connection of extraction pipes to wells should be considered so that, where possible, permanent sections can be installed in stages and the extraction and migration control systems can be cross-connected for security.

Gas control at the perimeter

6.70   At the perimeter of the landfill the leachate containment liner will provide a deterrent to off-site migration. Because of differences in the viscosity of gas and liquids clay and bentonite barriers are orders of magnitude less effective at restricting the flow of gas than that of leachate. The designer should consider whether the proposed leachate containment liner is sufficient for gas control or whether a higher specification liner is required for gas control purposes.

Interface with other design aspects

6.71   The detailed design of the landfill gas control system should be undertaken in conjunction with the site operator and specialist landfill gas contractors/engineers. The designer should consider the integration of the various components of the gas management systems with other elements of the landfill design, for example whether it will be affected by the leachate management system or whether there is sufficient depth in the restoration layers[31] to accommodate well heads, extraction pipes and pipework required for leachate extraction. Settlement can disrupt the cap around the well or cause down-drag to push the well against the lining system.

> Additional materials above the barrier layer may be required to accommodate landfill gas pipes in a pipework zone within the capping system[32].

> The layout of the gas control system to minimise disruption to the planned afteruse should also be considered.

Gas pumping compounds

6.72   In assessing the design of the gas pumping compound the designer should consider

- the environmental impact (for example, noise, visual intrusion and effects on the atmosphere)
- land availability
- access for maintenance
- utilisation options
- the electricity supply to drive pump equipment
- the likelihood of trespass and vandalism
- operator safety.

[31] See WMP26E.
[32] See paragraph 10.20 and Figure 10.1.

6.73   A description should be given of the likely equipment that will be provided at the pumping compound, for example

> pumping and flaring equipment, duplicated if necessary for back-up facilities

> condensate traps

> pipe layout

> flare design.

6.74   The pumps and flares should be designed with appropriate performance standards. Consideration should be given to the possible need for VOC destruction even for landfill gas of low combustion potential. The Environmental Protection Act 1990 and its associated regulations have extended waste regulators' responsibilities more widely. Those responsibilities take in the control of gas flares. Until guidance is available the waste regulatory body should take account of best practice and emission standards for comparable industrial processes.

> The components of best practice are likely to include, depending on the site, some or all of the following

- the probable variation of gas volumes and gas composition, including trace components, during the life of the site

- the landfill gas collection and pumping system

- the interrelation of the flare system with landfill gas utilisation

- flare design

- combustion temperature and residence time

- flare capacity, including the effects of turn-down on flare operations and emissions performance

- standby provisions

- continuous combustion monitoring

- process control of flare operation

- exhaust gas recycling

- emission monitoring

- safety

- maintenance.

Preparatory works

6.75   The design of the preparatory works required before the actual deposit of waste commences should be shown on a single plan. This can be developed in more detail at the construction design stage. Early drawings can be used to prepare estimates of the initial expenditure required to develop the site. The works will include the following elements, as described in the preceding sections

- highway improvements

- site fencing

- waste reception areas including weighbridges, wheel wash, offices, garaging

- access roads

- earthworks cut and fill areas

- area to be lined initially

- location of landfill gas and leachate management facilities

- site drainage including surface water, leachate disposal routes or irrigation plots

- site screening, including tree and shrub planting.

Monitoring requirements　6.76　Processes in a landfill are dynamic. There is a need to monitor the behaviour of a landfill continuously to determine

- its impact on its surrounding environment

- its rate of reaction and its progress towards stabilisation (see also WMP26A).

6.77　The data required by the designer to monitor the performance of the landfill design elements is shown in Table 6.2. Monitoring is described in detail in WMP26D.

6.78　The performance and regulatory monitoring will enable the designer to determine whether or not the landfill is behaving in the manner anticipated at the design stage. The designer should always seek to alter elements of the design to accommodate changes required by actual field experience.

Table 6.2

Performance monitoring of landfill design

Item	Data requirements
Earthworks	Whether the assumptions used in the earthworks balance have been borne out by construction and operational experience, which is generally related to void use
	Will demonstrate whether predicted site life and materials import/export requirements are correct
Fencing	Whether the fencing systems provided are proving effective, or whether specifications should be relaxed or strengthened
Groundwater drainage system	Check on efficiency and performance
Landfill gas	The designer will wish to know details of practical experience gathered by the operations team
Leachate collection system	Efficiency of designed removal system, monitored at secondary monitoring points located away from the removal sumps
	Durability of materials used in manholes, pumps and pipelines
	Leachate generation assessment should be checked against operational data
Liner system	As licence requirements
	Designer may wish to monitor the performance of the component parts of the liner system including materials but this may require intrusive investigation and generally should only be considered as part of a research programme
Maintenance schedules	The landfill designer and the site operator should monitor maintenance schedules to determine whether these are realistic, whether they are being followed, and whether they are in need of revision
Odour	Refer to paragraph 9.96
Settlement	Topographical surveys to check on actual settlement and test predictions
Stability	Checks on stability of temporary and permanent slopes to determine whether design assumptions were correct

7 Landfill Liners

Introduction

7.1   The general principles, objectives and standards for the design and construction of the overall landform are set out in Chapter 3. These principles summarise the risk assessment process which will determine the need for landfill containment and assist in the derivation of performance requirements for the landfill lining system. A liner system forms an integral part of a containment landfill. If a landfill is to be developed on this principle, a suitable liner system needs to be designed and constructed.

Purpose and scope of this chapter

7.2   This chapter describes principal factors in the design of alternative liner systems that may be used as appropriate to achieve the performance required by the design and provides guidance on

- the selection of the liner system, including the application of risk assessment methodology to assess the performance requirements (paragraphs 7.5 to 7.16)

- types of liner system, with reference to typical liner materials and the circumstances in which each liner type is commonly used (paragraphs 7.17 to 7.31)

- lining materials, including general suitability, construction methods and testing for a range of natural and artificial materials (paragraphs 7.32 to 7.46)

- the prevention of damage to liner systems after construction (paragraphs 7.47 to 7.53).

7.3   This chapter provides an overview of the issues to be considered when designing and constructing landfill liners. It does not set out detailed guidance for the designer but references a range of publications which contain data and detailed guidance on liner systems, types, materials and specifications. **These are not definitive and the designer must refer to current appropriate information at the time of design.**

7.4   **Two principal references have been used which provide more detailed guidance on all aspects of landfill lining systems, and to which the designer is strongly recommended to refer.** These are

- *Guidance on Good Practice for Landfill Engineering*[1], a guidance document published by the DoE and referred to throughout this text as the GGP report.

- *Quality Assurance and Quality Control for Waste Containment Facilities*[2], a guidance document published by the United States Environmental Protection Agency and referred to here as the USEPA document.

Selection of liner system

7.5   **The selection of a liner system is a complex process which should be**

---

[1] DoE: *Guidance on Good Practice for Landfill Engineering*, CWM 106/94 (in press).
[2] USEPA (1993): *Quality Assurance and Quality Control for Waste Containment Facilities*. Technical Guidance Document EPA/600/R-93/182, September 1993. Office of Research and Development, Washington DC 20460.

determined on a site specific basis. Considerable study must be undertaken in designing and constructing a suitable liner system. Where the landfill operator is inexperienced or not appropriately qualified to undertake the selection process, expert assistance should be sought.

Performance objectives   7.6   The performance objectives for a landfill liner system can be summarised as follows

- to control seepage of leachate from the landfill into the environment such that it does not cause an unacceptable level of contamination

- to assist in controlling the migration of landfill gas such that it does not cause an increase in the concentration of soil gases, over and above background levels, by the amounts defined in WMP27

  > Paragraphs 6.64 to 6.74 and 9.168 to 9.184 provide further advice on gas control and the limitations of clay liners.

- to retain consistent performance in its operating environment for the required design life and to be compatible with the expected leachate and gas composition and temperature

- to assist in the control of any groundwater ingress into the landfill which would cause an unmanageable increase in the volume of leachate generated or unacceptable uplift pressures.

7.7   Where accelerated stabilisation has been determined to be an objective of a specific site's design and operation, the rapid degradation of wastes should not compromise any general requirement for meeting the objectives defined above.

Application of risk assessment to liner selection   7.8   **The initial selection process for a liner system should involve a risk assessment.** The process to be followed is described in paragraphs 3.27 to 3.34 and should consider all sensitive receptors for both leachate and landfill gas.

> An acceptable level of leachate seepage from the landfill should be derived taking into account the sensitivity of the receiving waters, the depth and attenuating capacity of the unsaturated zone, the probable composition and generation rate of the leachate and dilution of leachate in the receiving waters.

> When addressing landfill gas, the geology and hydrogeology of the area and the presence of buildings, their occupancy, services, vegetation and manholes or other confined spaces in the proximity of the site should be taken into account in defining likely migration mechanisms (see WMP27).

> If a landfill is to be constructed below groundwater level, then the design of the liner should also take into account possible seepage of this groundwater into the landfill with its resultant impact on leachate generation, and control of uplift pressures on the liner (see paragraph 6.43), together with the long-term effects of groundwater levels.

7.9   The risk assessment methodology uses defined probability distributions of performance for each element of a liner system, and of the factors affecting them, such as leachate head, to determine a probable seepage rate under a given set of conditions. Methods for calculating seepage rates through liner systems are described in Appendix H, and the basis of a probabilistic model for estimating seepage rates through liner systems is described in Appendix E.

7.10   **In general terms, a liner system should not rely on the provision of only one level of protection.** In some circumstances the ground conditions under a site may provide some protection in terms of naturally low permeability, or attenuation/dilution of any seepage from the site. This will be taken into account in the risk assessment and may reduce the level of additional protection required. In other circumstances, multiple levels of protection need to be incorporated into the liner system. The degree to which multiple levels of protection or leakage interception are required will be determined by the risk assessment, and a combination of the probability of failure and the ease of potential remedial action.

Factors affecting selection   7.11   The selection of a liner system to achieve the performance objectives determined by the risk assessment will be influenced by the availability of materials, either on-site or locally. An assessment of costs will generally indicate that a liner system should only incorporate natural materials which are available within a reasonable distance of the site. Consequently, there will be regional variations in the design of a liner system based upon local geology. For example

> Clay will generally be used as a mineral component of a liner system where suitable clay is available on-site or nearby.

> If clay is not available but there are deposits of silty sand, the formation of a good quality bentonite enhanced soil (BES) will be facilitated.

> If no suitable materials are available, it is more probable that the liner will be formed from synthetic geomembranes (flexible membrane liners, FMLs) or geosynthetic clay liners (GCLs).

The choice of secondary protection will be similarly affected by the underlying geology of the site.

7.12   Liner systems should, in addition to the property of low permeability, **be robust, durable, and resistant to chemical attack, puncture and rupture**[3].

7.13   **Robustness, durability and puncture resistance** may be provided by

• the inherent strength of the liner components themselves

• the combination of two or more components acting synergistically

• physical thickness

• protective layers.

7.14   The designer should consider the performance of the liner materials both during construction, where the construction of each individual layer of the liner system must not endanger the layer(s) beneath it, and during operation, where the waste characteristics and method of waste placement will be relevant factors.

7.15   **Chemical resistance** and corresponding **durability** should be provided by considering the compatibility of the liner materials with the probable leachate and gas composition and temperature, particularly where accelerated stabilisation is to be practised. The effect of potential weaknesses or imperfections in the liner materials should be considered, together with the effects on secondary barriers of any leakage through the primary liners.

---

[3] There are procedures available for testing individual liner elements for some of these properties, but not for liner *systems* overall.

7.16   The stability of liner systems during site preparation and filling with waste must be assessed with regard to

- subgrade stability

- inter-liner stresses and slip planes in all potential circumstances

- the effects of leachate recirculation and potentially varying leachate head

- cellular filling and temporary slopes

- loss of mass on decomposition.

Liner types

7.17   A landfill liner system may comprise a combination of barriers and fluid collection layers, plus mineral or synthetic components fulfilling a separation or protection function. The principal types of liner system which can be fabricated from these components are illustrated in Figure 7.1 and the associated liner materials are shown in Table 7.1. The systems are described below. Cut-off walls and other types of system are also described.

Single liner system

7.18   This comprises a single primary barrier. This is typically overlain by a leachate collection system (LCS) with an appropriate separation/protection layer and where necessary can be underlain by a groundwater collection system (GCS), again with an appropriate separation/protection layer.

Table 7.1

Typical liner materials

Liner type	Primary barrier	Secondary barrier	Tertiary barrier
Single liner system	Clay, BES or hydraulic asphalt	N/A	N/A
Composite liner system	FML	Clay, BES or GCL	N/A
Double liner system	Clay, BES, GCL or FML	Clay, BES, GCL or FML	N/A
Multiple liner system	FML	Clay, BES or GCL	Clay, BES, GCL or FML

Notes: 1.   *Clay*   =   *Natural (reworked) clay liners*
            FML   =   *Flexible membrane liner (for example HDPE)*
            BES   =   *Bentonite enhanced soil*
            GCL   =   *Geosynthetic clay liner (bentonite matting)*

        2.   *Drainage layers can use either granular materials with geotextiles, or geonets, as shown on Figure 7.1*

Figure 7.1 Typical landfill liner system sequences *(not to scale)*
To be read in conjunction with Table 7.1

A: Single liner system

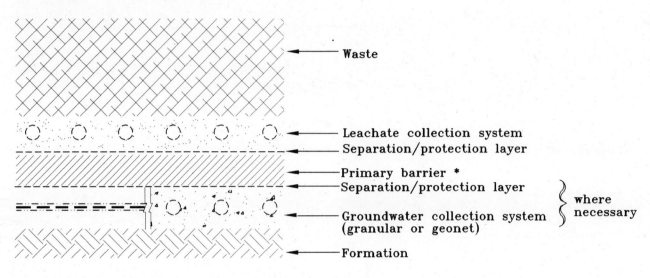

Waste

Leachate collection system
Separation/protection layer
Primary barrier *
Separation/protection layer
Groundwater collection system
(granular or geonet)
Formation

} where necessary

B: Composite liner system

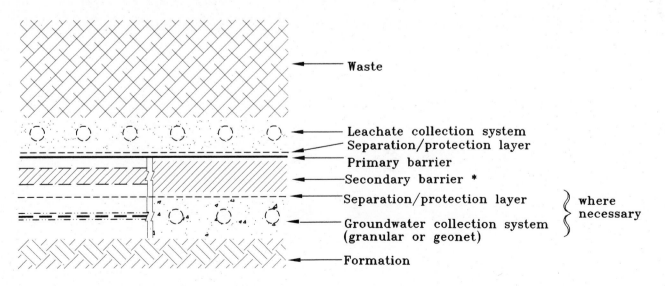

Waste

Leachate collection system
Separation/protection layer
Primary barrier
Secondary barrier *
Separation/protection layer
Groundwater collection system
(granular or geonet)
Formation

} where necessary

* Alternative materials see Table 7.1

Figure 7.1 Continued

C: Double liner system

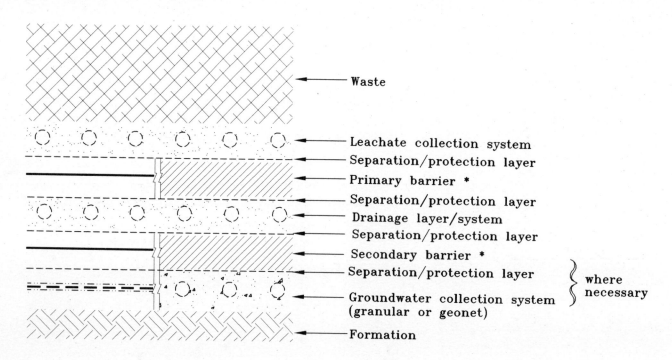

- Waste
- Leachate collection system
- Separation/protection layer
- Primary barrier *
- Separation/protection layer
- Drainage layer/system
- Separation/protection layer
- Secondary barrier *
- Separation/protection layer
- Groundwater collection system (granular or geonet) } where necessary
- Formation

D: Multiple liner system

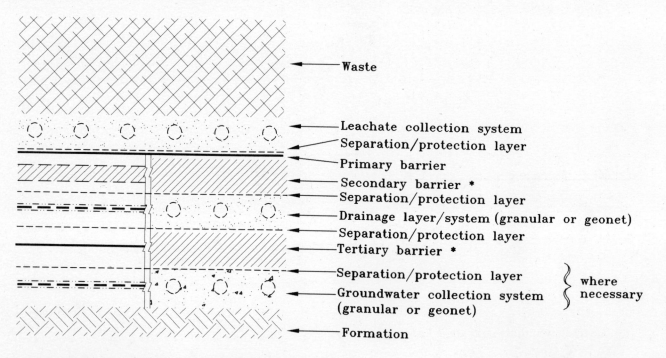

- Waste
- Leachate collection system
- Separation/protection layer
- Primary barrier
- Secondary barrier *
- Separation/protection layer
- Drainage layer/system (granular or geonet)
- Separation/protection layer
- Tertiary barrier *
- Separation/protection layer
- Groundwater collection system (granular or geonet) } where necessary
- Formation

* Alternative materials —see Table 7.1

7.19   This type of liner system is typically only used in low vulnerability[4] situations. Single liners can also be appropriate at landfills where part of the base is to be constructed below the level of the surrounding groundwater, provided that the flow rate into the site does not generate unmanageable quantities of leachate and where uplifting forces will not threaten the liner's integrity.

Composite liner system

7.20   Composite liners generally comprise two or more barriers (termed primary, secondary, etc) made of materials with differing physical properties placed in intimate contact with each other to provide a synergistic effect[5]. Typically, a primary geomembrane (flexible membrane liner - FML) is placed above a secondary low-permeability cohesive mineral barrier. Again, an LCS is typically placed above the primary barrier and a GCS may be constructed beneath the liner. Such a liner system combines the advantages of two different materials with different physical and hydraulic properties. It is essential that the FML is placed in intimate contact with the mineral liner to ensure that any flaws in the geomembrane will not lead to lateral migration along the interface between the two components[6].

7.21   The performance and robustness of this liner system is generally better than a single liner. This liner system has the sole objective of containment and does not allow any monitoring or removal of leachate or landfill gas which may seep through the liner, although the provision of a GCS may partially permit this.

Double liner system

7.22   This includes primary and secondary barriers with an intermediate high-permeability drainage layer to monitor and remove liquids or gases from between the barriers. The primary barrier is again overlain by an LCS, and the liner may be underlain by a GCS.

7.23   This type of liner system does allow the monitoring and removal of any fluids which may seep through the primary barrier, and in this respect is superior to a single liner system. In its most basic form, where geomembranes are used to form the barriers, the double liner system is generally inferior to a single composite liner in terms of performance and robustness.

Multiple liner system

7.24   This represents a combination of the above. The principle is similar to that of the double liner system in that an inter-barrier drainage layer allows the monitoring and removal of any fluids which may seep from the landfill. However, a composite liner is used, usually for the primary barrier, but potentially also for the secondary barrier, or vice versa. Again, an LCS is placed above the liner which may also be underlain by a GCS.

7.25   Such a system combines the containment ability and robustness of a composite liner with the monitoring and recoverability that a double liner system offers.

Cut-off walls

7.26   These may be constructed around a landfill to intercept off-site migration of landfill gas or to contain leachate. They may also be used to divert or lower groundwater levels up-gradient of a site. Cut-off walls are typically keyed into low permeability or saturated strata. They may be used as part of a landfill liner system

---

[4] *Vulnerability* is used in the context of the NRA's Policy and Practice for the Protection of Groundwater, and should be taken into account in the risk assessment.

[5] A synergistic effect in this context is where the performance in combination is greater than the sum of the individual components.

[6] See NRA, North West Region (1991): Note on composite lining systems for landfill sites (Letter to waste regulation officers).

or, for example, specified as pre-defined remedial works to be constructed in the event of seepage from the site being detected. Cut-off walls generally consist of physical passive barriers, providing a permeability contrast, and may be drained or undrained, but active pumped systems may also be used. A wide variety of techniques may be used to form cut-off walls[7]. Cut-offs may also be used to intercept and divert clean groundwater from entering a site. As with any liner material, the performance of a cut-off will vary according to its materials and quality of construction.

Other liner types

7.27   Within the liner types described a number of variants may become available. These should be considered on their merits for a particular site. For example, a composite hybrid of bentonite coated geomembrane is available. Whilst this may be of superior performance to a single geomembrane, the bentonite layer, whilst beneficial, lacks the thickness of a composite liner as described above (see also paragraph 7.41).

Lining of vertical quarry faces

7.28   Lining of near vertical quarry faces is problematic, but must be resolved if such sites are to be acceptable. Most conventional solutions use a variant of the 'Christmas tree' approach of a vertical series of edge bunds, either of clay and/or covered with geomembrane. Other solutions, variously using gabions, polystyrene, rock bolting, suspension of membranes, reinforced soil, and sprayed or cast concrete, are available. The designer faced with this challenge must meet the objectives set for the liner, together with any perimeter monitoring systems, whilst working within the constraints of the materials as described in this chapter[8].

Liner protection

7.29   Appropriate liner protection must be provided. Mineral liners are susceptible to erosion, weathering, desiccation and penetration of their upper surface by, for example, leachate collection system granular material. Geomembranes are susceptible to puncture, localised stress and point stress concentrations due to indentation, which can lead to stress cracking. A range of materials including granular materials, thick geotextiles, bonded shredded tyres and GCLs (if external to the liner) can provide appropriate protection to FMLs[9]. Protection to mineral liners is generally afforded by leachate collection layers, where provided, with geotextile separation above the clay. Thinner plastic membranes can provide benefit in moisture and erosion control if placed directly above the mineral liner. Stability can be a problem with interfaces between geosynthetics and mineral layers.

7.30   Where granular layers are used they are generally of sand or similar sized particles, 300 mm thick or more, overlain by a separation geotextile and the leachate collection system. Placement of the protection layer requires particular care to ensure that the placement machinery itself does not damage or over stress the liner. Erosion control will also be necessary, especially on sloping areas. The use of protective geotextiles is increasing. There is no accepted test or standard to assist in the selection of a suitable grade, but a German standard is in the course of

---

[7] DoE: *Guidance on Good Practice for Landfill Engineering*. CWM No 106/94 (in preparation 1995).

[8] Vertical wall installation is described in a NRA Internal Guidance Note No 7 *Landfill Liners*, December 1994.

[9] There are no recognised test procedures for such materials but bonded shredded tyres are a manufactured product subjected to manufacturing QA procedures. The following may also be of assistance:
- ASTM Standard DD5514
- BS 6906 methods of test for geotextiles

Reference should also be made to performance tests in NWWRO Document *Pollution Control Objectives for Landfill Design, Development and Operation* and in NRA Internal Guidance Note No 8.

preparation. Until a suitable standard is produced and accepted, the manufacturers' views should be sought. The adoption of quality assurance procedures in the manufacturing process should be emphasised.

Performance monitoring

7.31 Where a seepage detection system is installed, its performance should be carefully monitored and the results interpreted. For example, instances have occurred where the seepage intercepted has, on investigation, been demonstrated to be pore water expelled from the mineral liner component under the loading effect of the wastes. The designer should be clear whether a leakage detection system is for detection, interception and removal of any leakage through all or part of the liner system, or for detection only. Compartmenting the system can assist in the location of any significant leakage, and in its possible remediation. The use of geophysical leakage detection systems is becoming more common place, principally as an adjunct to CQA to check the quality of installations prior to waste deposition, but these would be used in addition to, and not instead of, a leakage interception system.

Lining materials and construction methods

7.32 The materials which can be used to form a landfill liner system, either singly or in combination, are shown in Table 7.1. For each material, general specification guidance is given in the following sections, followed by tables summarising guidance on factors affecting materials selection, methods of construction and testing methods, and listing useful current references.

General standards

7.33 The protection to be afforded by a liner system can only be achieved if its performance is equal to or better than that assumed in the risk assessment. The construction of the liner system is of vital importance to ensure that the system meets the assumptions made in the risk assessment. Engineering skills and standards form the key to successful installation of the liner systems; however, these have been augmented by new skills and standards from the polymer/ chemical industry for the successful installation of geosynthetic elements of liner systems.

7.34 Specifications for the construction of earth road embankments are in some respects relevant to the construction of clay liners, and in particular to subgrade preparatory works, with some modifications[10]. However, there are few equivalent UK specifications for the installation of other possible components of the liner system, for example, BES, GCL and geomembranes, and the designer must draw on standards and specifications prepared in the UK and overseas, either by government sponsored bodies, trade associations, manufacturer's data, research bodies or individual research projects.

Natural clay

7.35 Where suitable low permeability clay materials are available, either on-site or locally, these generally provide the lowest cost lining material and, as such, are commonly used. A typical specification is that the material should be placed and compacted in layers to form a homogeneous layer with a total thickness no less than 1,000 mm with a hydraulic conductivity no greater than 1×10^{-9} m/s.

7.36 Clay liners can be used to form a single liner system or in combination with other materials to form a composite, double or multiple liner system. In the latter case, if clay materials are in short supply, the thickness of the liner can reasonably be reduced and the permeability requirement can be relaxed if the risk assessment permits but the thickness of a clay liner should never be less than

---

[10] Department of Transport Specification for Road and Bridgeworks (1991).

600 mm. This represents a practicable minimum thickness for robustness and durability provided that a high level of CQA of material selection and construction can give assurance of consistent quality throughout its depth.

7.37   The basic requirement of a natural clay liner is that it attains and maintains a permeability below that specified. The factors which can affect the suitability and performance of clays are given in Table 7.2.

7.38   Before full scale construction of a clay liner commences, destructive field trials should be carried out on a sacrificial area to assess the adequacy of the proposed materials, methods of construction and CQA procedures.

7.39   The upper layers of in situ clays should be excavated and re-laid as an engineered layer of appropriate thickness, unless the overall deposit is of such quality and thickness that this is considered unnecessary. In that case perimeter cut-offs may be required to penetrate any weathered zone.

Bentonite enhanced soils

7.40   Where naturally occurring soils do not contain enough clay to achieve the desired permeability, bentonite can be added to improve their permeability characteristics. Liners formed from bentonite enhanced soils (BES) may be used as a replacement for clay. BES works by the swelling of the bentonite particles on hydration, which forces the hydrated bentonite around the soil particles to produce a synthetic clay.

> The contaminants in leachate can affect the hydration characteristics of the bentonite, potentially leading to a reduction in swelling or damage to BES that has been previously hydrated with clean water, and therefore to a reduction in its permeability[11].

> The suitability of the bentonite, and of the natural soil, for bentonite treatment is dependent on a number of characteristics which can only be determined by laboratory testing, preferably with similar leachate. The laboratory testing will also determine the quantity of bentonite that needs to be added to form the low permeability layer.

7.41   The GGP report advises that bentonite enhanced soils should generally be considered as direct replacement for natural clay liners and may be used by themselves in low risk situations or more typically as part of a composite or multiple liner system. The basic requirement of a bentonite enhanced soil liner is that it attains and maintains a permeability below that specified. The maximum coefficient of permeability of BES is frequently specified as 1×10^{-10} m/s. Although this provides a similar order of hydraulic flow resistance as one metre of clay at 10^{-9} m/s, the reduced thickness of BES is likely to require greater protection to give the same level of robustness and durability (see also paragraph 7.27). Factors affecting the suitability of a bentonite liner are given in Table 7.3.

Geosynthetic clay liners

7.42   Bentonite is also available as a composite matting comprising a bentonite layer approximately 6 mm thick between two geotextiles. The geotextiles are joined together either by needle punching or stitching, or by glue mixed with the bentonite. GCLs must be confined by either soils or FMLs with leachate collection systems, and can provide the synergistic behaviour with an FML as observed with composite liners. The geotextile layers can, if not adequately confined, provide a pathway for lateral leachate movement. Because of their inherent lack of

---

[11] See Building Research Establishment (1994): Bentonite walls.

Table 7.2

Natural clay liners

Factor	Comment	Useful references[1]
Materials suitability		
Particle size distribution (PSD)	In general terms, materials with a high clay content or a high silt and clay content will have a lower permeability. Materials with a high percentage of stone or with excessively large particles should not be used. The overall grading of the PSD is of importance, and suitably graded materials with a low clay fraction content can still perform acceptably.	DoE : GGP USEPA 1993 NWWDO 1991 NRA 1994 Elsbury et al Benson et al Daniel 1993 Rowe et al
Particle shape and (soil) fabric	Well-graded materials will tend to compact to a lower porosity (and hence permeability) than uniformly graded materials. In addition, fabrics present within the clay can lead to permeabilities being anisotropic.	
Plasticity	Although clays should be plastic if they are to form effective liners or liner components, highly plastic soils tend to shrink and crack on drying. As a general guide the plasticity index (PI) should be between 10% and 30%. Activity (PI/clay content) should be above 0.3. Higher PI clays can be suitable but require greater care to avoid shrinkage.	USEPA 1993
Strength	The material should be strong enough to be reworked (if appropriate) and to resist deformation under the imposed loading during the construction and operational phases.	
Mineralogy	X-ray diffraction techniques should be used to confirm that clay minerals and not rock flour comprise the bulk of the material.	
Construction		
Moisture content	Optimum permeability will frequently be achieved at moisture contents slightly wetter than that optimum for dry density. It is important that clays placed at a controlled moisture content are maintained at that moisture content by covering immediately, either with temporary plastic sheeting or components of the liner system which are to be placed above it. A frequent requirement is that the moisture content should be between: *lower moisture content:* OMC or plastic limit (PL) or 5% air voids, whichever is the higher, and *higher moisture content:* generally PL x 1.2 or 5% air voids whichever is the lower.	
Wetting of clays	If the natural moisture content is less than that for optimum permeability it should be adjusted by wetting. US practice recommends a pug mill or mixer, though careful spraying by bowser can be satisfactory if suitably quality controlled and if the clay is placed in thin layers, rotovated and allowed to wet-up satisfactorily. This may take 1-3 days.	

Table 7.2 *continued*

Factor	Comment	Useful references[1]
Construction *continued*		
Compaction	The purpose of compaction is to produce a uniform and dense liner. The compaction equipment should be chosen after field trials, and should be capable of both breaking down clods and keying them into previous lifts.	
Testing		
Permeability	Confirmation of suitability on excavation from deposit (generally done as part of site investigation and during field trials).	USEPA 1993 DoE : GGP
	Verification of remoulded permeability after construction, by previous establishment of inter-relationship between field trials and detailed testing.	NWWDO 1991
	Use of detailed triaxial testing for accuracy. Oedometer or fixed wall permeameters should be correlated to detailed tests, and are only suitable for rapid in-situ testing for consistent quality of construction across site. Important factors are: selection of sample; protection of undisturbed samples; replacement of liner at sample point.	BS 1377
Atterberg limits	Useful rapid tests of index properties; in combination with other parameters indicates acceptability of clay; useful for frequent testing for material consistency across site.	BS 1377
Moisture content and density	Provides basic level of construction quality control. Based on pre-determined relationship between permeability, density and moisture content. Several methods available for site or site office use, for example, a microwave and weighing scales. Nuclear Density meters provide a rapid method for the calculation of moisture content and density. They require skilled operation.	BS 1377
Particle size distribution	Essential for suitability of clay resources, in conjunction with other factors. Also similar to Atterberg limits in defining material consistency.	BS 1377
Thickness	Essential aspect of construction quality control for thickness of layers and total thickness of clay liner. Minimum of four layers, maximum thickness of layer determined from field trials.	
Chemical compatibility	Specific testing should be carried out for abnormal wastes, leachates or abnormal clays.	
CQA/CQC	Essential to ensure that specified performance is achieved uniformly. See Figure 3.2 for effect of variation on 1% of area.	Daniel 1993

Note: *1.*   *See bibliography for Chapter 7 for references in full.*

thickness, GCLs are sometimes used as a high quality layer above thicker deposits or layers of higher permeability clays or BES, to provide the requisite robustness. The factors that can affect the suitability of bentonite (see paragraph 7.40 above) also apply to GCLs. These factors are summarised in Table 7.4.

Geomembranes (flexible membrane liners)

7.43   Geomembranes (FMLs) are now widely used, and a substantial body of experience has been built up into their suitability, construction, CQA, performance, and their limitations. **These are not described here but are fully described in Section 3 of the GGP report, and Section 3 of the USEPA document**[12]. The designer of a landfill liner is recommended to study these documents, or such other authoritative texts as may become available.

7.44   The designer must consider the specification of FML against the criteria of

- materials selection (there are many different polymers available and under development, for example, high density polyethylene, low density polyethylene, very low density polyethylene, linear low density polyethylene, polypropylene, polyvinyl chloride, chlorosulphonated polyethylene)

- compliance tests to ensure that the material supplied is of the quality specified[13]

- installation tests to ensure that the FML is correctly jointed without damage to the membrane and to ensure that the FML is not damaged by the foundation, or during its installation or that of protective or drainage layers, or during the operation of the landfill

  > Criteria for definition of damage should be defined in the specification.

- protection, specification and construction of appropriate measures to ensure that the FML will meet its objectives in service

- appropriate CQA and CQC (see paragraphs 4.16 to 4.20).

Hydraulic asphalt

7.45   The use of asphalt or asphaltic concrete is a technology more familiar in dam construction. It is used as a liner in continental Europe and is available in the UK. Its use is described in the GGP report.

Interaction between construction materials

7.46   In the formation of all liner systems it is necessary to construct layers of different materials, either for separate or synergistic purposes. **The designer and contractor should consider all potential interactions between layers, both in use and under construction.** For example, a leachate collection blanket can act as a protection layer to a liner, but can also act either as a source of mechanical stress to a FML or of penetration to a thin mineral layer. Similarly the interface friction should be assessed between each layer under all conditions of use, both static and dynamic, temporary or permanent.

---

[12] DoE: *Guidance on Good Practice for Landfill Engineering* Report CWM 106/94 (in press). USEPA: *Quality Assurance and Quality Control for Waste Containment Facilities.* Technical Guidance Document EPA/600/R-93/182, September 1993. Office of Research and Development, Washington DC 20460.
[13] BS drafting committees TC 135 and BS 46/8 are preparing standards for geotextiles and geomembranes, and CEN TCs 189 and 254 are developing essential requirements, including test procedures, for all aspects of geomembranes.

108

Table 7.3

Bentonite enhanced soil liners

Factor	Comment	Useful references[1]
Materials suitability		
Bentonite composition	Sodium montmorillonite based bentonites have a greater swelling property than calcium montmorillonite (for example, Fuller's earth). While this is advantageous and requires less bentonite in the mix, because of the possibility of chemical reversion, the use of calcium based bentonite to provide a denser and potentially more stable BES should also be considered. Polymer treated compounds can offer greater resistance to leachate compounds and to desiccation. Specification of the grading of the bentonite should be considered.	NWWDO 1991 DoE : GGP USEPA 1993 Manufacturers' literature
Host material	The host material must be capable of thorough mixing, and must be chemically compatible with the bentonite (eg high soluble salts can cause difficulties). Clean sands will mix readily, as will silty sands which will also require less bentonite for a given permeability. More cohesive host materials are more difficult to mix due to balling, giving uneven distribution. Crushed rocks, PFA and other flue dusts may interfere with the swelling and cohesive properties of the bentonite, and should be tested for compatibility. Host materials should be sufficiently dry to permit thorough mixing (see below).	
Composition of mix	Must be established by prior testing, including permeability testing. Moisture content must be sufficient to allow good compaction, but not to allow hydration in an unconfined state. (One of the benefits of BES is that it swells under pressure below the confining liner).	
Construction		
Mixing	Mixing is generally recommended to be carried out in a mixer, although rotovation in a stockpile followed by excavation and laying can also be used. Direct spreading and rotovation in situ is no longer recommended.	
Placing and compaction	As for clay, having regard to the thickness of the layer and to any other liner layers beneath. Specific hydration is not normally required, and the BES should be covered by subsequent liner system layers as soon as possible after placement.	
Testing		
General	Confirmatory testing of properties as for clays.	
Bentonite distribution	Methylene blue provides a useful rapid site test for the correct dosage rate and uniformity of mixing, but not for bentonite/colliery shale mixes.	Alther 1983

Note: 1.   See bibliography for Chapter 7 for references in full.

Table 7.4

Geosynthetic clay liners

Factor	Comment	Useful references[1]
Materials suitability		
Bentonite composition	As for BES.	
Bentonite distribution	Generally 4000 g/m² of bentonite, uniformly distributed.	Manufacturers' literature
Geotextile suitability	Generally chosen to reflect the grade of bentonite. Can be woven or non-woven. Can be specified to provide mechanical strength and degree of chemical resistance (HDPE or polypropylene) if required.	Manufacturers' literature USEPA 1993 DoE : GGP
GCL characteristics	Internal frictional resistance after hydration must be considered, particularly for the glued product.	
Construction		
Laying	Attractively simple. Material is rolled out carefully over prepared and rolled formations.	
Jointing	Overlaps are marked @ 150-300 mm. Seams should be jointed with bentonite mortar to control lateral flow of leachate through the geotextile, and/or with bitumen.	
Hydration	The GCL should not be permitted to hydrate and swell if unconfined by FML and protective coverings/leachate collection system. Weight as well as covering is important, as the GCL can otherwise hydrate due only to condensation beneath the FML.	
Testing		
Shear strength	As the GCL is a manufactured product, its specification should be assured by compliance testing.	
Bentonite type, grading, content and thickness	- Ditto -	
Geotextile	- Ditto -	

Note: 1.   See bibliography for Chapter 7 for references in full.

Prevention of damage to liner systems after construction

7.47 Following the successful installation of the liner system there is a risk that damage will occur to the liner by a number of routes, such as

> accidental damage

> vandalism

> neglect.

7.48 *Accidental damage* may arise where bulky difficult waste, for example, lighting columns or concrete lumps, is tipped carelessly onto the drainage or protection layer, and is able to puncture and damage a liner system, especially a flexible membrane. Other examples of damage include

> posts supporting litter netting being driven into the drainage/protection layer causing damage underneath

> vehicles being allowed to travel over the liner system.

7.49 *Vandalism* can result in flexible membranes being punctured, torn and burnt.

7.50 *Neglect* may occur when too large an area of liner is prepared and is not covered with waste for long periods. During this period damage may occur by the drainage layer becoming blocked by washed-in fines, desiccation of a clay layer, wind uplift or erosion of liners or covering materials.

7.51 During the construction itself there is also a danger that mechanical placement of protective layers or drainage blankets can cause damage to the membrane.

Measures to prevent damage

7.52 The designer should consider all possible causes of damage for the proposed site, and in conjunction with the operator ensure that appropriate measures are taken to avoid them. Precautionary measures may include

> CQA[14] procedures for the initial waste infilling to minimise the risk of damage caused by waste

> training of the operating staff to increase their awareness of the purpose of the liner and the importance of its protection

> realistic sizing of phases to ensure that the risk of neglect is minimised

> working method statements and CQA for the placement of inter-liner layers.

7.53 The Site Manual will convey the details of the design and the underlying design principles to the operator at the operational stage of the site.

---

[14] See paragraphs 4.16 to 4.20 and Table 4.1.

Part 3
Landfill Operation

8 Planning and Design of Site Operations

Introduction

8.1   Parts 1 and 2 of this Paper provide background to the concepts of landfill design and operation, and guidance on the engineering construction of a landfill. As an engineering project, construction of the landform needs to be designed and carried out to predetermined and tested standards. These principles should also be applied to the emplacement of waste, the infrastructure which supports that process, to the capping of the landfill and monitoring of the degradation process.

8.2   All landfill operations require careful planning. The main operational features will have been determined by the operator and the designer at an early stage and consolidated in the working plan, in consultation with regulators, and submitted as part of the waste management licence application. A number of operational factors or conditions will be specified by the regulation authorities at the planning and licensing stages. The licence should be a working document and should accommodate the need for matters to be determined or amended as the life of the site progresses. Such matters should be dealt with in the working plan.

8.3   This chapter provides guidance on the general principles and planning of site operations, following the overall approach of landfill design and operation as an integrated project to construct a landform as described in Chapter 1. The chapter is arranged in the following order

- principles of site operation, including the key management considerations for the operator in relation to the main alternative design philosophies (paragraphs 8.5 to 8.12)

- skills and experience required for landfill operations, including standards and training of operators (paragraphs 8.13 to 8.16)

- record keeping, incorporating the Site Manual (paragraphs 8.17 to 8.26)

- waste acceptance procedures (paragraphs 8.27 to 8.50)

- legal requirements for regulation of operations, with reference to the legal framework in Chapter 2 and statutory guidance in WMP4 (paragraphs 8.51 to 8.58)

- landfill liaison groups (paragraph 8.59)

- general landfill safety, as part of the underlying requirement for protection of life, the environment and buildings (paragraphs 8.60 to 8.63)

- performance monitoring of operations (paragraph 8.64).

Definition of terms

8.4   The process of emplacing wastes in the prepared landfill has been traditionally referred to as *landfill operation* and has been retained as the terminology for this Paper, as has the term *operator* to describe the functionary. The operator is not necessarily the licence holder.

114

Principles of site operation

8.5   The quality, quantity and characteristics of waste used to build the landform need to be clearly understood and documented as part of the design, construction and operational stages of landfilling. Waste characterisation and the degradation processes are described in Appendix C.

8.6   The landfill designer will have determined at an early stage in the design process how the site will be developed. Wherever possible, bioreactive wastes should be managed for accelerated stabilisation in accordance with the priorities for meeting the aims of sustainable development, as illustrated in Figure 1.1. There are three main categories of landfill operation associated with these design considerations

- controlling waste inputs for low reactivity

- managing the landfill proactively as a reactor to achieve accelerated stabilisation

- managing the landfill with regard to long-term maintenance obligations.

Operating low reactivity sites

8.7   The control of waste inputs for low reactivity is an essential part of the operation for inert and low reactivity waste sites. However, there are relatively few genuinely inert wastes. For example, construction wastes typically contain small percentages of wood, carpet, paper and other potentially biodegradable components. Even the soil within such a site contains biodegradable matter and may differ chemically and biologically from the surrounding land. Thus, even though the organic content of the landfill may be kept low, unless it is entirely excluded some leachate and gas generation can be expected. This may need to be managed both to prevent pollution and to ensure that the site will stabilise according to the design criteria.

Managing landfills for accelerated stabilisation

8.8   In order to manage a landfill for accelerated stabilisation, the landfill has to be designed and operated to maintain as high a rate of activity as possible within a *biological reactor*. The operation is essentially a *process engineering* activity. This may require a fundamental shift in approach on the part of the operator. The following key steps may be identified for the operator

> Consider the waste as a feedstock and control the input accordingly.

> Inspect, categorise and, if appropriate, pretreat the feedstock.

> Place the waste in landfill cells (large biochemical batch reactors).

> Integrate monitoring and control systems as the waste is placed.

> Manage the site in the same way as any other process engineering facility by

- proactively commissioning the process, acquiring operating data such as leachate and gas quantity and quality and temperature and indirectly controlling the process

- optimising waste handling and placement procedures

- making adequate arrangements for site closure, aftercare, monitoring and maintenance.

8.9   Operators should consider potential advantages which may be offered by pre-treating the waste prior to depositing it into the landfill. Methods which might be considered include

- processing excavation and demolition waste to separate fines and aggregate for use on-site or elsewhere

- chipping timber to form a mulch for use in site restoration

- composting vegetation waste for restoration material

- pulverising biodegradable waste to create a more homogeneous feedstock for the accelerated stabilisation landfill

- shredding refuse delivered in plastic sacks to create a more homogeneous feedstock for the accelerated stabilisation landfill.

8.10   Pre-treating the waste and careful control of the incoming waste enable the site to be operated as a component landfill where discrete cells within the site accept different classes of waste, for example a bioreactive cell and an inert cell.

8.11   Further details of the factors affecting accelerated stabilisation are given in Appendix D.

Managing long-term containment sites

8.12   Where a long-term containment facility is considered to be the current BPEO, potentially polluting wastes are isolated from the environment by robust lining and capping systems in conjunction with long-term control measures for leachate and landfill gas. Design models will need either to incorporate the ability to install appropriate passive control measures retrospectively, or to utilise attenuation to minimise the long-term burden for future generations. For bioreactive wastes where accelerated stabilisation is not acceptable, the risk assessment will need to consider long timescales and very long-term maintenance obligations may be involved. In these circumstances, placement and management of the landfill cap and management of the long-term controls will be particularly important considerations for the operator and regulators.

Skills and experience of landfill operators

8.13   The landfill operator should recognise that the range of activities, the skills required and the standards to be met, have increased very substantially since WMP26 was first published in 1986. Modern landfill operators should regard themselves as being involved in a branch of engineering engaged in the process of building a landform, out of waste, whether it be a landfilling or a landraising operation. They should regard the waste entering into their site as a construction material and also, in the case of bioreactive waste, the process feedstock for the landfill reactor. Further skills are required for landfill gas and leachate management.

8.14   Where the landfill site is situated in, or is associated with, a working quarry the relationship and divisions of responsibility between the landfill manager and the quarry manager need to be clearly understood. WRAs should ensure that there is no conflict between the waste management licence conditions and statutory requirements governing the quarry operations including planning permissions and health and safety regulations.

8.15   The number of employees required to operate landfill sites effectively and safely will depend on many factors. The principal considerations are

- flexibility of both employees and plant is necessary to ensure that operators and machines employed can be used effectively

  > A form of shift system may be needed to avoid down time during meal breaks. Back-up will also be required to cover for sickness and holidays.

- where a number of vehicles use the site simultaneously, effective traffic control is important

  > A banksman controlling traffic flow and unloading may, therefore, be required close to the tipping area.

- if cover material is excavated on-site, additional staff and equipment may be required

  > This part of the operation may be subject to mines and quarries regulations.

- road maintenance, litter control and regular cleaning of fences and litter screens are essential

  > This may require additional seasonal man-power.

- where liquid wastes or other problem wastes are received, additional labour may be required to implement special disposal procedures.

Budgets should be included for record keeping, environmental control and leachate management staff.

Professional competence

8.16   The management of the activities authorised by the licence must be in the hands of a technically competent person. In the case of most landfill operations, technical competence is determined by the WAMITAB scheme of certification of technical competence. The law is set out in Part II of the Environmental Protection Act 1990 and statutory guidance is given in WMP4[1]. Other specific areas of work may also require specific qualifications or licences, for example, application of pesticides.

Record keeping

8.17   Maintaining accurate and comprehensive records of landfill operations is essential. Requirements for the surrender of waste management licences, under the provisions of section 39 of the Environmental Protection Act 1990, mean that a licence can only be surrendered if the WRA which granted it accepts its surrender and issues the site with a Certificate of Completion[2]. Thus good record keeping by the landfill operator will be of paramount importance when applying to surrender the licence upon completion of the landfill operations. Record keeping cannot be undertaken retrospectively and therefore plans for organising the maintenance of records should be instigated at an early stage in the design process.

8.18   The scope and quantity of these records will grow as the site develops and they will not be replaceable if lost. They must therefore be stored in a secure location and a complete duplicate set maintained at a separate location away from the site. A convenient method of storage which gives rapid access, makes use of up to date technology and occupies minimal space is storage on CD-ROM (compact disc - read only memory).

The Site Manual

8.19   It is essential that a means of ensuring effective transfer of information from the initial design concepts through to the final restoration and Certificate of Completion is provided. This forms part of the quality approach described in Chapter 4, which should be employed throughout the operational phase of the

---

[1] A brief introduction to waste management licensing which describes fit and proper persons and certificates of technical competence is given in DoE leaflet *A New Waste Management Licensing System: What It Means, How it Affects You*, DoE June 1994.
[2] See also WMP4.

development. A key concept of the approach is the maintenance of a *Site Manual*, which comprises a compilation of all relevant documents setting out all of the details of the site.

8.20   The Site Manual should include

- details of desk study and site investigation

- explanation of the landfill philosophy and objectives, including assessment of the approach to landfilling

- details of the landfill design and construction including risk assessments, specifications, drawings and CQA documentation

- planning and waste management licence applications and supporting documentation including changes and modifications

- detailed restoration and aftercare scheme

- formal environmental statement, or other details of informal environmental assessments carried out

- working plan for submission with licence applications, including amendments and modifications

- detailed restoration and aftercare scheme

- planning consents, waste management licences and supporting documents, including planning agreements and modifications

- statutory records relating to health and safety including health and safety plans, pesticides, accidents and fires

- survey records and plans including the changing capacity of the landfill[3]

- waste input details, special waste consignment and transfer notes and details of carriers, waste disposal locations, and development of working areas and phases

- details of landfill gas and leachate management

- photographic record

- environmental monitoring programme for leachate, landfill gas, noise, odours and dust as appropriate

- environmental monitoring data including factual and interpretative data and reports for leachate, landfill gas, noise, odours and dust as appropriate, together with calibration records

- registers of complaints, records of non-compliances and remedial measures

- visitor records

- record of performance monitoring including internal and external audits.

---

[3] Annual aerial survey with computerised volume calculation may provide an accurate and cost effective record of the changing capacity of the landfill.

118

8.21   Within the Site Manual, a register should be maintained of all the above items to enable search and cross-referencing, so that the Site Manual becomes a useful aid to communication between all parties involved in landfill design, construction, operation, restoration and aftercare. In the case of a partially completed site, as many as possible of the items should be included.

Weather and climate data

8.22   Weather conditions can have a critical effect on the efficient operation of a landfill site. The designer will have obtained historical data relating to the site during the desk study stage of the site investigation and will have taken into account the weather conditions likely to occur when designing leachate systems and surface water drains. These should be sized to take account of storm events.

8.23   Prevailing winds and the seasonality and direction of strong winds will have been taken into account when designing the sequence and direction of tipping so as to minimise the detrimental effects of odour, dust and litter on local communities.

8.24   The wind pattern should also be taken into account when locating permanent and temporary gas vents and landfill gas combustion exhausts so as to avoid exposure of local residents to vent and combustion emissions and potential odours. Atmospheric dispersion modelling of emissions may be necessary when permanent landfill gas flares and exhausts are planned, if the risk assessment shows that a receptor may be at risk.

8.25   The landfill operator should consider the installation of a simple weather station recording rainfall, barometric pressure and humidity. Site and parameter specific weather warnings may be obtained from the Meteorological Office. These will enable the operator to have advance warning, by telephone or fax, of critical weather conditions such as

>   exceptionally heavy rainfall

>   sharp falls in barometric pressure.

8.26   The operator can define the trigger levels and parameters against which the warnings will be issued.

Waste acceptance procedures

8.27   The waste that is accepted at a landfill site must fall within the categories of waste permitted by the waste management licence. The landfill operator may also impose restrictions on the acceptability of certain waste streams. **Waste acceptance procedures are complex and require careful consideration of the resources required and how to incorporate waste checking into the operation of the site.** The general approach is shown in Figure 8.1. Acceptance procedures for co-disposal wastes are discussed in WMP26F.

8.28   The Duty of Care Regulations have heightened awareness of the need to adequately describe and detail movements of controlled wastes. Site operators need to be aware of the nature of the wastes being deposited at their site in order to ensure compliance with licence conditions, operator policies and health and safety requirements. They will also need to maintain records of the wastes deposited.

Figure 8.1 Waste acceptance

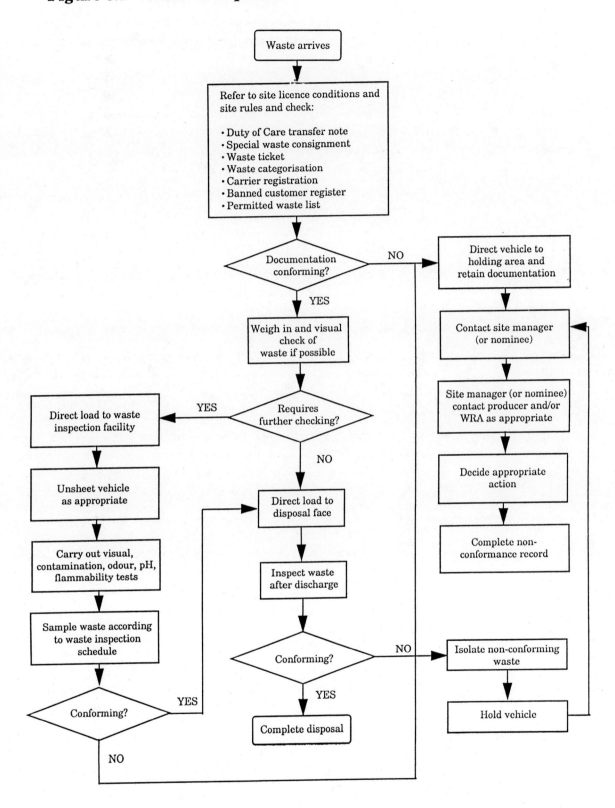

> All wastes received at a landfill site must be

- classified

- delivered by registered (or exempt) carriers

- covered by the appropriate documentation (Duty of Care transfer notes, Special Waste consignment notes and waste dockets)

- weighed in

- checked for conformity.

Classification

8.29   The waste classifications used in most existing licences are typically broad groups which are based on the legal descriptions given in the Environmental Protection Act 1990, and formerly the Control of Pollution Act 1974[4]. Guidance on a new waste classification system is in preparation[5].

- These classes may not be sufficient for the needs of the operator, particularly if the site is being operated for accelerated stabilisation. The operator will need to understand the physical, chemical and biochemical properties of the wastes rather than their origin alone.

8.30   Criteria for the acceptance of wastes at a particular landfill should be based upon the risk assessment carried out during the site design. Should changes to the waste input be required, the iteration process as described in Chapters 1 and 3 should be repeated.

Documentation and compliance testing

8.31   All wastes arriving at the landfill site should be covered by the necessary documentation, in accordance with legal requirements and the requirements specified by the operator, and should include an adequate description of the waste.

8.32   The Duty of Care Regulations require that a transfer note must be completed, signed and kept by the parties, to be transferred if the waste is transferred. The transfer note should include a description of the waste and provide information on the premises and process that produced the waste and chemical and physical composition.

> A correct and adequate description is of great importance to the landfill operator receiving the waste, who may wish to discuss the information requirements with the producer before agreeing to accept the waste. The description must provide enough information to enable the operator to avoid mismanaging the waste.

> To ensure that waste is suitable for acceptance at a particular site, it is essential that all of those responsible understand the waste acceptance criteria for that site and are aware of the information which is required for inclusion in the documentation. If this is not the case, a considerable amount of time and effort is likely to be expended dealing with non-conforming wastes.

8.33   The waste should be characterised and, where appropriate, tested. Useful advice is given in Annex II of the EC Landfill Directive[6], which sets out the following three level procedure

---

[4] See Appendix A for waste definitions.

[5] *A waste classification system for the UK*: Guidance in preparation by DoE.

[6] Waste acceptance criteria are incorporated in Appendix II of the Draft Landfill Directive (Ref 4103/95, 9 January 1995). The principles should be applied regardless of implementation of the directive.

- Level 1 : Comprehensive characterisation

- Level 2 : Compliance testing

- Level 3 : On site verification.

8.34   Testing and analysis of waste should be organised at three levels.

Level 1: Comprehensive characterisation

8.35   The waste is characterised by the producer to determine the acceptability of the waste for disposal at a particular site. Comprehensive characterisation constitutes a thorough determination of the chemical and physical properties of the waste.

Level 2: Compliance testing

8.36   Waste is re-tested at a specified frequency to look for changes in the basic characteristics of the waste. The frequency should be as specified by the waste regulatory body.

Level 3: On-site verification

8.37   Waste is subjected to simple checks and tests to ensure that the waste, when it arrives at site, matches the description in the documentation.

Input control at the landfill

8.38   The checks carried out will depend on the

> type of vehicle carrying the waste

> nature of the waste

> method used to contain the waste (for example drums and closed skips).

8.39   The checks carried out may involve

> visual examination

> sampling and analysis on-site (for example pH, flashpoint)

> checking the analyses provided, possibly using retrospective (Level 2) testing.

8.40   Three aspects of input control should be provided for

- documentation check

- on-site verification testing (Level 3)

- retention of samples for retrospective (Level 2) testing.

Documentation check

8.41   When waste arrives at the site the documentation should be checked for compliance by the designated person at the site reception or weighbridge. If the documentation is in order the waste should be weighed at the site reception or weighbridge, if not the vehicle should be directed to the holding area for further action (refer to Figure 8.1).

On-site verification

8.42   The weighbridge operator should direct the vehicle to either

- the disposal area

> The on-site check will be a visual check on the waste following discharge. The most complete visual examination can be made as the waste is spread and compacted.

- a designated waste inspection area

> A more detailed on-site verification check may be made prior to disposal.

Retrospective testing

8.43 Representative samples are taken at a specified frequency for Level 2 testing.

8.44 To minimise delay to vehicles using the site a schedule of the frequency and type of waste checking should be established. For loads which cannot be inspected before discharge a programme of spot checking should be established. A designated area should be provided for this purpose.

Competence of operatives

8.45 It is essential that all those responsible for checking the documentation accompanying vehicles and the site operatives at the disposal face are competent with respect to

- understanding the waste acceptance criteria for the site in terms of licence requirements, and company policies

- understanding the basic underlying reasons for the acceptance criteria for the site

- understanding the information which should be provided on the documentation accompanying loads

- ability to identify non-conforming wastes

- procedures to follow if either the documentation or the load is non-conforming

- safety.

8.46 The site operatives at the site reception and the disposal face will require training to ensure that they are technically competent in these areas. Waste inspection facilities are discussed in paragraphs 9.26 to 9.30.

Non-conforming consignments

8.47 Non-conforming consignments may be identified at

- site reception

- weighbridge

- waste inspection facility

- disposal face.

8.48 Non-conformances may be due to the documentation being incorrect, insufficient or inaccurate or due to the waste not conforming with the documentation, the waste management licence or other legal requirements.

> Operators should compile a written procedure detailing how to deal with non-conforming wastes. All site personnel should be aware of the chain of reporting and the actions to be taken. An area should be set aside for vehicles to be held, pending a decision regarding their future. The waste regulatory body should be contacted to provide advice regarding whether the load can be accepted or whether it should be reconsigned to another location.

> If a waste has been deposited before non-conformance has been established and is contrary to the waste management licence or is an unconsigned special waste, it should be isolated and the vehicle should

remain on-site pending a decision as to the necessary actions required to deal with it.

> Records of non-conformances should be kept and should include the actions taken to deal with them, who was contacted and the decision which was made for the disposal of the waste, and whether any offence was committed[7].

Communications

8.49   Effective communication links between weighbridge personnel, persons responsible for carrying out waste inspections and operatives at the disposal face are extremely important to ensure the following

- smooth transfer of wastes through the site

- wastes which require to be checked prior to proceeding to the face are directed to the appropriate area

- only conforming wastes are allowed to be deposited and are directed to the correct tipping area

- appropriate preparations and safety precautions are made for waste streams requiring special handling arrangements

- plant requirements for handling particular waste streams are provided at the appropriate location

- the emergency services and other parties can be contacted.

8.50   Options for maintaining communication links include the use of two way radios or portable telephones.

Regulation of landfill sites

8.51   Operational landfill sites are primarily subject to planning and waste management licence conditions which impose constraints on the way in which the operation is conducted. They will also specify performance standards to be maintained for various aspects of the operation. The legislative framework is outlined in Chapter 2 and Appendix B.

8.52   Conditions are legally enforced and the regulatory authorities may inspect the site at any time without prior notice. The inspectors may also inspect records and take away samples as they see fit.

8.53   The regulation of landfill sites is primarily the responsibility of waste regulatory bodies. Sites are also subject to other scrutiny by local authorities and the public, particularly as regards nuisance and litter.

Statutory nuisance

8.54   Local authorities are under a duty to inspect their areas for statutory nuisance under the Environmental Protection Act 1990[8]. If complaints are received from members of the public, the local authorities are obliged to investigate. A statutory nuisance could be caused by smoke, fumes, gases, dust, steam, odour, other effluent, flies, rodents, noise, escape of leachate, landfill gas or litter.

---

[7] Waste which is non-conforming and requires to be transferred to an alternative disposal point will require to be reconsigned under the Duty of Care provisions.

[8] Environmental Protection Act 1990 Part III Section 79. See also Chapter 2 and Appendix B. In Scotland, statutory nuisance is controlled by the Public Health (Scotland) Act 1987; however, the Environment Act 1995 provides for those sections of the 1987 Act to be repealed and for the nuisance section in the Environmental Protection Act to be extended to Scotland.

8.55   If the local authority considers that a statutory nuisance exists or might be likely to occur or recur, the local authority is under a duty to serve an Abatement Notice on the operator which must require either or both of the following

- the abatement of the nuisance or the pollution or restriction of its occurrence or recurrence

- the execution of works or other steps necessary to comply with an abatement notice.

8.56   The notice should specify the time within which compliance is required. Failure to comply with the notice is an offence.

8.57   In addition any aggrieved individual can lodge a complaint with the Magistrates Court[9]. If the Court believes that a statutory nuisance exists or is likely to be a recurring nuisance, it is under a duty to issue an abatement notice requiring the operator to abate the nuisance and to execute works within a specified time. A fine may also be levied.

Litter

8.58   It is an offence for any person to leave litter on public open spaces or on highways (roads) or on land of statutory undertakers. A member of the public who is aggrieved, for example, by litter persistently falling from vehicles travelling to and from a landfill site, can apply to the Magistrates Court for the issue of a Litter Abatement Order.

Landfill liaison groups

8.59   To ensure good relations with local people who may be affected by a landfill, many operators have found it beneficial to establish local landfill liaison groups.

- These serve as an avenue for the operator to explain his operation rather than be subject to uninformed speculation, and to provide a channel for members of the public with legitimate grievances to put their complaints directly to the operator without having to resort to law.

- Local landfill liaison groups often include representatives from the local councils and a representative of the WRA is often invited to attend.

General landfill safety

8.60   Employees should be competent, well trained and adequately supervised. Training should include site safety, fire safety, first aid and the handling of dangerous materials where appropriate. Since landfill sites can pose dangers to both site operator and users, emergency plans should be laid down and tested at regular intervals. Landfill sites should be regarded as potentially hazardous locations and the operator should have a written safety plan for the site. The health and safety plan should include matters

- for compliance with safety legislation including COSHH

- which although not required by statute are nevertheless required, for example to fulfil insurance requirements.

8.61   Hazards present at landfill sites may include

- moving plant and vehicles

- steep slopes

---

[9] In Scotland, the Sheriff Court.

- bodies of standing water

- contaminated, putrescible, toxic, flammable or infective material

- noxious, flammable, toxic or hazardous gas.

8.62   All employees and visitors to the site should be made aware of the potential hazards and the safety procedures to be implemented including fire safety.

8.63   The arrangements for visitors to the site should be such that they are not able to enter without reporting to the operator who can then ensure that they are aware of safety procedures, including fire safety, and are wearing appropriate protective clothing. Arrangements for visitors should always include check-in and check-out procedures. Regulatory inspectors visiting the site out of hours should be aware of and should comply with their own written safety plan for that site.

Performance monitoring   8.64   The performance of all of the landfill operations should be monitored according to a pre-determined schedule. Monitoring should continue throughout the operational phase and extensive guidance on this aspect is contained in WMP4, 26A, 26D and 27.

> Performance monitoring should include details of operational practices such as construction of earthworks, assessment of compaction performance, desludging waste water interceptors, landfill gas and leachate management systems. It should also include infrastructure components such as gates, fences, surface water drains and maintenance.

> Performance monitoring of some items is often prescribed by the WRA who may require records to be kept in a site diary.

9 Operational Practice

Introduction

9.1   The operational practices employed during the development of the landfill are an important element in determining the acceptability of the final landform in the environment. The operation of a site should

> reflect the design and construction requirements of the project

> satisfy all requirements for environmental protection, restoration and aftercare in accordance with the needs of the regulatory authorities

> present high standards to the public

> ensure satisfactory service to the users.

9.2   The purpose of this chapter is to provide guidance on the day-to-day operations of a landfill site. The chapter is divided into the following sections

- site infrastructure (paragraphs 9.4 to 9.51)

- internal movement of waste (paragraphs 9.52 to 9.56)

- waste discharge and emplacement (paragraphs 9.57 to 9.63)

- waste compaction (paragraphs 9.64 to 9.68)

- working areas (paragraph 9.69)

- daily cover (paragraphs 9.70 to 9.81)

- difficult waste (paragraphs 9.82 to 9.85)

- protection of local amenities (from for example, traffic, noise, odour, windblown litter, birds, vermin, insects, dust and mud on the road) (paragraphs 9.86 to 9.110)

- landfill fires (paragraphs 9.111 to 9.117)

- management of leachate (paragraphs 9.118 to 9.156)

- control of landfill gas (paragraphs 9.157 to 9.185)

- equipment[1] (paragraphs 9.186 to 9.197).

> In practice the subject areas are interlinked. The chapter gives guidance on the general considerations for each operational feature.

9.3   The details of the operations including the type of equipment used and the methods of waste emplacement will be dependent upon the waste streams accepted at the site, the rate of input, and the size and nature of the site itself. It is important for the operator to maintain records of various aspects of the operation to comply with legislation, including that for Certificates of Completion, and as good practice.

> Guidance on record keeping and performance monitoring is provided in Chapter 8, paragraphs 8.17 - 8.21 and paragraph 8.64.

---

[1] Many of these subject areas are also included in guidance notes published by the National Association of Waste Disposal Contractors (NAWDC). A list is included in the Bibliography.

Site infrastructure

9.4   The site infrastructure includes fixed installations which form the basis of the operation and without which the operation would not function smoothly. Many of these features will be common to most landfill sites, regardless of size and type, and are discussed below

- site entrance and security

- site control offices

- waste inspection facilities and laboratories

- weighbridges

- garages, workshops and mobile plant parking

- signs and directions

- lighting

- wheel cleaning facilities

- contaminated water treatment facilities.

Site entrance and security

9.5   The considerations which should be taken into account when designing the entrance are shown in Table 9.1. Prior to submitting a planning application for a landfill site, the landfill operator should consult with the local authority highways department to discuss access requirements. These requirements will depend upon a number of factors, including

- number and frequency of vehicles using the site

- size and type of vehicles using the site

- classification of the highway from which access is to be gained.

9.6   The measures taken to ensure security of the site and its facilities should be determined on a site specific basis. Typical intruders include children, fly-tippers, vandals, thieves, scavengers and animals. The operator of the landfill site should take all reasonable precautions both to protect his interests and to avoid being found negligent should an intruder incur an injury whilst on the site. Such measures may include the provisions given in Table 9.2.

Site accommodation and control offices

9.7   These may include

- site control and administration offices

- welfare (toilet, washing, first aid, lockers and messroom)

- stores.

9.8   The site accommodation will depend on the size and nature of the landfill operation.

> For example, the site office on a small site may incorporate the weighbridge office; however, larger sites may require individual offices to accommodate personnel such as the site manager, administrator and engineer, and possibly regulatory staff and independent consultants.

9.9   The construction of buildings will depend on the anticipated life of the site and the size of the operation, and may range from portable offices to purpose built brick buildings. Regardless of the number or type of buildings, certain features are common to all, including

Table 9.1

	Considerations for site entrance
Road safety	Entrance set back from the highway
	Main access road of sufficient length to ensure queues do not extend onto the highway
	Entry and exit lanes of adequate width to cope with the size and type of vehicles using the site and to allow vehicles to pass
	Good sight lines
	Acceleration/deceleration lane
	Appropriate visibility splays at junction
Logistics of entry to and exit from the site	Gate should be far enough off the highway to allow the first/last vehicle of the day to park safely while the gate is being operated
	Weighbridges should be situated as far into the site as possible, to avoid queuing on the highway
	Desheeting/sheeting areas should be clearly marked and should be located clear of the site entrance
	Wheelwashes should be strategically placed to avoid queuing, preferably at the landfill end of the access road
	The main access road should be constructed to highway standards with a tarmac or concrete surface, kerbs and suitable drainage
	The main access road should be kept clean, and free of pot holes to assist the free flow of traffic
	Suitable road markings
	Adequate, clear direction and instruction signs
Visual impact	The appearance of the site is a major influence on how the site is perceived by the public and so the site entrance should incorporate:
	• landscaping
	• tree planting
	• screening of the operational areas
	• presentable, clean and tidy site offices
	• good tarmacadam/concrete surface parking facilities
	• direction and instruction signs
	• site lighting

Table 9.2

Measures to prevent unauthorised site access

Gates	Gates should be provided which match the fencing specification
	The gates should span the full width of the access road
	A suitable locking mechanism should be provided and a register kept of key holders
	Gate tops may be cranked with strands of barbed wire
	Gates and fences should be maintained in good repair and inspected by a nominated person at regular intervals
Fencing[1]	Perimeter fencing should be provided at all landfill sites, to prevent unauthorised access
	Security fencing may be appropriate for vulnerable locations (the suggested minimum height for security fencing is 2 m with cranked top and barbed wire strands)
	Perimeter fencing should be inspected regularly by a nominated person
	The fencing should be maintained in good repair at all times
Security cameras	*Advantages*
	Provide a record of incidents which may be admissible as evidence
	Disadvantages
	Often difficult to provide an adequate power supply in remote parts of a site perimeter
	Challenging to vandals
Security guard	*Advantages*
	Full-time security is very effective - part-time less so
	Disadvantages
	Requires patrols and good quality paths around and within the site
Intruder alarms, lighting, shutters and bars on accommodation	*Advantages*
	Low manpower demands
	Disadvantages
	Require regular inspection and maintenance

[1] Appropriate specifications may be found in British Standard BS 1722 and the Manual of Contract Documents for Highway Works: Volume 3 *Highway Construction Details*. HMSO.

- compliance with planning, building, fire, and health and safety regulations and controls

- security and resistance to vandalism

- durability and the possible need for relocation during the lifetime of the site

- ease of maintenance and cleaning

- suitable appearance

- provision of services including gas, electricity, water, drainage and telephone

- landfill gas monitoring and safety measures.

Site control and administration offices

9.10   The site control office should be located away from the site entrance, adjacent to parking facilities for visitors and staff private vehicles. The location should be chosen to avoid the need for pedestrians to cross the access road. The door should not open directly onto the road or operating areas.

9.11   The site control office may serve as the reception area for visitors to the site. There should therefore be clear signs from the car park and a logging in and out system for visitors to use, in the interests of site safety and security. The site control office should provide secure accommodation to house records relating to the operation.

9.12   Details on the purpose and type of records which should be kept are discussed in paragraphs 8.17 to 8.21. There are requirements for some documents to be kept on display and a suitable notice board should be provided.

9.13   For larger sites, the accommodation may consist of a number of units or rooms to accommodate the office administrator/receptionist, site manager, site engineer, sales staff, meeting room, a visitor centre and possibly a laboratory. Future quality assurance developments may also require the provision of accommodation for the regulation authority and independent consultant.

9.14   Security against intruders is essential because of the value of the information and equipment stored in the office, such as monitoring devices, computers, facsimile and photocopying machines. The offices should have solid doors and lockable shutters or bars on the windows.

Welfare facilities

9.15   Welfare facilities should be designed according to the number of personnel working at and using the site. The facilities may include

- toilets (separate for male and female employees) and washrooms

- emergency shower (located close to the potential risk area)

- messroom for heating food and providing hot water, a fridge and tables and chairs for use during meal breaks

- canteen facilities (for larger sites)

- lockers

- drying and changing facilities

- first aid facilities

- accommodation for the crew/passengers of vehicles where the site rules permit only the driver to proceed to the disposal area

- means of communicating with other personnel on-site and in the site control office, which may be in the form of a telephone in the messroom, a radio base or other suitable means of communication

- services such as water, electricity, drainage and telephone.

9.16 Consideration should be given to the use of separate entrances or one-way systems to prevent or discourage access from dirty areas to clean areas other than through the changing/washing areas.

9.17 The welfare facilities should be located in a quiet location. The area in which these facilities are located should be landscaped to make them pleasant to use and to give a good impression to visitors using the site. As with the site control office, security is important and all doors should be of a solid type with lockable shutters or bars on the windows.

Stores

9.18 Secure facilities should be available for the storage of materials. The stores should be secure, well ventilated and dry with heating where appropriate. The storage requirements will be site specific, but may include storage space for

- general items

- hazardous materials

- fuels

- other materials.

9.19 *General items* include safety and protective clothing, tools, litter picking equipment, stationery and paperwork, fencing pegs, wire, pumps and mobile lighting, surveying equipment and monitoring equipment.

9.20 *Hazardous materials* include pesticides and herbicides, paints, flammable substances, containers of liquefied gas, gas cylinders, oils and greases, and special, difficult and hazardous wastes awaiting disposal. They should be stored separately in appropriate secure areas. The fire prevention officer should be contacted over the provision of hazardous storage areas. Typical features of stores holding hazardous material include

- security measures

- warning signs

- fire extinguishers

- stock list of chemicals and COSHH data

- first aid provision

- provision to contain and clean up spillages

- segregated areas for incompatible materials

- good ventilation

- washing facilities.

9.21 It may be appropriate to limit access to all stores, with a nominated person being responsible for access and maintenance.

9.22   *Fuel* and oil for plant and machinery on-site should be stored in correctly marked tanks or containers. These should be surrounded by a secure bund which is able to contain at least 110% of the capacity of the tank. This is to reduce the potential for pollution from spillages and to contain the fuel in the event of a fire. Bunded tanks should preferably be roofed to prevent the bund filling with rainwater.

9.23   The location and specification of fuel storage tanks should be specified in the working plan but may need to be relocated during the life of the site. The waste regulatory body and the fire prevention officer should be notified when fuel storage facilities are to be relocated.

9.24   Other materials which may need to be stored include drainage and lining materials, soils, selected processed wastes for road construction or other uses, and water for fire control, road spraying and leachate treatment.

9.25   Care should be taken in the storage of topsoil to prevent unnecessary deterioration of soil quality. Further details of the management of materials for use in restoration are contained in paragraphs 6.32 to 6.40 and WMP26E.

Waste inspection facilities and laboratories

9.26   Waste acceptance and reception procedures are described in detail in paragraphs 8.27 to 8.50. In order to ensure compliance, facilities should be provided to allow the checking of wastes prior to final deposit. The facilities required will depend, to an extent, upon the range of wastes which are permitted. There are essentially two areas where waste checking can be carried out

- the reception area

- the tipping face.

9.27   The weighbridge is usually the first point at which the vehicle will undergo checks to assess the suitability of its load for acceptance at the site. The documentation accompanying the load will be checked at this point. If the load is open-topped, it may be possible to make a visual inspection at the weighbridge office, possibly using closed circuit televisions or mirrors. This will not be sufficient to check full compliance of the load, however, as only the surface of the load may be seen. The checking which can be carried out at the reception area is also limited by the type of vehicle delivering the waste. It is impractical to inspect or sample wastes in closed vehicles at the reception area.

9.28   The loads of such vehicles are best checked by random waste inspections before the load reaches the tipping area. All loads should also be checked at the tipping area. There will therefore be a need to provide a separate waste inspection area. Where hazardous materials are not involved, a designated hard standing at the reception area with equipment to gain safe access to the load may be sufficient.

> In addition to its technical objectives the waste reception area portrays the public image of the operation and should be planned, operated and maintained in a clean, tidy and workmanlike condition.

> For sites accepting potentially hazardous materials, a more comprehensive inspection area will always be required. This should include

- a laboratory for carrying out waste checks to ensure conformity with the waste description

- storage for samples taken for sending for conformity analysis

- means of gaining access to loads, for example, a platform, steps or an elevating platform vehicle

- secure area for retaining non-conforming wastes which can be separated from the rest of the load

- an emergency shower

- fire extinguishers

- the ability to contain spillages and any contaminated rainwater, for example a concrete or tarmacadam base with falls to a collection sump

- communications link with the weighbridge, site control office and the disposal face and emergency services

- services including water, electricity, drainage and telephone.

9.29   The waste inspection facilities must be an integral part of the landfill design. It is important that these are considered at the development stage to avoid potential traffic flow problems. Where there is a need to unload for inspection prior to acceptance, an area should be set aside for this purpose.

> Such an area should have retaining bunds or walls and a hard surface which can be cleaned.

> Drainage water should be regarded as potentially contaminated and should be collected in an interceptor for analysis prior to discharging.

> The location of the area should be carefully chosen to prevent visual intrusion, odour nuisance and risk should hazardous materials be encountered.

9.30   An area should be set aside for holding vehicles whose loads are found to be non-conforming. In such an event the waste regulatory body should be contacted to determine the actions to be taken[2].

Weighbridges

9.31   An accurate record of waste inputs is essential for effective waste management and may be required to enable returns to be made to the waste regulatory body. On-site weighbridges are the best way of providing such data.

> It is good practice to weigh both on entry and exit from the site. Twin weighbridges may be located on either side of an island on which the weighbridge office is situated.

9.32   Considerations when selecting the type of weighbridge are given in Table 9.3. The weighbridge should be located sufficiently far from the highway to avoid congestion on-site and to provide space for queuing off the main highway. Sites with large input rates may require several weighbridges and the provision of specific queuing lanes. The weighbridge office will normally be located on the off-side of the weighbridge. It should be positioned so that the weighbridge operator can easily see vehicles approaching, leaving and using the weighbridge. The office should be elevated so that the weighbridge operator can speak to the vehicle driver.

---

[2]   Under the Duty of Care Regulations, loads which are not accepted and are sent for disposal elsewhere, must be accompanied by a new waste transfer note.

Table 9.3

Considerations for type of weighbridge

Platform weighbridge - flush with the road	*Advantages*
	No ramps are required
	Disadvantages
	Once installed relocation is difficult
	Sufficient access beneath the weighbridge is required for the clearance of debris and mud which may accumulate
	If built on infilled area, settlement may occur and access could be restricted unless appropriate engineering measures are undertaken
Platform weighbridge - raised	*Advantages*
	Easy to install
	Less engineering work required
	Moveable and can be relocated at reasonable cost
	Disadvantages
	The bridge is some 350 mm above road surface and, therefore, ramps are required
Axle weighers	*Advantages*
	Low cost
	Disadvantages
	Not suitable where accurate weighing is required

9.33   The operator may need to control traffic using the weighbridges by means of traffic lights or a lifting barrier. Easy communication between the drivers and the weighbridge office should be provided, together with the means for the exchange of tickets.

> Computer based technology in weighbridges increases efficiency and the free flow of traffic to and from the site. Modern weighbridges are usually linked to a computer which will record the identity of the carrier and the size and nature of the load. Although designed primarily to facilitate billing, their recording systems provide a valuable basis for more detailed waste input records.

> Methods of data acquisition and transfer include magnetic cards, bar code readers, and vehicle mounted transponders. These are principally suitable for regular site users. The facility to deal with occasional loads must also be included.

9.34   Security of the weighbridge office is an important consideration. Services (electricity, telephone and possibly water and drainage) will be required. To handle the full range of road going disposal vehicles, the weighbridge should be able to weigh up to 50 tonnes gross vehicle weight.

9.35   If the documentation is in order, the weighbridge clerk will direct the vehicle either to a designated area for inspection or to the disposal area. Effective communication between the weighbridge and the tipping face, and a sound knowledge of the acceptability of waste streams are required by all personnel involved in the transfer of waste from reception to final disposal, in order to ensure

- smooth running of the site

- only permitted wastes are accepted

- safety of operatives dealing with the waste

- accurate recording of waste inputs and disposal locations.

Garages, workshops and mobile plant parking

9.36   At larger landfill sites, garage and workshop facilities for plant and equipment, repair and maintenance may be required on-site. When designing workshop and garaging facilities consideration should be given to the need for

- adequate lighting, heating, ventilation, insulation and electricity supply

- sufficient headroom to enable tipping bodies to be raised

- a floor which can withstand the loads likely to be imposed on it

- adequate space for easy movement around the vehicle/s being worked on in the workshop

- security to prevent unauthorised access

- workbenches and tool storage space

- welding facilities

- lockable area for gas cylinders

- steam cleaning facilities

- fire extinguishers

- storage facilities for flammable/hazardous materials.

9.37   In the interests of efficiency, parking for mobile plant should be located near to the operational area. The parking area should not require the vehicles to cross or use the main site access road, to avoid damage by tracks or compactor wheels. Plant parking space should preferably be a hard standing and may require a secure enclosure to prevent unauthorised access to the vehicles.

Signs and directions

9.38   It is important that adequate information for the operation and regulation of the landfill site is displayed at the site for the benefit of both users and employees. The requirements will include the following

- site notice board at the entrance to the site

- direction signs

- instruction signs

- information signs

- safety signs

- warning signs.

9.39   Signs are used to convey information from the site operator to users, personnel and visitors to the site. This process is facilitated if signs are well designed, constructed and maintained. Standard designs and colours impart information more effectively than one-off signs and should be used wherever appropriate. In the case of safety signs, this is a statutory requirement[3]. The use of modular signs facilitates the amendment of the information contained on the sign.

Site notice board   9.40   This should be displayed at the entrance to the site and should be of a size and located in a position such that it can be easily read.

> The site notice board frequently gives visitors their first impression of the site. It should therefore be carefully designed, well maintained and sensitively located.

9.41   The WRA usually requires that it states the following information

- site name, address and telephone number

- site operator's name, address and telephone number

- site opening times

- emergency contact numbers

- name, address and telephone number of the WRA.

Direction signs   9.42   On leaving the highway and entering the site, drivers should immediately be made aware of traffic routing, access restrictions and weighing-in procedures by means of clear and well placed signs.

9.43   The signs should inform drivers carrying different waste streams where they need to go for reception and waste checking, and to deposit the waste.

> Colour coded signs or shapes or a combination of both are a useful means of providing directions where there are multiple routes.

> Some operators have found it useful to issue a coloured tally at the weighbridge to remind the driver of the correct route and to confirm to the tipping face supervisor that the load has arrived at the correct location.

Instruction signs   9.44   Instruction signs are necessary to enable users of the site to carry out their functions in a safe and efficient manner. Examples of instruction signs include

- use of weighbridges

- unsheeting procedures

- use of wheel cleaning facilities

- disposal at the tipping face.

Information signs   9.45   Examples of information signs include the location of car parks and site reception.

---

[3]   The Safety Signs Regulations 1980 (SI 1980 No 1471) which require that any safety sign giving specific health or safety information (other than signs used for regulating traffic, which should comply with the Road Traffic Regulation Act 1967) should comply with BS 5378 : Safety signs and colours.

Safety signs

9.46   Safety signs will relate to personal conduct on the site, speed restrictions to control and regulate traffic and the location of first aid and fire extinguishers.

Warning signs

9.47   Warning signs are extremely important on landfill sites as they draw attention to areas of high risk such as deep water, liquid filled trenches and overhead wires. A sign should be provided at all landfill sites before the exit to warn drivers that it is their responsibility to ensure that their vehicle is free of mud before exiting the site (see paragraph 9.49).

Lighting

9.48   Lighting will be required whenever the site is operational during hours of darkness, usually defined by reference to standard lighting up time.

> The site reception area, car park, weighbridge and wheel cleaning facilities, access road and important signs including all safety signs should be lit whenever the site is operational during hours of darkness or bad visibility.

> Effective portable lighting should be provided and strategically positioned to facilitate safe working under conditions of darkness or bad visibility.

Wheel cleaning facilities

9.49   The deposit of mud on the public highway is an offence (usually the responsibility of the driver of the vehicle) under the Highways Act. It is dangerous and is almost certain to cause adverse public reaction. It is essential that drivers using the site are provided with one or more effective means to remove mud and debris from their vehicles prior to leaving the site.

9.50   There are numerous options for wheel cleaning which can be used to ensure effective cleansing. Table 9.4 summarises the advantages and disadvantages of the options which are available.

Contaminated wash water

9.51   Run-off water and wash water from roads, garages, workshops and wheel cleaning facilities is likely to be contaminated. It should therefore not be discharged directly from the site. Interceptor pits or lagoons will be necessary to trap suspended sediment. Surface water should be tested before discharge to ensure compliance with the terms of the discharge consent. Leachate treatment facilities should not be used for the disposal of this contaminated water until the relevant documents in the Site Manual have been consulted to ensure that such disposal is permitted.

Internal movement of waste

9.52   Regardless of the size and type of the landfill, there is a key requirement to move the waste effectively and safely to the disposal face. Due account should be taken of all amenity impacts, for example dust, litter and mud, that may arise during this process. Mitigation measures should be adopted to minimise such effects[4].

---

[4] Refer to paragraphs 9.86 to 9.110.

Table 9.4

Wheel cleaning options

Site road construction and maintenance	*Advantages*
High specification, long site roads will assist the removal of any mud and debris before the vehicle reaches the highway	Long access roads allow for speed build up which helps to shed mud
Roads can incorporate sleeping policemen to further assist shedding of mud	Sleeping policemen are relatively cheap and are fairly effective
	Disadvantages
	This method is unlikely to be sufficient on its own
	Regular road sweeping, to clear mud which has been shed, will be required which may hold up traffic
	Long haul roads may not be feasible at smaller sites
Wet wheel spinner	*Advantages*
A combination of centrifugal force, the effect of rollers and the action of water jets removes mud from the wheels and underside of the vehicle	This system is relatively effective
	Disadvantages
	Requires a water supply and the disposal of dirty water and sludge
	Can freeze in winter
Dry wheel spinner	*Advantages*
A combination of centrifugal force and the effect of rollers removes mud from the vehicle wheels	This method is a relatively cheap option for the removal of mud from the wheels
	Disadvantages
	This method is only effective if it can be combined with at least 100 m of surfaced access road after the spinner
	The mud collected will require regular removal
Sunken bath or cattle grid	*Advantages*
This involves the provision of a shallow trough, formed in concrete or similar material, filled with water, through which all traffic leaving the site must be driven	This system is a relatively low cost, effective option
	Disadvantages
A set of humps or bars set into the road surface within the bath provides vibration which assists in shaking off loose material	Care must be taken to ensure that vehicles do not enter the bath at too high a speed
	There also needs to be a water supply and means of draining the dirty water and clearing the accumulated slurry
	Jarring of vehicles

Table 9.4 continued

Shaker bars	*Advantages*
This is essentially an oversized cattle grid, set level with the road	Relatively cheap and effective
	Disadvantages
Alternatively it can be elevated with a ramp at either end	The sump requires regular cleaning
Vibration from the vehicles passing over the bars causes the mud and trapped material to drop through the grid bars into a trough or sump	Jarring of vehicles
Automatic underbody spray	*Advantages*
This system involves the installation of side and underbody water washing spray equipment, comprising a steel frame mounted over a pit on which pumps, tanks and control equipment are installed	This option is very effective and cleans the underbody of the vehicle as well as the wheels
	Disadvantages
	This is a more expensive option
Vehicles are driven slowly through the machine which automatically starts high pressure spray jets aimed at all underbody surfaces, mudguards, wheel and side members	May freeze in winter
	A water supply, drainage and an area of hardstanding are required
Manual high pressure water jet	*Advantages*
Hand held high pressure water jets can be used to complete the cleaning cycle	This system will effectively remove mud from under the wheel arches and underbody and can be used for general cleaning of the vehicle
A water supply and drainage will be required in an area where vehicles can be parked up	*Disadvantages*
	Slow, therefore the facility needs to be strategically located to avoid traffic queues
	Drivers may be tempted to clean the whole vehicle which would be time consuming and would disrupt the general smooth running of the operation
	A water supply, drainage and an area of hardstanding are required

9.53 The provision of well maintained, high quality site roads is necessary to ensure the free flow of traffic and a fast turn around of vehicles. The construction details of three types of typical site road are illustrated in Figure 9.1. Depending on the size of the site and the traffic density, a combination of these road types will be required. Special protection should be incorporated where access routes cross liners.

Main access road

9.54 The main access road should lead from the highway, through the waste reception area and along the main haul road to the landfill operational area. The road should have a tarmacadam or concrete surface, and be graded to facilitate drainage towards the sides of the road. Between the highway and the reception area the road should normally have kerbstones set in concrete. The main access road should be wide enough for two way vehicle traffic or single track with passing bays at (say) 50 m intervals. Plant and machinery should not be allowed to travel on the main site access road as this is likely to cause damage.

Arterial roads

9.55 These roads lead from the main access road to the tipping area. They will be of a semi-permanent type but should be of a good quality to cope with heavy usage. Advance planning of the operational phasing will allow arterial roads to be retained for the maximum time and therefore reduce the investment required for reconstruction. They can therefore be constructed to a relatively high standard.

Temporary site roads

9.56 The temporary site roads lead from the arterial roads to the disposal face and therefore will have a short life. The roads are typically made of waste construction material which has been delivered for disposal at the site. The site roads are likely to become heavily compacted and should be taken up or ripped before emplacing further lifts of waste.

Waste discharge and emplacement

9.57 The overall objective is to emplace the waste into its final position within the landfill in accordance with the design objectives without compromising safety, the environment or local amenity. Landfill involves the application of established engineering practices for construction. Areas where waste is to be placed should be set out for line and level in advance of tipping so that waste is placed in accordance with the detailed construction plans.

Methods

9.58 The particular methods employed by the site operator will depend on the nature of the waste input and the requirements of the site. Factors which should be taken into account include

- physical condition of the waste
- weather conditions at the time of emplacement
- special requirements to avoid hazards inherent in the waste
- design objectives.

9.59 Considerations for a range of waste emplacement methods for untreated household, commercial and similar industrial and commercial wastes are given in Table 9.5. Procedures for co-disposal practice are given in WMP26F.

Procedures

9.60 Procedures should be closely controlled as the discharge and emplacement of waste is potentially hazardous.

9.61 All drivers using the site must be aware of the site rules regarding the discharge of waste and must obey instructions from the site personnel. The rules will be site specific but examples of practices which are likely to be universally applicable are as follows

Figure 9.1   Construction details of site roads

Section: Typical main access road

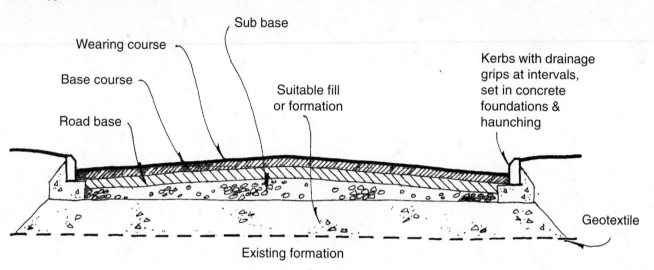

Section: Typical arterial road

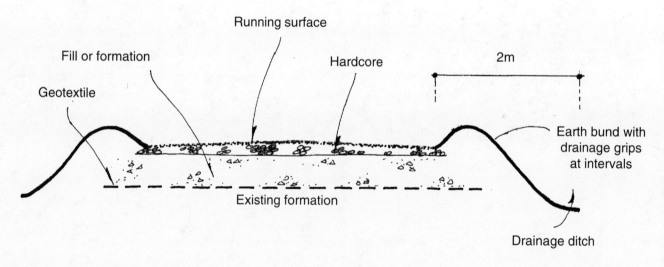

Section: Typical temporary site road

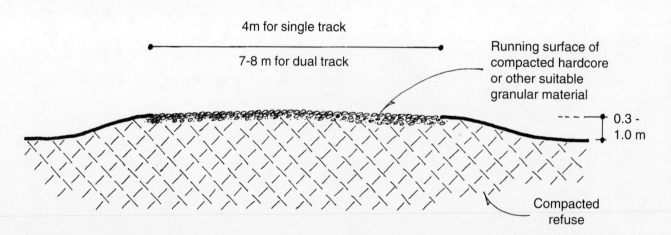

Table 9.5

Waste emplacement methods

Face tipping method

A horizontal or near horizontal platform is created by tipping over an advancing face with levelling and compacting from above

The maximum height of the face is usually limited by the waste management licence and is typically not more than 2.5 m after compaction

The compaction equipment operates on the flat surface at the top of the face

Advantages

Machine operators find this method easy

It is easy to apply daily cover

Temporary access roads can be provided easily

Bulky objects are easy to bury

Problem wastes can be tipped at the toe of the face

Disadvantages

The face can be unsightly

It is difficult to apply temporary cover to the face

Waste easily becomes wind blown when tipped over the edge of the face

The surface of the landfill becomes over compacted through the repeated passage of vehicles, encouraging the development of perched water tables within the landfill

Onion skin tipping

Similar to face tipping but creates an inclined surface where thin skins of waste are deposited instead of a face

The compaction equipment operates on the inclined surface

Advantages

It is easy to apply daily cover on both flat and inclined surfaces

Waste is less likely to become windblown than with the face method

High lifts can be achieved

Disadvantages

It is more difficult to bury bulky objects

Working upwards

This method can be a variant of either the face or the onion skin method whereby the waste is deposited on the lower surface and pushed upwards by the compaction equipment

Advantages

Waste is less likely to become windblown when discharged from the delivery vehicle

Temporary access roads, intermediate cover and compacted waste can easily be removed ahead of the advancing layer so reducing the risk of perched water tables

Disadvantages

Additional machines may be required to apply cover on the flat surface above the wastes

- restrictions on the number of vehicles in the discharge area at any one time

- passengers not allowed to alight in the discharge area

- pedestrians on the operational area to wear high visibility clothing, safety boots and other relevant personal protective clothing

- prohibition of smoking on-site

- special procedures to unload overloaded vehicles

- special procedures for tipping bulk vehicles in circumstances where they might become unstable when their bodies are raised.

9.62   Every discharged load should be visually inspected by a designated operative. This may be a banksman or the machine driver depending on the traffic density. Working area personnel should be trained and competent at waste identification in order that they can recognise waste which may be non-conforming. In the event of reasonable doubt as to the waste acceptability, the operative should inform the waste reception facility and/or the site manager immediately and the consignment should be isolated pending further inspection.

9.63   Once the waste has been discharged from the vehicle, it should be consolidated and layered to ensure that tipping areas remain well defined and tipping slopes are maintained at the designed gradients.

Waste compaction

9.64   It has become conventional practice since the 1970s to level and compact the waste as soon as it is discharged at the working area. Compaction offers many benefits including

- enabling the maximum amount of waste to be emplaced within the space available

- reducing the impact from litter, flies, vermin, birds and fires

- minimising short-term settlement.

> Steel wheeled mobile compactors are generally accepted as the best equipment for this purpose (see paragraphs 9.188 to 9.189). They have largely replaced the small tracked machines which previously were in general use.

9.65   Greater understanding of landfill biological processes has shown that there are also disadvantages which should be taken into account where the rate of degradation is an issue. For example, excessively high waste densities may inhibit biodegradation by restricting leachate and landfill gas movement and may cause perched water tables within the site.

9.66   Waste density is discussed in paragraph 6.15. Some operators have reported in situ densities in excess of 1.2 tonnes/m^3 in mixed household waste using steel wheeled compactors. Research[5] suggests that a density of about 0.8 tonnes/m^3 is the optimum for the biodegradation processes in mixed household waste. If this is the case, then excessive use of steel wheeled compactors should be avoided if there is a need for rapid biodegradation. The economic and other benefits of higher rates of initial compaction must also be considered.

---

[5]   Young A (1994): *Applications of computer modelling to landfill processes.* DoE report CWM 039A/92

9.67   Research[5] also indicates that biodegradation processes benefit if the waste mass can be made more uniform in particle size and density than is normally the case. Although not primarily used for the purpose, the high power of mobile compactors enables them to move easily and hence to homogenise the waste. The operator of an accelerated stabilisation landfill should ensure that waste emplacement procedures

- specify the number of passes of the compactor to achieve a predetermined density (this may be less than for a conventional site)

- use the compactor to blend and homogenise the waste as much as possible.

9.68   If the operator of an accelerated stabilisation landfill concludes that he needs to use little or no compaction then he should provide alternative measures to prevent nuisances from litter, flies, vermin, birds and fires.

Working areas

9.69   Key considerations for the delineation of the working areas are given in Table 9.6. The size of the working area and the way it is defined will be controlled by the waste management licence after taking into account

- safe working practice

- the prevention of nuisance (ie odour, flies, birds, visual impact)

- the area required for manoeuvring of discharging vehicles and site plant

- the size of the discharging vehicles

- peak site input rates

- the configuration of the operational cells and phases

- the exclusion of air (if advanced stabilisation is an objective)

- minimisation of uncontrolled rainwater ingress

- the benefits of controlled progressive working

- stability of the waste, particularly in steep temporary faces and having regard to potential slip planes in the liner system.

Daily cover

Objectives

9.70   The advantages of using daily cover are primarily in preventing windblow and odours, deterrence to scavengers, birds and vermin and in improving the site's visual appearance. It is also advocated as a means of shedding surface water during the filling sequence, thereby assisting in leachate management, although its effectiveness in this respect is doubtful.

> Substantial windblown litter arises at the time of discharge of waste from the delivery vehicle. Daily cover is applied after this operation and therefore serves no or very little purpose in preventing windblown litter[6] from this source.

---

[6] NAWDC Guidance Note No 17 *Litter Control.*

Table 9.6

Delineation of working areas

Tipping cells	*Advantages*
These are created by constructing bund walls between which the waste is deposited	The tipping area is confined
	Litter is reduced and the installation of temporary litter fences is facilitated
	Disadvantages
	Increased demand for inert material to create bunds
	Bunds may restrict leachate and gas circulation in the completed landfill unless they are removed
Temporary markers	*Advantages*
When the configuration of the site requires a linear pattern of tipping, traffic cones, painted barrels or marker posts can be used to define the extent of a working area	Very simple low cost method which has no impact on the final landfill
	Disadvantages
	Requires a high standard of control as poorly positioned or inadequate markers will lead to waste being deposited outside the working area

> Odours at landfill sites are associated with landfill gas, leachate, malodorous waste and incoming and newly deposited refuse. The application of daily cover will not affect the generation of leachate or landfill gas as it is loosely placed but may reduce the effects of odours from the combined sources. Malodorous wastes should be covered immediately with non-odorous waste which will often act as a scrubber for the malodour.

> The season and weather conditions may have an impact on odour and the use of daily cover may be beneficial under conditions of high heat and humidity. These conditions are usually short lived in the UK and as a result there may be a different requirement for daily cover during the summer. Fly infestations, which do occur under these conditions, are also mitigated by daily cover.

9.71   It is important that site location and waste inputs are taken into account when considering the type and application of daily cover. In many cases the application of daily cover will improve the visual aspect of the working area.

> Soils will give a pleasing uniform appearance from the site boundary. To achieve this a thickness of about 150 mm is usually adequate. About 300 mm needs to be used to avoid paper, etc being seen from close proximity. This is excessive for other purposes and the visibility of waste through daily cover should not be regarded as the sole criterion of effectiveness.

> Exposed compacted or processed waste itself produces a uniform appearance from a distance and it is the visual impact from outside the site which is significant.

9.72 Vermin and birds can be controlled by employing specialised deterrence techniques as well as by the use of cover.

Impact of using daily cover

9.73 Where cover is used for public health or nuisance protection, the cover material should be such that the permeability of the waste and cover as a whole should (eventually) be sufficient to allow leachate to pass and gas to be extracted without creating perched conditions or preferential paths. Commercial considerations will require that void space for waste is maximised. Imported cover takes up valuable void space for primary wastes and if a 150 mm deep layer is placed over every 2 m layer of waste some 7.5% of the void space is lost. The covering of faces and flanks will cause even more loss of void space and most operators estimate that the total loss of void space is between 10% and 20%.

9.74 If compacted, daily cover can have a relatively low permeability which results in the partial containment of each layer of waste. As a result leachate becomes perched and difficult to extract. Landfill gas then moves preferentially sideways giving greater potential for migration off-site and both gas and leachate become difficult to extract.

9.75 Traction for road going vehicles is often difficult during wet weather even when very little cover is applied. The resulting mud may be carried onto site access roads and increases the importance of keeping public highways clean.

Availability of daily cover

9.76 Traditionally soil material has been used for daily cover and the thickness to be applied is specified in the waste management licence. Whenever possible, daily cover is obtained by planned excavation from within the landfill area and thereby causes no net consumption of void. This will optimise the commercial value of the wastes accepted. Where a site is deficient in appropriate resources, daily cover may come through the gate from construction activities. However, in many areas this source is diminishing.

> Construction waste is now recycled or used to form screening bunds and for landscaping at the construction site. As a result, better quality soils and clays, which would be better used for engineering and restoration materials, are sometimes used as daily cover and in extreme cases quarried materials have to be imported to landfill sites for daily cover purposes.

Alternative daily cover materials

9.77 There is considerable interest in finding alternative materials for daily cover. Some of the materials being considered include

- heavy duty reusable plastic sheets (tarps)
- non reusable plastic films
- fibre matting, geotextiles
- spray on foams
- paper pulp (low clay content)
- shredded green waste.

9.78 Results so far have failed to identify any single method which can be used as a simple substitute for soil materials and all of them have given rise to secondary impacts or costs which only become apparent under operational conditions. Nevertheless, the disadvantages of using soil material for daily cover are significant and site testing and experimentation with alternatives should continue.

> The use of alternative cover materials must be based on an assessment of their value and impacts, and the suitability of the material for inclusion in the site.

9.79   Vehicle fragmentiser waste has been used as cover in some areas. It is becoming increasingly less acceptable because of concerns about conductivity, dust, heavy metals and polychlorinated biphenyls.

9.80   Shredded tyres and plastics may be used, but with the advent of recycling and the reduction of waste, these are becoming less available.

9.81   Sites operating in active mineral workings may use mineral rejects for cover. Improved quarrying techniques and alternative uses for these materials may affect their availability.

Disposal of difficult wastes

9.82   Difficult wastes are those wastes which, though acceptable for disposal to landfill in terms of their overall properties, have some characteristics which require a particular method of handling at the site which is not part of day to day procedure.

9.83   The definition of a difficult waste will depend partly on the waste itself and partly on the site receiving it. Difficult wastes will include

- finely particulate material

- empty containers

- very large objects

- sludges

- very light materials, for example expanded polystyrene

- malodorous wastes

- tyres.

9.84   Difficult wastes may be identified during the risk assessment and will not necessarily be classified as special wastes[7]. Because all difficult wastes require specific techniques to enable them to be deposited in the landfill site without risk, a written code of practice should be compiled specific to each one, setting out in detail the procedures to be adopted.

Example of difficult waste practice

9.85   Wastes giving rise to dust when tipped or run over by site machinery should be handled and deposited in such a way that dust is not released.

> Measures may include requiring all particulate wastes to be delivered to the site in sealed bags, or to be pre-conditioned by spraying with water containing a wetting agent. Tipping should normally be at the base of the active face, or in a prepared excavation, and carefully covered with incoming waste, or waste stockpiled for the purpose immediately following deposit.

---

[7] See Appendix A for waste definitions.

> Dusty wastes should not be used in the formation of site roads.

> Bulk waste likely to give rise to dust when being tipped (such as demolition waste) should be wetted prior to deposit or sprayed during tipping or processing.

Protection of local amenities

9.86   Measures are needed to ensure that the landfill operation does not adversely affect the amenities of the locality.

> Monitoring the emissions of the landfill decomposition process such as landfill gas and leachate is dealt with in WMP4 and WMP27. The potential impacts of the landfill site should be addressed during the planning application stage and measures to mitigate the impacts should be included in the landfill design.

> Local impacts should be carefully examined to minimise adverse effects on the community. The importance of developing good relationships with the local community cannot be overemphasised. The potential nuisances which are commonly of concern to the local community include

  - increased traffic, giving rise to nuisance from noise, vibration, exhaust emissions, dust, dirt, visual intrusion, damage to local roads, increased risk to pedestrians

  - noise

  - odour

  - windblown litter

  - birds

  - vermin, insects and other pests

  - dust

  - mud on the road.

9.87   Measures to mitigate these factors should be set out by the operator in the working plan which accompanies the waste management licence application.

9.88   Amenity nuisances are generally raised as complaints to the operator or the WRA but may be focused on the local media.

> Operators may appoint community liaison officers to be available to visit complainants and establish the nature and source of the problem. This is reported to the site manager so that corrective measures can be taken.

Traffic

9.89   Heavy lorry traffic can give rise to nuisance, damage to road surface and verges and routing problems.

9.90   Traffic impact is a major factor for consideration at the planning stage and is often dealt with by planning conditions or by means of a legal agreement[8]. The design of the site should include consideration of

---

[8] Town and Country Planning Act 1990, Section 106. In Scotland, Section 50 of the Town and Country Planning (Scotland) Act 1972.

- routing vehicles to and from the site via major roads wherever possible

- routing to avoid residential areas

- using one-way routes to avoid traffic conflict in narrow roads

- carrying out road improvements, for example, strengthening road haunches, improved provision of footpaths, improvement of sight lines, provision of passing places or lay-bys, provision of new roads

- limiting the number of vehicle movements

- restrictions on working hours

- limiting vehicle size

- alternative means of transporting waste, for example rail, barge and conveyor transport.

Noise

9.91   Adverse impacts on the local community from noise may arise from a number of sources including

- throughput of vehicles

- reversing bleepers

- fixed and mobile plant, for example compactors, generators, gas flares, leachate treatment equipment

- audible bird scaring equipment.

9.92   Noise impact studies are an effective means of predicting and assessing noise levels in order to evaluate the relative importance of the sources and the need for remedial actions. They should be undertaken as part of the initial design process so that mitigation measures can be incorporated in the design and included in the application for planning permission and the waste management licence. Measures to minimise noise impacts are given in Table 9.7.

Odours

9.93   Offensive odours at landfill sites may emanate from a number of sources, including

- waste materials, such as wastes from transfer stations, which have decomposed significantly prior to landfilling

- old waste disturbed by digging

- malodorous wastes

- agricultural and sewage sludges

- leachates and leachate treatment systems

- landfill gas

- odour counteractants.

Table 9.7

Options to minimise noise levels

General site noise	Construction of a buffer zone between the site and the external environment[1]
	Soil bunding, tree planting and acoustic fencing
Reversing bleepers	The importance of site personnel safety generally outweighs the nuisance caused by noise from reversing bleepers (although this may be alleviated by the installation of some of the acoustic measures listed above)
Fixed plant	Where fixed plant, generators or pumps are required to operate continuously for long periods, or where local residents are nearby, silencing and acoustic screening should be incorporated
Temporary plant	Portable acoustic screens or straw bale enclosures can be used to reduce the noise from temporary plant

---

1   A buffer zone should not be arbitrarily imposed but should take into account need, topography, direction of working, method of operation, and prevailing wind. The design should be site specific and not prescriptive. Buffer zones may also reduce the visual impact from wind blown litter. Such considerations should be incorporated into the design.

9.94   Good landfill practices will greatly reduce general site smell and reduce impact from odours which could lead to complaints from the local community, site users and site operatives. Good practice includes

- adequate compaction

- speedy disposal and burial of malodorous wastes

- effective use of appropriate types of daily cover

- progressive capping and restoration

- effective landfill gas management

- effective leachate management

- use of covered trenches for liquid waste disposal[9]

- rapid burial of excavated waste

- consideration of prevailing wind direction when planning leachate treatment plants, gas flares, and direction of tipping.

9.95   Most odour counteractants use a masking agent. Sensitivity to odours is a subjective matter and some find the masking agents in counteractants as offensive as the odour nuisance itself.

9.96   Quantification of the environmental impact of odours is difficult and may involve a panel of human detectors[10]. Odour control should be incorporated into performance monitoring systems by maintaining a record of the number of complaints and the actions taken in response to them.

Litter

9.97   Poor litter control both on and off site is particularly offensive to neighbours. Good operational practice should be adhered to in terms of waste discharge, placement, compaction and covering to minimise the occurrence of windblown litter. Measures for controlling litter include

- consideration of prevailing wind direction and strength when planning the filling direction and sequence

- provision of an emergency tipping area, for lightweight wastes such as paper, for use when winds are high

- strategically placed mobile screens close to the tipping area or on the nearest downwind crest

- temporary banks and bunds immediately adjacent to the tipping area[11]

- permanent catch fences and netting to trap windblown litter

- full enclosure of the tipping area within a mobile litter net system

- closure of the site to specific or all waste types may be appropriate when conditions are particularly adverse.

9.98   Restricting incoming vehicles to only those which are sheeted and secured will reduce litter problems on the highways. Another major source of litter along the highways around the site is waste retained in open bodied vehicles after they have tipped. Drivers should ensure that all waste has been removed from the vehicle before leaving the site.

---

[9] Co-disposal is dealt with in detail in WMP26F.
[10] Refer to WMP26D.
[11] The maintenance of temporary bunds around the active area can also be of considerable benefit in visual screening of operations, and can be a convenient stockpile for daily cover.

9.99   Litter pickers should be employed to collect litter which escapes the preventative measures. Litter screens, fences, nets and perimeter ditches should be maintained free of litter.

9.100   Examples of good practice include

- immediate immobilisation of wastes likely to become wind-born by using appropriate plant such as compactors with steel-cleated wheels

- ensuring an adequate supply of cover material which is used promptly.

Bird control   9.101   Birds are attracted to landfill sites in large numbers, particularly where sites receive appreciable amounts of food wastes. Usually only large birds such as gulls are regarded as a nuisance. Potential concerns relating to the presence of scavenging birds include

- the deposit of excrement and scraps of food on mobile plant and vehicles on-site, reducing driver's visibility and damaging nearby land

- causing bird-strike damage to aircraft[12]

- the introduction of pathogens to nearby water bodies and crops

- the introduction of alien species to sensitive local habitats.

9.102   Operators should be aware that not all birds found on landfill sites are nuisances; endangered and rare species sometimes take up residence[13]. Bird control techniques should be carefully planned taking into account the species likely to be affected. Measures which can be used to mitigate bird nuisance include the employment of good landfill practice, with prompt disposal, consolidation working in small active areas and progressive covering (if appropriate) of waste, together with the use of bird scaring techniques. These techniques include

- flying birds of prey over the site

- bird kites mimicking birds of prey

- shell crackers - containing flare and banger

- rope bangers

- gas cannons

- scarecrows - fixed or mobile

- amplified recordings of bird distress calls (species specific)

- electronic sounds imitating calls of distress

- bird corpses or dummies.

9.103   There are advantages and disadvantages to all of these methods and the degree of effectiveness can best be assessed from experience.

> Measures involving explosions or distress calls have inherently adverse environmental impacts in terms of noise and may scare desirable species living in the vicinity of the site.

---

[12] Where the site is within the vicinity of an airfield there may be a requirement from the Civil Aviation Authority or the Ministry of Defence to ensure adequate means of bird control.
[13] Certain species are protected under the Wildlife and Countryside Act which should be consulted prior to choosing control methods. Lethal methods of control may be subject to licensing by DoE.

> Experience has shown birds of prey to be effective and to have minimal consequential environmental impact.

> The effectiveness of any method deteriorates with time and will need to be changed regularly. The licence should therefore not be prescriptive when discussing scaring techniques.

9.104   A log of techniques employed should be maintained by the site operator to demonstrate compliance with requirements and as part of the performance monitoring system. The log will also assist in assessing the effectiveness of the different methods employed.

Vermin and other pests

9.105   Landfills have potential to harbour flies and vermin, particularly where the waste contains food materials. Modern landfilling techniques including prompt emplacement, consolidation and covering of wastes in well defined cells are effective in the prevention of infestation by rodents and insects. Rats and flies are the main pests which require control. Sites with extensive non operational land can become infested with rabbits.

> Rodents can burrow through and damage liners and control measures are therefore particularly important at sites which incorporate such materials.

> Fly infestations commonly arise from waste which has been awaiting collection for some time. Ideally the time lapse from the initial collection of waste to final disposal should be kept to a minimum to reduce the risk of infestation, but this is often outside the control of the landfill operator.

> Sites accepting animal carcasses, tannery wastes and food wastes are particularly susceptible to fly infestation. The risk of infestation can be reduced by prompt burial of all biodegradable wastes. To interrupt the reproductive cycle of the house fly, any putrescible waste needs to remain buried for more than 10 days. The potential for fly infestation to develop should be considered if engineering works require waste to be re-excavated.

9.106   Pest control measures should be specified in the working plan, and a log should be kept of measures taken so that compliance with regulations and quality management system can be demonstrated.

> Effective measures to deal with rodent infestation include

  • effective site management involving well defined, tightly controlled tipping areas and prompt capping of completed areas

  • regular visits by pest control contractors or fully trained operatives

  • inspection and treatment of areas where rats live, for example sewers, culverts and drains.

> The use of insecticides on exposed faces and flanks of the tipping area, by spraying and fogging, is an effective means of exterminating insects. It should only be undertaken by fully trained personnel. Great care should be taken to ensure that this does not lead to secondary impacts including the contamination of water courses and leachate.

9.107 The local environmental health department or specialist contractors may be employed to provide advice and assistance in relation to pest control issues.

> Chemicals used must be appropriate for the task. The concentration should be as specified by the manufacturer and quantities used must be kept to a minimum so that they will not appear in the leachate and cause problems with treatment and discharge.

> Personnel applying insecticides must possess certificates of competence and must be provided with appropriate protective clothing.

> Pesticides must be kept in a secure store.

Dust

9.108 Dust from landfill operations is mainly a problem during periods of dry weather but can also arise from dusty waste as it is tipped. Dust is generally associated with

- the drying out of site roads

- site preparation and restoration activities

- the disposal of waste comprising fine particles, for example powders

- carriage of dust/mud onto the highway.

9.109 Dust suppression can be effected by

- limiting vehicle speed

- regular mechanical sweeping of the highway and access roads

- spraying roads with water

- only accepting fine particulate waste in secure bags

- seeding bare earth surfaces as quickly as possible after soil materials have been emplaced.

Mud on the road

9.110 Mud on the public highway is one of the most common causes of public complaint[14]. Preventative measures should be incorporated into the site design to reduce the potential for mud to be carried off-site. It is, therefore, in the interests of the landfill operator to provide adequate wheel cleaning facilities to ensure that mud is not carried off site by vehicles. Depending on the soils or the length of the haul road, permanent wheel cleansing facilities may be needed (see paragraphs 9.49 to 9.50 above).

> The main site access road should be as long as possible to enable vehicles to shed the bulk of mud collected from the site before going onto the highway. Wheel cleaning facilities should be installed at strategic places along the main site access road. Main site roads should be maintained in a mud free condition by employing a mechanical sweeper.

> In the event that mud does escape, warning signs to inform users of the highway of the potential hazard should be erected on the highway following approval by the highway authority and road sweepers should be employed immediately to clean the affected highway.

---

[14] The deposit of mud on the highway is an offence under the Highways Act 1980.

Landfill fires

General management

9.111   Fires in waste on landfill sites are uncommon but do occasionally occur and it is important for site operators to be aware of the dangers, how to treat fires and to address the problems associated with them. All fires on-site should be treated as a potential emergency and dealt with accordingly.

> All sites should have an emergency tipping area set aside from the immediate working area where incoming loads of material known to be on fire or suspected of being so can be deposited, inspected and dealt with.

9.112   Waste that is burning on delivery should be doused with water or more preferably covered progressively with adequate supplies of damp soil/cover followed by cooling and finally removal to its disposal point. It should not normally be allowed to burn itself out as this will give rise to nuisance from smoke and odour and may constitute a health risk. Firefighting techniques should be appropriate for the waste type.

9.113   Fires within the operational area are either surface fires or deep-seated fires. The former usually occur in recently deposited and as yet uncompacted materials adjacent to the current working area whilst the latter are found at depth in material deposited weeks or months earlier.

> Site operators should have a plan to deal with each type of fire and have a code of practice for their operatives stating exactly how to tackle any outbreak. Regardless of the circumstances, no individual should ever tackle a landfill fire alone.

> To control fires by the addition of large volumes of water may form large volumes of leachate and so cause water pollution.

Surface fires

9.114   In most cases, the best way to tackle any fire is to smother it with large volumes of wet or damp soil/cover material, working progressively inwards from the edges of the fire to slowly cover and compact the area and then to allow it to cool before moving the whole to its final resting place.

> Such an operation can take some time especially if the fire is a large one and it may be necessary to have the fire brigade attend initially to wet the area and extinguish any flames. Once the area is wetted and cooled the process of covering should go ahead as quickly as possible.

Deep seated fires

9.115   Deep seated landfill fires should always be taken very seriously. They can create large voids, invisible from the surface, can give rise to carbon monoxide in hazardous concentrations and can destroy containment liners.

9.116   The existence of a deep seated fire[15] is a major problem, and often only detected by the presence of smoke emanating from some part of the site or by the presence of carbon monoxide in the landfill gas. In the majority of cases, deep seated fires are beyond the reach of most common landfill plant, and to attempt to dig them out with inappropriate plant may exacerbate the situation by admitting air. In such cases it is better to delineate the area concerned and surcharge the site

---

[15] Many deep seated fires are starved of oxygen and produce carbon monoxide as well as carbon dioxide. Carbon monoxide is not produced biogenically and so its presence in concentrations of more than 1 or 2 ppm can be taken to indicate underground combustion. It is not always produced by deep seated fires and so its absence does not necessarily indicate the absence of a fire. Carbon monoxide is a toxic gas and is also extremely flammable with a flammability range in air of 12% to 75%.

with large volumes of clay-like material. This minimises the number of outlets for gases to escape and reduces the influx of air to the area, thus containing the problem as far as is possible. Daily checks of the area are necessary and immediate remedial action must be taken before any significant fire breakthrough is noted.

> It is advisable to temporarily cap any nearby landfill gas vents as these will serve as chimneys for combustion products to escape or for fresh supplies of air to be drawn in. Plugging all outlets will reduce the combustion process and the fire will eventually cease.

> Landfill gas extraction in the vicinity of the fire will exacerbate the situation and should normally be suspended until the fire is extinguished. The impact of this suspension on landfill gas safety may be assessed and appropriate measures will need to be taken which would include the provision of additional extraction wells and additional monitoring.

9.117   If it becomes apparent during any outbreak that it will be necessary to isolate the area in order to stop the fire spreading further this should be done by excavating deep trenches beyond the burning area and backfilling them immediately with clay material so as to create a cut off barrier around the fire.

Management of leachate

Background

9.118   Leachates generated from recently emplaced wastes, which are in the acetogenic phase of degradation, contain high concentrations of organic compounds (typically in the order of 5,000 - 20,000 mg/l TOC). Such leachates are also characterised by lower pH values, a product of organic compounds whose volatility may also produce unpleasant smells, and of dissolved carbon dioxide. Acetogenic leachates also contain ammonium ions (typically in the order of several hundred mg/l) which result primarily from the breakdown of proteins and other nitrogenous compounds in the wastes.

9.119   Those leachates generated from wastes which have been emplaced for several years, and which have commenced the methanogenic phase of degradation, have a lower concentration of organic compounds (typically of less than 1000 mg/l TOC) a neutral to alkaline pH-value, and a relatively low ratio of BOD to COD. The concentration of ammonium ions remains in the order of several hundred mg/l. Variations in leachate composition between the acetogenic and methanogenic stages of waste degradation are given in Table I.1 in Appendix I.

> The composition and volume of leachate generated at a landfill site will vary with time. Reliable and proven landfill leachate treatment strategies will be required which meet these long and short term variations.

9.120   As landfills decompose anaerobically over many years, the putrescible wastes they contain have the potential to generate highly polluting leachates. To avoid severe environmental impacts, proper control and disposal of these leachates is essential.

> Discharge limits for parameters such as rate, organic loading, pH-value, ammoniacal nitrogen, and metals, may be specified. They may be subject to a trade effluent consent/agreement from a Water plc/Regional Council, or a discharge consent agreed with the NRA (RPA Scotland).

> If certain prescribed substances are present in the leachate at greater than background concentrations, the regulation authorities may involve HMIP (England and Wales) or HMIPI (Scotland). In such cases the regulation authority would refer to the leachate as a special category effluent, containing substances, or arising from a process, that is defined in regulations made under section 138 of the Water Industry Act 1991.

> The collection and removal of leachate is described in Chapter 6 paragraphs 6.48 to 6.63.

Objectives of leachate treatment

9.121   In general, the objective of leachate treatment at all landfill sites should be to attain the required standards for discharge, whether to sewer, water course, land or tidal water. A variety of physico-chemical and biological techniques is available for the on-site treatment of leachate prior to discharge.

> These techniques vary in cost, approach, applicability and effectiveness. Treatment strategies must meet individual leachate volume, composition and discharge conditions, and will inevitably be site specific.

9.122   The major components in the leachate whose treatment to more acceptable concentrations may be required prior to discharge include[16]

- high concentrations of degradable and non-degradable organic materials

- concentrations of specific hazardous organics and inorganics

- ammonium and, increasingly, nitrate ions

- sulphides

- odorous compounds

- suspended solids.

9.123   All leachate treatment facilities should satisfy the following design criteria

- the leachate treatment system should be adequate for the varying volumes and composition of leachate generated through all stages of landfill development and restoration

- the treatment facilities should be robust, to ensure that performance requirements are maintained throughout (and beyond) the operational life of the landfill.

9.124   It is essential that leachate treatment plants are designed by experienced designers with waste water engineering expertise. As increasing reliability and consistency of effluent quality are required, there is no place for inadequately designed systems.

Physico-chemical treatment

9.125   Many physico-chemical processes, including the first four listed here, are not true treatment processes, but concentration steps or cross media processes

---

[16] It should be noted that the site specificity of leachate discharge requirements means that not **all** of the above components require treatment or removal from **all** leachates.

where a quantity of relatively unpolluted effluent is produced, leaving the contaminants as a concentrate or brine which requires further action.

Air stripping of ammonia

9.126   Air stripping of ammonia is frequently considered as a treatment method for leachate. The process can be undertaken in a lagoon or in a purpose built stripping tower. The pH of the leachate is adjusted to values of 11 or above prior to being exposed to large quantities of air. Gaseous ammonia is then released to the atmosphere.

9.127   Several factors must be considered when the use of air stripping of ammonia from leachate is proposed.

> The environmental impact of releasing ammonia gas into the atmosphere is difficult to mitigate. Considerable quantities of ammonia with a significant odour would be released unless removed by subsequent scrubbing. Gas scrubbing might be used to prevent this ammonia discharge to the atmosphere but the capital and running costs of such a system may render the overall process relatively expensive.

> The power costs associated with the provision of large quantities of air, which must be supplied for the stripping process, are likely to be high. In addition, because of the half-life nature of the reductions in ammonia values, it may well prove extremely expensive to achieve very low effluent concentrations which are often required.

> The pH of the treated effluent will require adjustment prior to discharge in accordance with the discharge consent requirements. The adjustment of pH will also require potentially large quantities of alkali and acid reagents.

Activated carbon adsorption

9.128   Granular activated carbon (GAC) is a highly porous material with a high surface area to volume ratio. GAC (and powdered activated carbon - PAC) have been used to adsorb residual quantities of organic materials from leachates which have previously had the majority of their organic contaminants removed using other treatment methods.

> Suspended solids must be removed from the leachate prior to treatment, to prevent blockage of the carbon filter. This can be achieved by several means including plate separators and pressurised sand filters.

> The activated carbon can be regenerated after it has become completely saturated with adsorbent. The regeneration cycle cannot be undertaken in situ. In situations where small volumes of GAC (often in modular units) have been used, the GAC may be disposed of by incineration rather than sent for regeneration.

9.129   This method of leachate treatment can be used in an effluent polishing situation to reduce COD loading, non-volatile organics and hazardous organics. The treatment can be highly effective with up to 99% removal attainable, but is generally very expensive if significant quantities of residual COD require treatment.

Reverse osmosis

9.130   Reverse osmosis removes suspended and colloidal materials, ammoniacal nitrogen, heavy metals, and most dissolved solids, and reduces COD and BOD. It

160

may be suitable for application to leachates with a high inorganic loading and low volumetric flow rates.

9.131   The process does not treat or degrade any contaminants, but, using ultra filtration membranes (operated at elevated pressures of 40 Bar or more), is able to concentrate soluble constituents of leachate into a brine or concentrate which can comprise 25 to 40% of the volume of the influent leachate, and a permeate which can achieve high standards of purity.

9.132   Various means have been used for the disposal of this concentrate.

> Recirculation back into the landfill has been the simplest, cheapest, and generally adopted option, but may not be acceptable in the longer term as a landfill where leachate contaminants are simply being returned into the wastes will not achieve accelerated completion. Should it be possible to tanker the concentrate off site, the overall trade effluent costs associated with what is basically concentrated leachate are likely to be unaffected, although transport costs will be less because of the reduced volume.

Evaporation

9.133   This is a two to four stage process which concentrates contaminants in leachate by evaporation and distillation. Leachate is pre-treated by the addition of acid to reduce the pH-value and to convert volatile ammonia into soluble ammonium salts. The leachate is evaporated, and separated into distillate and residual liquor.

9.134   As with reverse osmosis the process is one of concentration, rather than treatment. The resulting concentrate (typically 1/20th of the original volume) requires disposal. If the concentrate is returned to the landfill there is concern, as with reverse osmosis, that the contaminant loading will build up within the leachate over a period of time. As no waste products are actually being removed from the landfill the long-term environmental risks may increase as a result.

Oxidation with hydrogen peroxide or hypochlorite solution

9.135   Oxidation of leachate by the addition of oxidising agents and pH adjustment may be used for the removal of sulphides, sulphite, formaldehyde, cyanide, and phenolics. The principal use of this type of treatment is in situations where odours caused by sulphides are a particular problem.

> The performance of the process depends on the reaction time and on the oxidising agent chosen. Agents other than hydrogen peroxide may be used, including calcium and sodium hypochlorite, ozone, and chlorine gas with caustic soda. Caution should be exercised in the use of oxidising agents to ensure their safe handling.

> Treatment may be carried out as a batch or continuous process, using dilute solutions of the oxidising agents. A ratio of hydrogen peroxide to soluble sulphide of unity, at a neutral pH, with a contact time of about ten minutes is usually adequate to remove sulphides.

9.136   Organic material may also be removed by oxidising agents such as ozone, although high dosages are often required to bring about significant reductions in COD. Ozone has been used in wastewater treatment plants to control odour, improve suspended solids removal, oxidise pesticides and improve biodegradability of other organic compounds.

Wet air oxidation

9.137   This is a type of combustion process which may be suitable for leachates with high organic strength, for example with COD between 5,000 and 150,000 mg/l. The process can be undertaken in conjunction with other physico-chemical or biological treatment process, and used as a final or polishing stage of leachate treatment.

9.138   Leachate is mixed with air, and is pumped into a series of heat exchangers under pressure. Oxidation takes place in a reactor at temperatures of up to 310C, and at pressures up to 200 Bar. The resulting gas phase is passed through an air purification system, and vented to atmosphere, and the liquid phase is recycled into a heat exchanger.

> This technique is expensive but can be used to treat very high strength leachates.

Coagulation, flocculation and settling

9.139   The addition of reagents to leachate, followed by mixing and settlement, might occasionally be useful either before or after other methods of treatment. The reagents can result in a reduction in suspended solids, heavy metals, turbidity, colour and some organic loading concentrations.

> Reagents which have been used in the process include lime, sodium and magnesium hydroxide, ferric chloride and sulphate, and polymeric coagulants.

Aerobic biological treatment

9.140   Aerobic biological processes have consistently provided successful and reliable treatment of landfill leachate, both in the UK and overseas. Such treatment can readily reduce high concentrations of BOD and COD, present in leachates during early stages of waste decomposition. Older, methanogenic landfill leachates can be treated, with suitable low cost nutrient addition. Nitrification of high concentrations of ammoniacal-N, which is particularly important, can be achieved efficiently by adoption of an extended aeration cycle of plant operation. Where leachate recirculation is to be used as part of a process of accelerated stabilisation, it is also likely to be necessary to de-nitrify the treated leachate to avoid problems of reintroduction of nitrogen to the waste Aerobic biological processes can be categorised into **attached growth** and **non attached growth** operations.

Attached growth processes

Trickling or percolating filters

9.141   The use of this technique as a single-stage treatment for high strength leachates is limited, because increasing organic and inorganic loadings tend to cause clogging, due to the build-up of slimes (microbial growth) and the precipitation and build-up of inorganic (especially iron) salts. The accumulation of these materials restricts liquid flow, causing ponding.

> Problems of clogging by inorganic salts might be avoided by physico-chemical pre-treatment, or by a long retention time in an open lagoon prior to treatment, which enables precipitation or settlement of iron and calcium salts.

Rotating biological contactors (RBC)

9.142   Rotating biological contactors consist of rows of rotating shaft-mounted discs. As the discs rotate, attached micro-organisms are alternately immersed in leachate and exposed to air. Although percolating filters have generally not proved successful in leachate treatment because of an inability to handle the high strengths of COD and ammoniacal-N present in leachates, RBCs have proved more successful.

9.143   At least two full scale RBC plants have been constructed in the UK[17] and the process has proved successful in treating strongly methanogenic leachate from old landfill sites, and achieving nitrification. Heating may be necessary to allow this to occur consistently.

Non-attached processes

9.144   In the use of **non-attached growth** processes in aerated lagoons or tanks for aerobic leachate treatment, aeration encourages the formation and growth of suspended biological flocs, which break down and metabolise the polluting components of the leachate. Mean periods of retention from 10 to 20 days are capable of greater than 90% removal of COD and ammoniacal nitrogen.

> Extended aeration treatment plants have been shown to be robust, both biologically and mechanically. Mechanically, extended aeration plants can be engineered to require little maintenance, and to provide automated discharge of treated leachate as appropriate to a specific discharge consent.

> The microbial flocs are resistant to shock loads. They can acclimatise to the presence of toxins and metal ions as well as to high ammoniacal-N and chloride levels, partly because the large volume of an extended aeration system enables them to rapidly dilute incoming leachate doses.

> The extended aeration plants developed for leachate treatment[18] differ in their operation from standard activated sludge processes (which were initially developed for treatment of domestic sewage and have been installed at some landfills). The short residence time of the activated sludge plants enables reduction of COD but only limited removal of ammoniacal nitrogen.

9.145   To ensure sufficient phosphate levels for microbial growth within an extended aeration process, occasional addition of phosphoric acid is generally required. Regular inputs of alkali, preferably sodium hydroxide, may also be needed to counteract reductions in pH which occur during the nitrification process.

9.146   Extended aeration treatment lagoons, if operated correctly to a daily cycle in accordance with recent leachate treatment research[19], have been found to be a most flexible form of leachate treatment. They can readily cope with a wide range of flows and strengths of leachate. Easily altered parameters such as volume of leachate in the lagoons, and retention times, makes the plants resistant to shock loads (due to the large volume of aerated lagoon into which these increased concentrations or flows of leachate are discharged).

Anaerobic treatment

9.147   Anaerobic treatment of leachate uses similar biodegradation processes to that of the landfill. The process has shown some success in the removal of high concentrations of BOD and COD by degradation of organic materials to methane and carbon dioxide.

9.148   The disadvantages of anaerobic treatment of leachate are

---

[17] Knox K (1987): Design and Operation of a Full Scale Leachate Treatment Plant for Nitrification of Ammonia. Proc First International Landfill Symposium, S. Margherita di Pula, Sardinia, Italy.
[18] Robinson H D, Barr M J and Last S D (1992): Leachate Collection, Treatment and Disposal. Journal of the Institution of Water and Environmental Management, Vol 6 No 3 June 1992.
[19] Robinson H D (1994): Treating Landfill Leachate. Landfill Completion Seminar, IBC Technical Services Ltd, Industrial Division, 27 October 1994.

- once landfilled wastes themselves ultimately achieve substantially methanogenic conditions, with effective conversion of organic compounds to landfill gases, an anaerobic plant could become largely redundant

- removal of ammoniacal nitrogen, perhaps the major long-term contaminant in many landfill leachates, cannot be achieved in any anaerobic system.

Reed bed treatment systems

9.149   The ability of reed bed systems to treat waste waters relies on the transfer of oxygen to their extensive rhizomatous root system, thereby stimulating the growth of aerobic bacteria in the surrounding soil medium. Oxidising zones are thus created close to the roots, with areas remote from the roots forming reducing zones. This mosaic of areas allows both anaerobic and aerobic reactions to break down organic substances and other contaminants. Other constituents of the effluent may be immobilised or absorbed by the plants themselves.

9.150   Reed bed treatment systems have become an established component of treatment systems for domestic sewage, with 81 beds at 27 sites having been set up by 1988[20]. Water authorities frequently use reed bed systems to treat domestic sewage in conjunction with rotating biological contactors. Severn Trent plc intend to have 160 reed bed/RBC systems installed by the middle of 1994[21].

9.151   Many researchers have demonstrated good removal of organic components of effluents, but poor removal of ammoniacal nitrogen is also a common finding, and this is likely to limit the value of reed beds for treating raw leachates. However reed bed treatment systems may have considerable potential for secondary polishing of leachates which have initially been pretreated by other means.

9.152   A DoE research project[22] has investigated the treatment of a high strength landfill leachate using a treatment sequence comprising an automatic aerobic lagoon plant, followed by a reed bed treatment system established in gravel media. Preliminary results indicate that the system can provide very effective reliable removal of suspended solids, COD and BOD. Investigations are continuing into the ability of the system to carry out nitrification and denitrification.

Land treatment

9.153   Spray irrigation of leachate onto grassland, coniferous and broadleaf woodland, and peat slopes has been widely practised in the UK. Spraying can give rise to a significant reduction in leachate volume due to evapotranspiration. The method has been successfully applied to the spraying of low strength leachates over large land areas in wetter areas of the UK. Spray irrigation is unlikely to be a successful method for treatment of stronger leachates and certainly there may be a contradiction in engineering a landfill to provide an appropriate degree of containment, and then irrigating untreated leachate onto adjacent uncontained grassland. However, irrigation of pretreated leachate over a capped completed landfill surface or onto grassland or other media such as peatlands, has significant potential for effluent polishing.

---

[20] Parr T (1989): *1988 Survey of reed growth in the UK reed bed treatment systems.* WRC/NERC contract report TO2058el. Medmenham, UK.

[21] Knox K and Gronow J (1993): A review of landfill cap performance and its application for leachate management. Proc Fourth International Landfill Symposium, S. Margherita di Pula, Sardinia, Italy.

[22] DoE: *A Review of the Composition of Leachates from Domestic Wastes in Landfill Sites (in preparation).*

164

9.154   Land treatment involves a combination of biological and physico-chemical processes, for example, nitrification and denitrification, plant uptake, oxidation, transpiration, evaporation and precipitation, absorption and adsorption. As the leachate percolates through or across the soil, there are opportunities for microbial degradation of organic compounds, uptake of ammoniacal nitrogen by plants, and removal of inorganic ions by precipitation or ion exchange.

9.155   Slotted pipes (trickle irrigation), sprinklers and spray nozzles have been used to distribute leachates. Typical application rates are up to 45 m^3/ha/day, but higher rates have been used for weaker leachates.

> Evaporative losses are maximised by using fine sprays (rain gun devices intended for farmers to irrigate crops are designed to **minimise** evaporation) and regular intermittent spraying provides more effective evaporation than a single daily application.

> Inappropriate application of leachate may damage both soil structure and vegetation. Problems that may occur include the compaction of the soil surface, and the formation of a ferric hydroxide pan (hard pan) both of which reduce infiltration. There is also some evidence to suggest reductions in soil phosphate, and an increase in the salinity of the soils.

> The spraying of leachate containing high levels of metals or persistent organics is not recommended because of the potential for accumulation in soils and plant materials. Consideration should also be given to potential odour problems in the vicinity of the treatment area, and to the effects of possible dispersion of fine droplets in windy conditions.

Leachate recirculation   9.156   The recirculation of leachate through areas of emplaced wastes, or by spraying onto areas of uncapped wastes, can use a landfill as an uncontrolled anaerobic filter/reactor, and provide a medium for some additional microbial degradation of organic contaminants especially during the initial acetogenic phase of decomposition. Leachate recirculation can also make more effective use of the absorptive capacity of the landfilled wastes and enhance the production of landfill gas by improving the moisture distribution within the site.

> At existing sites, leachate recirculation may be difficult to achieve except on current tipping areas. Sub-cap irrigation systems may provide a means of overcoming this, but it is a technology in early stages of development.

> Partial treatment prior to recirculation (for example nitrification of ammoniacal-N) has some potential, and has shown some promise in pilot-scale trials[23], but would not overcome problems of recirculation of ions such as chloride or some metals. Recirculation of even a proportion of these must inevitably further extend completion timescales.

---

[23] Morris J (1993): Royal Reeds Reap Rewards in Water Bulletin 565, 9 July 1993.

Control of landfill gas

Importance

9.157   Uncontrolled landfill gas poses risks, through its explosive asphyxiant and greenhouse gas characteristics. Virtually all landfill sites will produce gaseous emissions for a long period of time. The extent to which this will occur, the composition of the gases and the control and monitoring arrangements which will be needed will have been considered as part of the landfill design process. Landfill gas management and monitoring are discussed in detail in WMP27.

9.158   The quality and quantity of intermediate and top cover used in operations and restoration will influence the extent of lateral gas migration.

> For example, the specification of a low permeability cap as part of the restoration may well encourage lateral migration by effectively preventing gas escape through the landfill surface.

Problems arising from landfill gas

9.159   Potential problems arising from landfill gas fall into the following categories

- explosions or fires due to gas collecting in confined spaces, such as buildings, culverts, manholes or ducts on or near landfill sites

- asphyxiation of people entering culverts, trenches, manholes or buildings on or near landfill sites

- ignition of landfill gas when released through fissures at the surface, with a risk of setting fire to the waste

- detrimental effects on crops and vegetation on or adjacent to landfill sites

- risks to human health

- nuisance problems, especially odour.

9.160   Migration pathways and receptors will be identified during the desk study phase of the design process and the effect of external factors such as sharp changes in barometric pressure should be considered during risk assessment. To be able to design and operate landfill gas control systems effectively it is necessary to understand that two largely independent mechanisms for migration exist

- gaseous diffusion (concentration gradient)

- advection (pressure gradient).

9.161   For this reason, as well as the need to build in a design safety factor, it is usually necessary to have more than one level of control at any site, specifically designed to meet the requirements of that particular site.

> Landfill gas systems designed to control vertical and lateral migration must take priority over, and must not be confused with, any utilisation systems which may be installed. Nevertheless, a well designed system for landfill gas utilisation can and should complement a migration control system where practicable.

Trace components in landfill gas

9.162   A large number of minor constituents have been identified in household waste landfill gas at low concentrations. Some of these compounds are responsible for unpleasant odours and some of them may represent a health hazard. Odours from landfill gas differ from those from leachate since the smell of the latter is predominantly due to carboxylic acids which are only present at low concentration in landfill gas.

9.163   Landfill gas is typically diluted in the air above a site by a factor of between a thousand and over a million. The numerous organic compounds which may be present at significant concentrations at source are usually diluted to below the toxicity threshold. Measurements of metals as volatile derivatives or in particulate matter have shown that concentrations in landfill gas are very low at both household and industrial waste sites. At sites taking chemical wastes, care must be taken to ensure that toxic gases are not generated by the reaction between incompatible wastes or do not volatilise from the waste itself.

Landfill gas odours

9.164   Landfill odours can cause considerable nuisance, as sufficient dilution to eliminate the smell may not be achieved under some weather conditions. Potential sources of odour and control options are discussed in paragraphs 9.93 to 9.96.

Greenhouse gas emissions

9.165   Both methane and carbon dioxide are greenhouse gases. Methane is estimated to be about 20-30 times more damaging than carbon dioxide. Therefore conversion of methane to carbon dioxide is less damaging to the environment than allowing the landfill gas mixture to be discharged to the atmosphere unchanged.

9.166   The combustion of landfill gas either in flares or as part of an energy recovery process converts methane to carbon dioxide, and should be undertaken whenever the landfill gas yield is capable of supporting combustion. When the methane content is too low or too variable to support combustion, consideration should be given to using a support fuel but this should only be implemented if a risk analysis shows that clear benefits can be gained.

9.167   Passive gas venting systems and migration through the surface cover of a landfill site pose a potential environmental hazard. However, the microbial oxidation of methane in soils may offer a powerful means of reducing the methane emissions. Research[24] indicates that in the near future this process may be enhanced or controlled through controlling the soil type and humidity. Operators should maintain an overview of this research so that operational systems can be implemented as soon as possible.

Objectives of landfill gas management systems

9.168   Landfill gas management systems should be part of the site infrastructure and will normally be subject to waste management licence conditions. The objectives of landfill gas management systems are to

- minimise the risk of migration or accumulation off-site

- eliminate so far as possible the risk of explosion or asphyxiation

- prevent unacceptable risk to human health, detriment to the environment or nuisance.

Types of system

9.169   Three types of system may be used to control lateral migration of landfill gas, either individually or in combination

a)   passive venting

b)   barriers

c)   pumping.

[24] Whalen S C, Reeburgh W S and Sanbeck K A (1990): Rapid Methane Oxidation in a Landfill Cover Soil. Applied and Environmental Microbiology, Vol 56, pp 3405-3411.

a) *Passive venting systems*

9.170 **Passive venting systems should only be used in situations where the rate of gas generation is low, for example biologically old sites, and inert waste sites.** They rely on the inherent property of gases to move from a location with high pressure and/or concentration, to one where pressure and/or concentration is lower. Such systems can be implemented by a number of means including venting columns and drilled vents as set out in Table 9.8 and shown on Figure 9.2.

9.171 Stone-filled venting trenches rely on their acting as a permeability contrast and the importance of such vents admitting oxygen from the air into the ground should not be overlooked. The reduction of efficiency with depth means that simple venting trenches will not effectively prevent lateral migration at depths of more than about 3 metres because gas concentrations reach an equilibrium between the deeper parts of the trench and the surrounding ground. Performance can be improved by installing a low permeability geomembrane on the side of the trench away from the waste.

b) *Physical barriers*

9.172 Physical barriers range from stone-filled trenches to low permeability constructions including flexible geomembranes, bentonite cement, and slurry walls, piled cut off, and combinations thereof. Bentonite cement and other clay barriers are not fully effective against gas migration unless they incorporate a geomembrane. The performance of all physical barriers is considerably improved when combined with a means of removing the gas, such as by passive venting or pumped extraction.

c) *Landfill gas extraction systems*

9.173 These systems depend on suction to remove landfill gas from the waste. They comprise five main components

- gas wells or drains in the waste[25]

- pipework leading from the wells to the pumps

- condensate traps to remove condensed liquid from the system

- pumps which remove the gas from the waste

- landfill gas diffusers, flares or utilisation plant.

9.174 **Gas wells and drains**: Landfill gas wells comprise either drilled boreholes constructed after the waste has been emplaced or stone collectors constructed as part of the waste emplacement process.

- Drilled wells - comprise large diameter boreholes drilled into the placed waste and completed with an inner perforated well pipe surrounded by a gravel packing. The top of the borehole is completed with non-perforated pipe surrounded by a bentonite seal to allow for settlement. A typical well is illustrated in Figure 9.3.

  > As a general principle, the performance of a well improves with increasing diameter and boreholes are now being drilled up to 1 m diameter. The well pipe is generally about 150 mm internal diameter HDPE with between 10% and 20% open perforated area.

---

[25] Migration control systems can, in suitable geological conditions, incorporate wells located in natural ground just outside the waste, where ground conditions can provide more predictable behaviour than the waste. The risks of pulling gas out of the site into the surrounding ground must be assessed before adopting this approach.

168

Table 9.8

Passive and low permeability barrier landfill gas management options

---

Drilled vents

These are drilled using conventional percussion or flight auger methods after substantial thicknesses of waste have been emplaced

Advantages

A relatively cheap method of providing pressure relief

Do not interfere with day to day operations

Can easily be converted to a suction system

Disadvantages

Risk of drilling through basal liners

Limited effectiveness when pressure gradients are absent

Small surface area inhibits diffusion of air into the ground resulting in poor flushing capabilities

---

Stone columns

Stone columns built as tipping proceeds, typically 1 m diameter or 1 m square

Advantages

Relatively cheap to construct

Effectively relieve positive pressure

More effective than drilled wells at diffusion venting because of greater surface area

Promote downward migration of perched leachates

Disadvantages

Intrusive in working area

Liable to damage by mobile plant

Lack vertical stability

Promote rainwater infiltration

Vibropiled columns

An uncased stone column or stone filled pipe is inserted into the site after tipping has been completed using vibropiling techniques

Advantages

Do not intrude into operational area

Costs comparable with conventional drilling

Effective in relieving pressure

Disadvantages

Relatively small diameter makes diffusion venting poorly effective

Same as for drilled wells

Table 9.8 *continued*

Stone filled venting trenches and pits	*Advantages*
These are excavated into or around the waste and filled with clean graded stone usually as part of the restoration works	Simple to construct
	Can be cost effective
A geotextile is frequently used to separate the stone from the waste	Effective for shallow sites (<5 m deep)
	Large surface area allows inward diffusion of air hence good flushing characteristics
	Disadvantages
	Difficult to prevent ingress of surface water
	Lose effectiveness with depth and will not prevent migration at more than 3 m depth
	Intrude in restoration scheme
Stone filled venting trenches with barrier	*Advantages*
As above, but with a low permeability membrane such as MDPE or HDPE on the side of the trench away from the waste	Effectively control migration provided that the trenches and membranes penetrate to the water table or to a low permeability strata
	Disadvantages
	Difficult and expensive to construct at depths greater than about 5 m
Stone filled venting trenches with headwork venting columns	*Advantages*
	The surfaces of the trenches can be sealed thus reducing the risk of infiltration of surface water and improving compatibility with some land uses
	Disadvantages
	Reduced surface area of venting columns impairs diffusion mechanism

Figure 9.2 Passive landfill gas venting pit *(not to scale)*

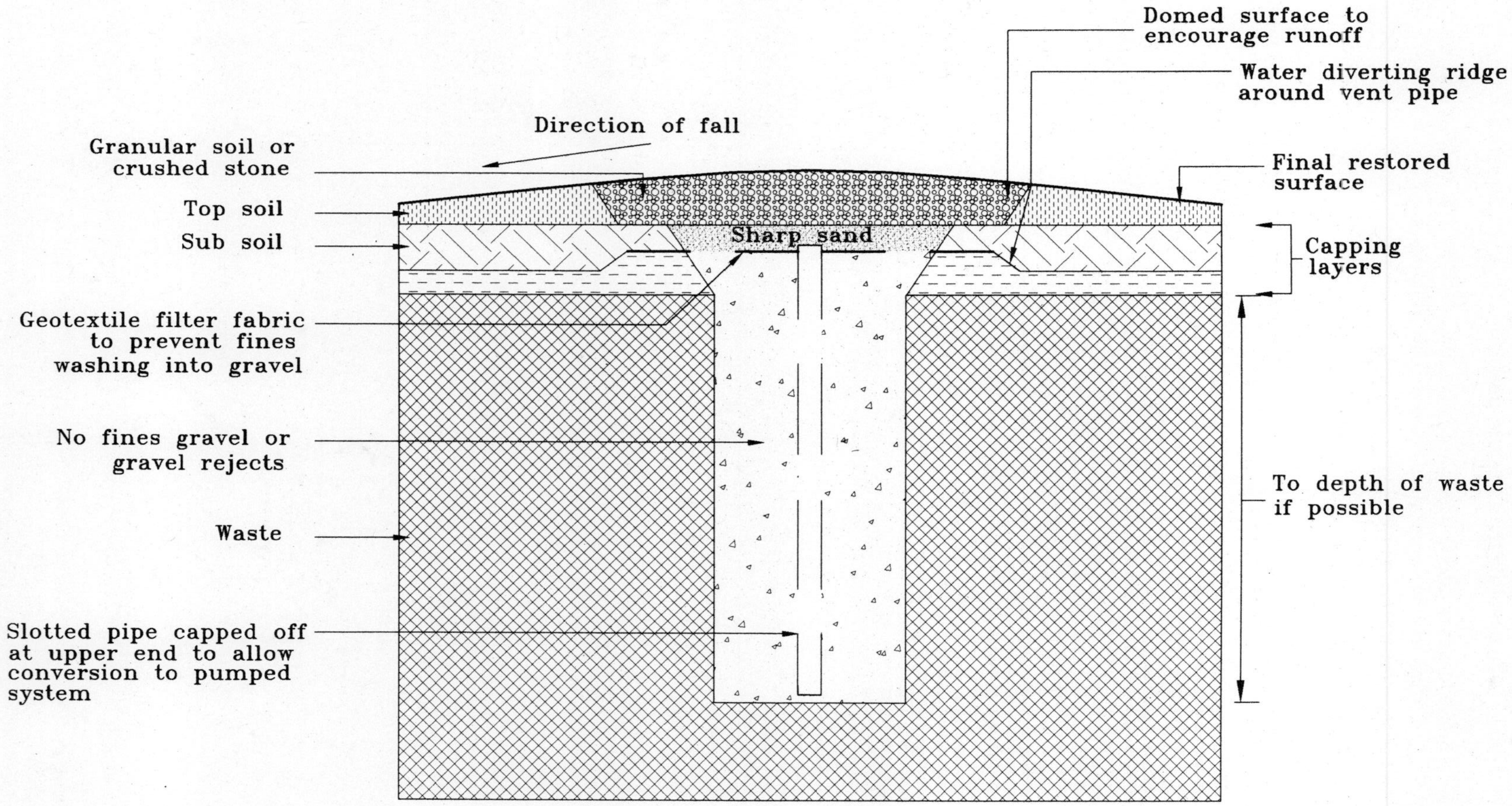

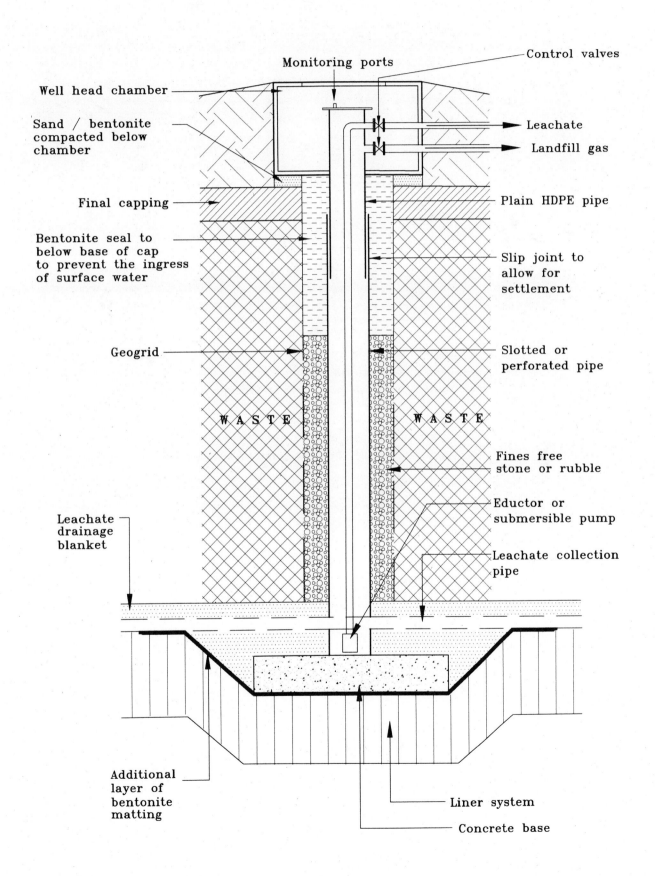

Figure 9.3   Typical combined leachate and landfill gas collection well

- Horizontal drains - are usually constructed in the waste as it is emplaced and comprise a horizontal stone bund or a stone-filled trench with a perforated collection pipe which is connected via risers to the gas pumping system.

9.175   Gas collection systems are subjected to very considerable forces as the waste compacts, degrades and settles, and this should be taken into account when the system is designed and constructed. Substantial downward drag forces are imposed on the relatively incompressible vertical wells and stone columns which, in extreme cases could punch the wells or columns through the landfill base liner. Drilled wells should therefore terminate at least 3 metres above the base of the waste in all containment sites and incorporate sliding joints at their upper end. Constructed stone columns should have a substantial foundation pad designed to withstand the forces likely to be imposed.

9.176   Because of the heterogeneous conditions within a landfill, the forces imposed on a vertical structure will be not be confined to the vertical plane. Lateral forces will deflect the structure out of vertical alignment and may crush or shear the well pipes.

9.177   All gas extraction systems are subject to a progressive loss of performance due to the build up of silt, chemical precipitates and biomass. Small diameter wells, ie <150 mm internal diameter, are so badly affected that they can become unserviceable within 3 or 4 years of construction[26].

9.178   Vertical wells will only extract gas effectively from unsaturated waste. The reduced permeability of degraded waste, accumulation of condensate and the physical displacement of pore water often result in a build up of leachate within landfill gas wells to the detriment of their performance.

9.179   As a result, vertical wells are not effective in extracting gas from wet sites. Even in unsaturated sites the operator may well find it necessary to arrange for leachate removal from vertical gas wells using either pumps or ejectors.

9.180   Operators have achieved good results with a horizontal gas collection system installed beneath the capping of saturated sites where vertical wells have failed to achieve good results on account of the high leachate levels. Horizontal collection systems are much more likely to be damaged by loading forces than vertical wells and their use at depth in landfill sites has now been largely discontinued.

9.181   **Pumping mains and pipework**: Landfill gas pipework systems are generally made of smooth bore HDPE piping with fusion welded joints. The pipes should be sized to suit the anticipated flows and may range from 150 mm internal diameter at the well head to 300 mm or more, close to the pumps. Temporary systems are generally constructed from flexible HDPE pipe, typically 150 mm diameter.

9.182   **Condensate traps**: Regardless of whether the pipework is permanent or temporary, careful attention should be paid to the removal of condensate from the system. Landfill gas is saturated with water vapour as it is generated within the waste, and this is carried into the wells and pipework along with the gas. Variations

[26] In situ falling head permeability tests of 150 mm internal diameter wells drilled in waste have shown permeabilities of the order of 1×10^{-8} m/s in household waste emplaced for about 10 years.

in the temperature and pressure within the extraction system cause some of the water vapour to condense and drain to low points in the system where in extreme cases it can cause blockages.

> The pipework system should be designed to drain the condensate to low points which may drain either back to the wells themselves, or to self draining condensate knockout pots which discharge the condensates back into the waste, or to condensate collection tanks.

> Most regulatory authorities take the view that discharging condensate back into the waste from which it originated does not require a separate waste management licence although it may be a condition of an existing licence. Otherwise condensate is a controlled waste and is subject to regulation for its disposal or discharge. Condensate may be a highly contaminated liquid[27].

9.183   **Gas extraction pumps**: Gas extraction pumps now generally take the form of centrifugal compressors driven either by diesel engines or by electricity. They are available in a range of sizes typically between 150 m^3/hr and 500 m^3/hr. The smaller units are available skid or trailer mounted complete with a condensate trap, flare or diffuser and the necessary controls and monitoring equipment. These are generally used for temporary systems either to deal with emergencies or for pumping tests.

> Gas pumping equipment may be required to pump gas/air mixtures which fall within the explosive range (ie 5% - 15% methane, in 18 - 21% oxygen). They cannot be made intrinsically safe and so it is essential that flame arrestors are fitted to prevent ignition within the compressor propagating back through the pipework to the site.

9.184   **Flares and diffusers**: Landfill gas extracted from the waste should be disposed of by combustion in a purpose built flare. Where the gas contains insufficient methane to support combustion, and a risk assessment precludes the use of a support fuel, it should be discharged to the atmosphere through an elevated diffuser stack to ensure adequate dispersion.

> The landfill designer should have estimated the quality and quantity of landfill gas likely to be generated and should design measures to ensure that the emission does not cause a nuisance or health risk to local residents using atmosphere dispersion modelling where appropriate.

> It is not possible to predict the occurrence of malodorous or hazardous trace components in the landfill gas and so it is necessary for the operator to investigate the landfill gas itself and the products of combustion from the flare or utilisation plant to verify that the predicted performance is being achieved. These investigations should be undertaken as part of the plant commissioning trials and should be repeated once a year from then on.

> Operators should be aware that the combustion efficiency of many landfill gas flares is very poor.

Landfill gas utilisation   9.185   Energy recovery is a mature, successful technology in the UK and where it

---

[27] Condensate often forms a two phase mixture; an organic rich 'oily' phase and an aqueous phase. If chemical analyses are required, the presence of the two phases should be taken into account.

has the prospect of being economically attractive and environmentally beneficial is encouraged by the Department of Trade and Industry.

> Landfill gas utilisation complements and helps offset the costs of landfill gas control.

> Direct use of the gas is more efficient than electricity generation but requires local users.

> Electricity generation is an alternative where there are barriers to direct use.

> Energy recovery should always be considered in preference to flaring without energy recovery.

Equipment used on landfill sites

9.186   The items of mobile plant most commonly used on landfill sites are

- steel wheeled compactors

- tracked dozers and loaders

- rubber tyred loaders

- scrapers

- hydraulic excavators.

9.187   Mobile plant may also include fork lift trucks and telescopic handlers. Auxiliary equipment may also be required to carry out specific tasks such as spraying with water to reduce dust problems, the application of pesticides and road sweeping, pumping, high pressure spraying and electricity generation.

Steel wheel compactors

9.188   Steel wheel compactors have been developed specifically for landfill operations and are used extensively. Different patterns of cleated wheels are designed to break up and compact waste. For small sites receiving low volumes of waste, a compactor alone may be adequate to spread and compact the waste as well as handle and place cover material. However, a compactor is not designed to be a multi-purpose machine and at busy sites it is more usual to provide a tracked or wheeled bucket loader. If cover has to be excavated or transported any distance a dumper may also be provided. Properly trained operators, emplacing waste in thin layers, enable compactors to be used in an efficient manner. Compactors

- chop and homogenise the waste

- reduce the void fraction of the waste

- produce an even and stable surface

- pin down waste to minimise litter and make the site less attractive to birds and vermin.

9.189   Landfill compactors are available in a wide range of sizes and operating weights. Apart from size, the more obvious differences between machines are the cleat patterns on the wheels and the wheel configuration. The wheel configuration is relevant when determining the number of passes required to achieve the desired amount of compaction.

Tracked dozers and loaders

9.190   These are very versatile machines with a wide range of sizes. Tracked machines can be fitted with a variety of blades, buckets and track cleats. Correct selection of fittings is important and is determined by the intended use of the machine.

> The advantage of a tracked machine for landfill operations is that it can operate where the underlying ground is soft because of its low ground pressure. It is also very stable and manoeuvrable when working over rough or sloping ground.

> Tracked machines are not as effective for compacting waste as steel wheeled compactors because their ground pressure is lower. However, by operating on a sloping working face, a tracked machine increases its effective ground pressure. Special track plates are available to chop up waste. Track life can be adversely affected by the wastes.

9.191   A tracked dozer/loader with a multipurpose bucket can

> separate bulky items from incoming waste and place them where required

> grade the waste surface

> maintain secondary roads

> tow bowsers

> extract trapped vehicles

> carry out a range of other general site maintenance work.

Rubber tyred wheel loaders   9.192   These are versatile machines and may be useful for small sites where construction waste predominates, or as back-up machines on large sites. Tyred loaders have the advantage that they can travel on highways without damaging the surface. Because of their greater speed they are more efficient than a tracked machine except in soft ground conditions. Punctures can be a serious problem but may be minimised by providing tyre guards, using foam filled tyres and raising tyre specifications.

Scrapers   9.193   These are used on landfill sites for excavating and moving cover materials in the course of site preparation and restoration. Essentially there are two types, tractor and box, and motorised. Since these are single purpose machines they are normally found only on large sites, although they may also be employed during the site preparation and restoration stages.

Hydraulic excavators   9.194   These are commonly used on landfill sites where their main function is excavation, mainly related to site preparation and restoration, but also for excavation of co-disposal trenches.

Auxiliary equipment   9.195   This includes tractors, dump trucks, slave vehicles (when waste is brought to the site in containers), fuel and water bowsers, lighting set, road brushes, pumps and pipework. Water bowsers are particularly useful during the summer for damping down dusts.

Equipment selection   9.196   No one machine is capable of performing all the tasks required to operate a landfill. When selecting plant, the operator should consider a variety of factors including

• site characteristics

> Landfill sites vary. There will always be site specific factors which affect the type of equipment required for their operation. For example, pumps will be required to remove uncontaminated

rainwater; separate pumping systems will be required to deal with leachate.

- site preparation

  > Where landfilling is being carried out in conjunction with minerals extraction, the operator may be filling part of the site while preparing another. This may involve the excavation of material from the base to form a cover or a liner, in which case a scraper or hydraulic excavator and dump truck will be required.

- quantity of waste

  > The number, type and size of machines required will clearly depend on the quantity of waste arriving at the site each day. Waste impact should be matched with the handling capabilities of the selected equipment.

- type of waste

  > Waste must be pushed, compacted and covered at the working area, and as a minimum therefore a compactor or bladed machine will be needed.

- density of waste

  > In general, optimum use of void space requires wastes to be compacted to a high density. The highest density can be achieved most quickly using steel wheel compactors. Density values achievable range from about 0.5 tonnes/m^3 using a tracked vehicle pushing waste from the top of a working face to over 1 tonne/m^3 using a compactor working on thin layers of waste. Densities over about 0.8 tonne/m^3 may reduce the rate of biodegradation (see paragraph 9.66).

- cover

  > There may be a need to win cover on-site. For large operations where cover is to be won, a hydraulic excavator or drag line can be used in conjunction with dump trucks or a box scraper. When cover is carried only short distances, either a tracked or wheeled loader may be suitable. At sites where cover is delivered it may be possible to use the machine that is normally compacting waste.

- back-up requirements

  > The advantage of operating more than one machine is that if the machine used for spreading and compacting refuse is out of service, incoming waste can still be handled. Alternatively, contingency plans must be made either to direct waste to another site or to bring in a suitable machine. Some equipment manufacturers offer a repair or replace policy. The reliability of equipment and availability of spares should always be considered when selecting equipment. It is most important not to undersize plant; apart from the problems of overworking that will then arise, operating standards may suffer.

- safety and operator comfort

> It is desirable that the cabs of all machines used on landfill sites should be air conditioned and protected by appropriate dust filters. They should also be fitted with rear spotlights, ROPS and FOPS[28] cab protection and audible reversing signals. It is essential that machine operators are properly trained in the safe operation of their machines and that adequate supervision is provided.

Inspection and maintenance of plant

9.197   Machinery breakdown can be costly. The operator may have to contend with repair costs, replacement machine hire charges, problems resulting from poorly compacted waste, the absence of cover, or temporary closure of the site. It is therefore prudent to have a programme of daily and weekly inspection of machinery. With a schedule of preventative maintenance, the maintenance check-list supplied by the machinery and plant manufacturer should be adhered to. Specific time should be allocated for maintenance, particularly for weekly inspection. Adequate facilities for maintenance should be provided. Makeshift arrangements for major refits of heavy plant can lead to accidents.

---

[28] ROPS = roll over protection structure
FOPS = falling object protection structure.

10 Capping Design and Construction

Introduction

10.1   The capping system is the final component in the construction of the landform. It comprises the engineering and restoration layers. This chapter describes the overall objectives for the capping system and gives guidance on the factors to be considered in the design of the technical aspects of the engineering layers. Detailed guidance on the design and construction of the restoration layers consistent with the intended afteruse is given in WMP26E. In accordance with the holistic approach to design, the reader should refer to WMP26E in determining the overall design model for the capping system.

Objectives of the capping system

10.2   The objectives of the engineering cap are to

- contain the wastes

- manage leachate production by controlling the ingress of rain and surface water into the underlying waste

- prevent uncontrolled escape of landfill gas or the entry of air into the wastes

- provide protection for the emplaced wastes

- accommodate the environmental control measures.

10.3   The objective of the restoration layers is to enable the planned afteruse of the site to be implemented and therefore to provide a suitable growing and rooting medium for plants as appropriate.

Containment of wastes

10.4   The engineering cap provides a cover for the emplaced waste materials and the foundation for the restoration and afteruse of the site. Depending on the nature of the waste and the intended afteruse, the cap may vary from a suitable soil cover to a fully engineered system which incorporates barriers to water and gas movements, and associated control measures. A soil cover appropriate to the afteruse placed directly over the wastes may be suitable for inert wastes, while the effective management of bioreactive wastes for accelerated decomposition will require a stringent capping design. These will be determined by the overall design objectives and risk assessment.

Control of moisture entering the landfill

10.5   The control of moisture entering the emplaced wastes is an important factor for all bioreactive landfills, including both those where accelerated stabilisation is attempted and those where the site is managed for slow release over a very long period. Where any wastes are contained in an excavation, either naturally or by a liner system, an effective cap will be required as part of the overall controlled leachate management system to ensure that the site does not accept uncontrolled additions of water. Water balance calculations, as described in paragraphs 6.49 to 6.51, will be essential.

> Studies have shown that caps constructed from properly selected and engineered clays with effective drainage, and sufficient depth of soil cover, will reduce infiltration to very low rates, at least over

the relatively short term (up to 60 months) covered by the research[1].

10.6   For the enhanced bioreactor site, the landfill will need to be managed to achieve accelerated decomposition[2]. Research indicates that controlled introduction of moisture is one way to achieve this objective. In order to retain control over leachate management, recirculation of leachate beneath a high quality, low permeability cap will be required.

Control over gas emissions and air entry

10.7   An effective engineering cap forms an integral part of the landfill gas management systems described in Chapters 6 and 9. The role of the cap is to act as a deterrent to uncontrolled escape of gases through the surface of the waste, and to encourage gases to move through the control system of pipes, vents or trenches. It is also essential to ensure the proper functioning of the restoration layers above.

Prevention of erosion

10.8   The design model will need to ensure that the finished landform is protected from water erosion and that slope stability is maintained. The design gradients will depend on the overall design model determined through the risk assessment process and the requirements of the afteruse[3].

Afteruse and access provision

10.9   The holistic approach to landfill development encompasses landfill engineering, landscape design and planned afteruse, with the landscape architect playing an important role in the restoration concept. The landfill designer must therefore take account of the landscape and planned afteruse requirements in the technical design of the engineering layers.

10.10   The landscape master plan should be prepared in consultation with the owner/operator and the engineering design team, taking into account the requirements of the planning authority and other relevant consultees. The design team as a whole should consider what specific provisions will be necessary to accommodate the landscape and afteruse proposals without compromising the performance of the engineering cap and should consider the overall profile of the capping system required. WMP26E deals specifically with the restoration layers of the final cap including the handling and placing of the soil layers and the requirements for vegetation establishment. The depth of soil cover will be site specific, consistent with the planned afteruse and the presence of environmental control systems.

10.11   The landfill designer, landscape architect and restoration specialists should ensure that the landscape proposals and the landfill requirements are compatible, for example

> the size and layout of phases should be organised where possible to reflect existing or proposed land use patterns, enabling field boundaries to be established as part of a phased restoration scheme[4]

> adequate storage areas for on-site or imported soils should be planned within the site boundary to allow separate handling, storage and maintenance of soil quality in respect of landscape restoration materials

---

[1] Knox K and Gronow J (1993): "A review of landfill cap performance and its application for leachate management". Proc Fourth International Landfill Symposium, S. Margherita di Pula, Sardinia, Italy.
[2] See Appendix D.
[3] See paragraphs 6.4 to 6.7 in Chapter 6.
[4] See also paragraph 6.18.

> the use of many and varied soil types in one restoration phase should be avoided

> the layout of pipework and environmental monitoring points should be designed to enable the use and maintenance of the planned landscape to take place with minimal disruption

> access routes provided for monitoring and maintenance of the landfill gas and leachate management systems should be planned to avoid compromising the planned afteruse.

10.12   When considering the design of the capping layers, the designer will need to determine what types of vehicle access provision will be required, for example, large vehicles for heavy repairs and maintenance or light vehicles for routine monitoring and repairs. Access tracks should be kept to a minimum; they need to be constructed of suitable materials and their construction should not damage the engineering cap profile nor the restoration layers. Their alignment should be designed to minimise both soil damage and interference with the planned afteruse of the site.

Capping system

Key features

10.13   The design of a capping system should consider

- the system—s ability to withstand the effects of frost and hot weather

- availability of required materials

- construction of maintenance vehicle access tracks and public footpaths (as appropriate)

- durability of the system

- installation of gas well heads and collection pipework

- installation of leachate collection manholes and pipework

- landscape requirements including additional subsoil needs

- low permeability to minimise gas emission and surface water infiltration

- the relationship between the phasing of construction and the landscape design for the afteruse

- recirculation of leachate if required

- robustness against settlement stresses

- stability on proposed restoration slopes

- surface water drainage

- the effects of roots and burrowing animals on its integrity.

Capping layers

10.14   Components of the capping system are shown on Figure 10.1. For the purposes of this Paper, the surface layers constitute the *restoration layers*, which are discussed in detail in WMP26E. The underlying components comprise the *engineering layers*, which are discussed in the following text. However, the design of the protection layer and any drainage zone will be affected by both restoration and engineering considerations and **the designer should consider the capping system as a whole.**

182

Figure 10.1 Capping system – five possible components

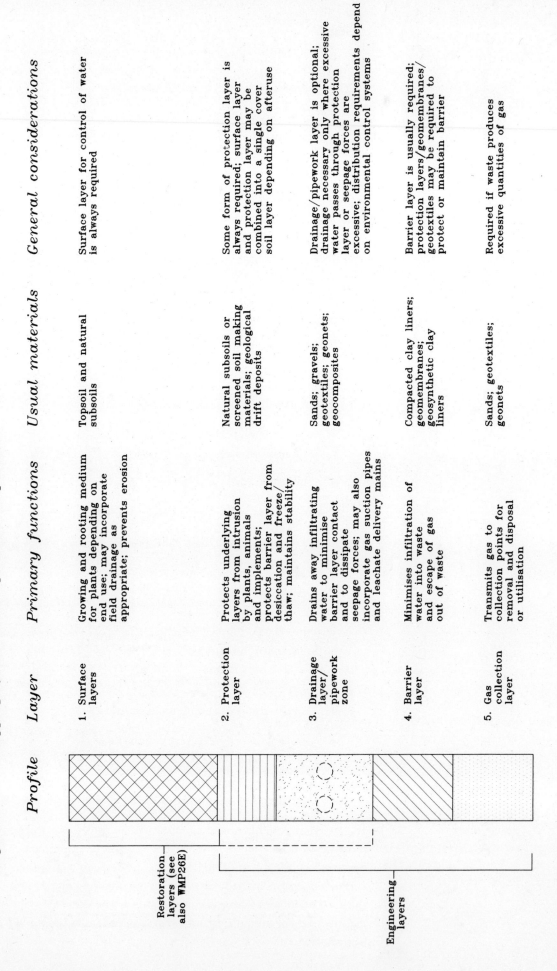

Profile	Layer	Primary functions	Usual materials	General considerations
	1. Surface layers	Growing and rooting medium for plants depending on end use; may incorporate field drainage as appropriate; prevents erosion	Topsoil and natural subsoils	Surface layer for control of water is always required
	2. Protection layer	Protects underlying layers from intrusion by plants, animals and implements; protects barrier layer from desiccation and freeze/thaw; maintains stability	Natural subsoils or screened soil making materials; geological drift deposits	Some form of protection layer is always required; surface layer and protection layer may be combined into a single cover soil layer depending on afteruse
	3. Drainage layer/pipework zone	Drains away infiltrating water to minimise barrier layer contact and to dissipate seepage forces; may also incorporate gas suction pipes and leachate delivery mains	Sands; gravels; geotextiles; geonets; geocomposites	Drainage/pipework layer is optional; drainage necessary only where excessive water passes through protection layer or seepage forces are excessive; distribution requirements depend on environmental control systems
	4. Barrier layer	Minimises infiltration of water into waste and escape of gas out of waste	Compacted clay liners; geomembranes; geosynthetic clay liners	Barrier layer is usually required; protection layers/geomembranes/geotextiles may be required to protect or maintain barrier
	5. Gas collection layer	Transmits gas to collection points for removal and disposal or utilisation	Sands; geotextiles; geonets	Required if waste produces excessive quantities of gas

Restoration layers (see also WMP26E)

Engineering layers

> For example, the prime function of the *surface layers* is to enable the planned afteruse to be achieved. If these surface layers offer the required level of protection for the underlying environmental control systems, barrier and gas protection layers, then a separate *protection layer* may not be required. However, the designer should look at the overall depth of cover required to achieve both the required level of protection for the engineering components and the requirements of the projected afteruse.

> Similarly, in addition to the restoration layers, the drainage layer/ pipework zone, which is primarily concerned with the accommodation of the environmental control systems related to the underlying waste, may also be effective in providing drainage for the planned afteruse.

For all layers, the designer should make use of on-site or indigenous materials where possible.

10.15 The low permeability element of the *barrier layer* may be constructed to a similar specification to the landfill liner constructed on the base (see Chapter 7). In the UK, low permeability layers generally comprise

- mineral capping layers, for example, compacted clay or BES

- flexible membrane liners (FML), formed from overlapping or welded sheets protected above and below by suitable earth or sand or by geotextiles

  > The FMLs can be thinner and of lower specification than those used in the base liner.

- geosynthetic clay liners.

10.16 Composite capping layers and multiple capping layers are sometimes specified for sensitive locations. Construction methods, materials specifications, testing and CQA procedures are essentially the same as those used for construction of the landfill liner (see Chapter 7).

10.17 Where a site is designed in anticipation of a long period of slow activity, a high quality engineered cap, well protected above and from the underlying wastes, is likely to become the principal control on leachate generation and landfill gases and therefore on long-term environmental protection.

10.18 Protection from damage is a requirement for both clay and membrane barrier layers. Depending on the construction of the barrier layer, the depth of soil materials for the *protection layer* should be sufficient to prevent desiccation of a clay layer[5] or physical damage, for example, by installation of underdrainage or deep cultivations.

10.19 The depth of cover should also be sufficient to bury and provide cover for the gas and leachate management systems within the *pipework zone*, for example, well heads and suction pipework[6]. In addition, on sites where a piped underdrainage system is required for the planned afteruse then an additional depth of cover may be needed to ensure that the landfill gas and leachate pipes can be laid safely below the drainage system.

[5] Knox K and Gronow J (1993): "A review of landfill cap performance and its application for leachate management". Proc Fourth International Landfill Symposium, S. Margherita di Pula, Sardinia, Italy.
[6] Generally a minimum of 450 mm of cover is required over any pipework.

Drainage layer/pipework zone

10.20   Drainage layers are sometimes placed between the surface and the barrier layers where it is necessary to minimise the head of water on the low permeability layer in order to provide positive drainage to the subsoil and topsoil layers, or to increase slope stability by reducing pore water pressure in the overlying soil layers. The drainage layer may be formed from granular material or from geosynthetic drainage nets. Drainage outlets for water collected by the drainage layers will need to be provided. These can be to surface water ditches or to landscape planting areas[7].

Stability and settlement

10.21   The ability of the overall cap to remain stable is of prime concern, especially on steeper restoration landforms or those incorporating low friction layers such as flexible membranes. Where necessary, the stability of the various capping layers should be checked using recognised techniques[8]. Erosion control may be required on steep slopes where large volumes of run-off can be expected. Such controls may include the early establishment of grass cover or the provision of drainage channels. Further details are given in WMP26E.

10.22   Uniform settlement of the waste can normally be accommodated by the capping materials. However, serious problems, such as cracking of the capping layers, may arise as a result of differential settlement at phase boundaries, across the site or on the site perimeter.

10.23   The designer should consider where differential settlement may occur and make provision to accommodate the settlement and the associated stresses. This provision will take the form of

- additional thicknesses of capping materials to accommodate differential movement or allow removal of material if settlement does not occur as predicted

- the possible need for irregular edges and boundaries to compensate for predicted settlement differentials, as shown on Figure 10.2.

10.24   It is important to ensure continuous surface water drainage across areas of differential settlement. In extreme cases, ponding may occur or surface water may flow into the underlying waste through cracks in the cap.

---

[7] Further detail on the design of drainage systems is given in WMP26E.

[8] See Tables 7.2, 7.3 and 7.4 in Chapter 7. Reference also Alexiew D, Berkhout H & Kirschner R (1995): "On the slope stability of landfill capping seals using GCLs" in *Geosynthetic Clay Liners*, ed Robert M Koerner, Erwin Gartung & Helmut Zanzinger; published by AA Balkema/Brookfield. ISBN 90 5410 5194.

Figure 10.2   Construction methods – edge details

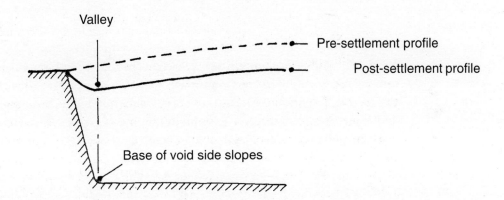

A: Waste and/or cap profile forms a gentle gradient around the edge of the site on completion of restoration. Settlement results in the formation of a hollow or "valley" over the base of the void side slopes. The valley may need reinforcement against erosion.

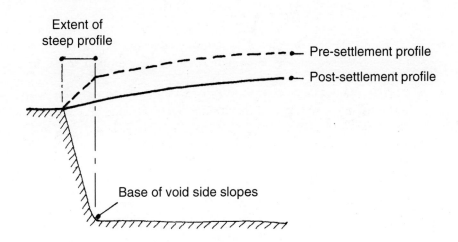

B: Waste and/or cap profile forms a steep gradient around the edge of the site on completion of restoration. This steep profile extends into the site only as far as the base of the void side slopes. After settlement, suitable gradients are maintained for surface water runoff.

Monitoring and remedial maintenance

10.25   Processes in a landfill are dynamic. The settlement of the waste mass and its effect on the integrity of the cap will need to be monitored regularly. Monitoring generally takes the form of walk over surveys, checking the surface for

- ponding of water (differential settlement, slackening gradients, blocked land drains)

- severe differential settlement of surface layers

- vegetation under stress or failure because of poor drainage or landfill gas emissions or both.

10.26   In addition, monitoring of leachate flow after restoration will enable unusual increases in leachate to be detected, which may indicate that damage to the cap may have occurred. Any such occurrences should be monitored closely, and if necessary investigated, to determine whether or not the overall cap construction is damaged, and what remedial measures are required. Simple remedial work may require only the infilling of low spots where water is ponding. More extensive differential settlement or failure of the cap may require its excavation and reconstruction. Regular topographical surveys will be required to assess the progress of settlement.

10.27   Such operations need to be timed and conducted in ways that minimise damage to placed soils and minimise interference with afteruses.

Glossary

Glossary

Note: the definitions in this glossary are specific to WMP 26B.

ABSORPTIVE CAPACITY
The difference between the initial moisture content of the waste and its moisture content at field capacity, ie when it can retain no further water against the pull of gravity.

ACETOGENIC PHASE
The initial period during the decomposition of refuse in a landfill when the conversion of organic polymers, such as cellulose, to simple compounds, such as acetic and other short-chain fatty acids, dominates and little or no methanogenic activity takes place.

ACCELERATED STABILISATION
The active enhancement of biodegradation processes so as to increase the rate of breakdown of the bioreactive waste materials towards a stable and largely non-reactive state.

ADSORPTION
The uptake of one substance on to the surface of another.

AERATION
Exposure to the action of air.

AEROBIC PROCESS
A process which requires the presence of molecular oxygen.

AFTERCARE
i) The steps necessary to bring the land to the required standard for the planned afteruse. [after MPG7]

ii) The period prior to the granting of a certificate of completion during which maintenance and monitoring work is needed to ensure that the restored landfill does not cause pollution of the environment, harm to human health or adverse effects on local amenities.

AMMONIACAL NITROGEN
The combined concentrations of nitrogen as ammonia and ammonium compounds, generally derived from the anaerobic biological degradation of proteins, and other nitrogenous wastes. Concentrations of above a few mg/l can be directly toxic to fish.

ANAEROBIC PROCESS
A process which requires the complete absence of molecular oxygen.

ANISOTROPIC
Having different physical properties in different directions.

AQUIFER
A permeable geological stratum or formation that is capable of both storing and transmitting water in significant amounts. A *confined aquifer* is where upper and lower layers are low permeability which confine the groundwater under greater than atmospheric pressure. An *unconfined aquifer* is where the upper surface of a saturated zone forms a water table within the water-bearing stratum.

ATTENUATION
A decrease in concentration caused by any of a variety of mechanisms, individually or in combination, including dilution, adsorption, precipitation, ion-exchange, biodegradation, oxidation, reduction.

BED VOLUME
The total moisture content of the wastes in a particular landfill or container, including free leachate and any absorbed moisture. The bed volume and the rate of inflow of rain or groundwater determine the average hydraulic retention time of water in the landfill.

BIOMASS
Term used to refer to the mass of biologically active material contained in a reactor, such as a landfill or a biological effluent treatment plant.

190

BIOREACTIVE WASTES	Wastes which are capable of undergoing biological degradation.
BOD (Biochemical Oxygen Demand)	A measure of the amount of material present in water which can be readily oxidised by micro-organisms and thus a measure of the power of that material to take up the oxygen in water.
BUFFERING CAPACITY	A measure of the ability of a substance, for example waste, to neutralise acid or alkaline substances added to it.
BUND	A small bank of soil or other inert material used to define limits of cells or phases or roadways. Not a structural embankment which may be required to retain waste or liquid, but may be a permanent part of a landfill base, incorporating a liner.
CAPPING	The covering of a landfill, usually with low permeability material. Permanent capping is part of the final restoration following completion of landfill/tipping. Temporary capping is an intermediate cap which may be removed on resumption of tipping.
CELL	The compartment within a landfill in which waste is deposited. The cell has physical boundaries which may be a low permeability base, a bund wall and a low permeability cover.
COD (Chemical Oxygen Demand)	A measure of the total amount of chemically oxidisable material present in liquid.
CONSTRUCTION	In this Paper, the actions to build a landform, using waste materials, incorporating all parts of the landfill facility.
CONTAMINATION	The addition of chemicals to groundwater, watercourses or soils at concentrations that can be measured and are significantly higher than background concentrations. (see also Pollution)
DENITRIFICATION	See Nitrification.
DESIGN	The formulation of the plan for the landfill project, including all the details and drawings for the particular site. Three stages of detail are given in this Paper; the *conceptual, main* and *construction* design.
DIFFUSION	The process by which molecules and particles migrate and intermingle, the sole energy source being that due to the natural random motion of the molecules.
EARTHWORKS	Engineering work associated with the movement of soils and materials on a landfill.
EFFECTIVE RAINFALL	Total rainfall minus actual losses due to evaporation and transpiration. Effective rainfall includes both surface run-off and that which percolates into the ground below the soil zone.
EMISSION	A material which is expelled or released to the environment. Usually applied to gaseous or odorous discharges to atmosphere.
ENVIRONMENTAL IMPACT	The total effect of any operation on the environment.
EXOTHERMIC REACTION	A chemical or biochemical reaction which results in the release of heat energy.
FIELD CAPACITY	The total amount of water that may be retained against gravity by landfilled solid wastes, for example after saturation and draining.

FLAMMABLE RANGE The range of percentage volumes of a mixture of flammable gas with air which will propagate a flame at 25°C and at atmospheric pressure. The lowest percentage is referred to as the Lower Flammable Limit and the highest is the Upper Flammable Limit. Where flammable gas occurs in a confined space such that an explosion might occur, these might be referred to as the Lower Explosive Limit (LEL) and the Upper Explosive Limit (UEL) respectively.

GROUNDWATER The mass of water in the ground below the phreatic zone, occupying the total pore space in the rock and moving slowly downhill where permeability allows.

HEAVY METALS Elemental metals having a high relative density and properties that may be hazardous in the environment. The term usually includes the metals copper, nickel, zinc, chromium, cadmium, mercury, lead, arsenic, and may include selenium and others.

HYDRAULIC RETENTION TIME (HRT) The total moisture content of the wastes in a particular landfill or portion of landfill, divided by the rate at which water passes into, and out of, that portion of the landfill.

HOLISTIC DESIGN The overall concept of landfill design, construction and operation, restoration and aftercare as an integrated project where action on one part affects all the others.

INERT MATERIALS Materials that will not physically or chemically react or undergo biodegradation within the landfill.

LANDFILL The engineered deposit of waste into or onto land.

LANDFORM The profile of the completed surface of a landfill.

LANDFILL GAS A by-product of the digestion by micro-organisms of putrescible matter present in waste deposited in landfill sites. The gas is predominantly methane (64%) together with carbon dioxide (34%) and trace concentrations of other vapours and gases.

LEACHATE The result of liquid seeping though a landfill and, by so doing, extracting substances from the deposited wastes.

LINER A natural or synthetic membrane material, used to line the base and sides of a landfill site to reduce the rate of leachate and gas emissions.

MOISTURE CONTENT Percentage of water contained in a sample of waste or soil. Usually determined by drying the sample at 105°C to constant weight.

NITRIFICATION/ DENITRIFICATION Nitrification is an aerobic biological process in which ammoniacal-N is converted to nitrite and then nitrate. De-nitrification is an anoxic biological process in which nitrate is reduced to nitrogen gas.

ODOUR THRESHOLD VALUE Lowest concentration of an odorous gas which can be detected by sense of smell.

OPERATION (OF A LANDFILL) The process of emplacing waste, and the associated management activities for the prepared facility.

PERCHED WATER An accumulation of liquid at a level above that of the adjacent water table. Often caused by zones of low permeability strata (or wastes) which inhibit downward percolation.

PERMEABILITY A measure of the rate at which a fluid will pass through a medium. The coefficient of permeability of a given fluid is an expression of the rate of flow through unit area and thickness under unit differential pressure at a given temperature.

PHASE (OF A LANDFILL) A prepared operational, temporarily restored or restored area.

PHREATIC ZONE The zone of soil and rock in which pores are completely filled with groundwater.

POLLUTION, POLLUTANT The addition of materials or energy to an existing environmental system to the extent that undesirable changes are produced directly or indirectly in that system. A pollutant is a material or type of energy whose introduction into an environmental system leads to pollution. cf Contamination.

POROSITY The ratio of volume of void space to the total volume of a rock or strata.

PREPARATION The engineering works associated with the base, lining, monitoring, environmental control and infrastructure items of the facility prior to emplacing waste in a phase.

PUTRESCIBLE A substance capable of being readily decomposed by bacterial action. Offensive odours usually occur as by-products of the decomposition.

SATURATED ZONE Zone of an aquifer where all fissures and pores contain water (in other words, the zone below water table).

SETTLEMENT The amount by which a landfill surface sinks below its original level due to compaction by its own weight, and degradation of the waste. For example, a tipped waste thickness of 40 m settling by 8 m would have undergone 20% settlement. (This example is for finished surface levels only and does not consider the age or rate of degradation and settlement).

STABILISATION As applied to landfill, this term includes the degradation of organic matter to stable products, and the settlement of the fill to its rest level. The process can take many years to complete. The term also refers to the use of plants and/or geotextiles to prevent soil erosion from the surface of a landfill or spoil heap.

SURCHARGE To fill a landfill above final contours to allow for subsequent settlement. For example, if 20% settlement is predicted and a 100 m finished waste thickness is required, then a surcharge of 25 m of waste is required, in other words, the total placed waste thickness would be 125 m.

SUSTAINABILITY Returning the contents of a landfill site to the environment in a controlled manner, at a rate which the environment can accept without harm, generally using pro-active measures over a limited timescale to diminish polluting capability, in a way which does not leave a long term legacy of active monitoring and management.

TRANSMISSIVITY The rate at which water is transmitted through a unit width of an aquifer under a unit hydraulic gradient. In the English Engineering System, transmissivity values are given in gallons per minute through a vertical section of an aquifer one foot wide and extending the full saturated height of an aquifer under a hydraulic gradient of 1. In the International System, transmissivity is given in cubic metres per day through a vertical section of an aquifer one metre wide and extending the full saturated height of an aquifer under a hydraulic gradient of 1.

UNSATURATED ZONE The zone of a stratum which lies above a water table in which the pore space in the soil is not saturated with water.

VERMIN Used collectively to describe insects and small wild animals who are associated with harm to human health or adverse effects on local amenities.

VOID SPACE The capacity of a landfill for waste, plus cover, plus construction material, plus the engineering and restoration layers.

WASTE See Appendix A

WATER TABLE Top surface of the saturated zone within the aquifer.

WORKING AREA The area or areas of a landfill in which waste is currently being deposited.

Abbreviations

Abbreviations

Abbreviation	Term in full
ACE	Association of Consulting Engineers
BES	bentonite enhanced soil
BGS	British Geological Survey
BOD	biochemical oxygen demand
BPEO	best practicable environmental option
BS	British Standard
BSI	British Standards Institution
CAD	computer aided design
CD-ROM	compact disc - read only memory
CIRIA	Construction Industry Research and Information Association
COD	chemical oxygen demand
COSHH	Control of Substances Hazardous to Health [Regulations]
CQA	construction quality assurance
CQC	construction quality control
DoE	Department of the Environment
DTM	digital terrain model
EA	Environmental Assessment [Regulations]
EC	European Communities
FML	flexible membrane liner
GCL	geosynthetic clay liner
GGP	Guidance on Good Practice [Report - see Chapters 3, 6, 7]
HDPE	high density polyethylene
HMIP	Her Majesty's Inspectorate of Pollution (England and Wales)
HMIPI	Her Majesty's Industrial Pollution Inspectorate (Scotland)
HSE	Health and Safety Executive
ICE	Institution of Civil Engineers
IWM	Institute of Wastes Management
LCS	leachate collection system

MAFF	Ministry of Agriculture, Fisheries and Food
NAMAS	National Measurement Accreditation Service
NAWDC	National Association of Waste Disposal Contractors
NRA	National Rivers Authority
NWWDO	North West Waste Disposal Officers [Reports - see Chapters 3, 6, 7]
PCB	polychlorinated biphenyl
RBC	rotating biological contactor [see Chapter 9]
RPA	River Purification Authority (Scotland)
UK	United Kingdom
USEPA	United States Environmental Protection Agency [Report - see Chapter 7]
VOC	Volatile organic compounds
WAMITAB	Waste Management Industry Training and Advisory Board
WMP	Waste Management Paper
WRA	waste regulation authority

Appendix A
Waste Definitions

Appendix A
Waste Definitions

The following waste definitions are derived from a number of sources as follows:

DoE: Environmental Protection Act 1990 Part II [EPA 1990]

DoE: The Controlled Waste Regulations 1992 SI 1992 No 588 [CWR 1992]

DoE: The Control of Pollution (Special Waste) Regulations 1980 [COPA 1980]

DoE: The Waste Management Licensing Regulations 1994 SI 1994 No 1056 [WML 1994]

EC: Directive 91/689/EEC on *Hazardous Wastes* [HW 1991]

The definitions of difficult, inert, municipal and toxic wastes are general descriptions of terms in common usage.

WASTES, COMMERCIAL

Commercial waste is waste, defined in the Environmental Protection Act 1990 Section 75 (7), which, subject to subsection (8), comes from premises used wholly or mainly for the purposes of a trade or business or the purposes of sport, recreation or entertainment excluding:-

a)   household waste;

b)   industrial waste;

c)   waste from any mine or quarry and waste from premises used for agriculture within the meaning of the Agriculture Act 1947 or, in Scotland, the Agriculture (Scotland) Act 1948; and

d)   Waste of any other description prescribed by regulations made by the Secretary of State for the purposes of this paragraph.

WASTES, CONTROLLED

Controlled waste means household, industrial and commercial waste or any such waste. [EPA 1990]

WASTES, DEMOLITION

Masonry and rubble wastes arising from the demolition or reconstruction of buildings or other civil engineering structures. [CWR 1992]

WASTES, DIFFICULT

Wastes that create difficulties in disposal because of their physical or chemical properties.

WASTES, DIRECTIVE

Any substance or object in the categories set out in Part II of Schedule 4 of the Waste Management Licensing Regulations 1994 which the producer or the person in possession of it discards or intends or is required to discard but with the exception of anything excluded from the scope of the Directive by Article 2 of the Directive. [WML 1994]

This definition will be incorporated in primary legislation in the Environment Act 1995, once the relevant sections and Schedules are brought into force.

WASTES, DOMESTIC

Waste or refuse that arises from private houses; synonymous with household waste. [see below]

WASTES, HAZARDOUS Any waste covered by the Hazardous Wastes Directive 91/689 EEC and listed in the schedule. [HW 1991].

However, more commonly hazardous waste is regarded as any waste that, by virtue of its composition, carries the risk of death, injury, or impairment of health to humans or animals, the pollution of waters, or could have an unacceptable environmental impact if improperly handled, treated or disposed of. The term should not be used for waste that merely contains a hazardous material or materials. It should be used only to describe wastes that contain sufficient of these materials to render the waste as a whole hazardous within the definition given above.

WASTES, HOUSEHOLD Household waste is defined in the Environmental Protection Act 1990 Section 75 (5) as waste, subject to subsection (8), from:-

a)   domestic property, that is to say, a building or self-contained part of a building which is used wholly for the purposes of living accommodation;

b)   a caravan (as defined in section 29(1) of the Caravan Sites and Control of Development Act 1960) which usually and for the time being is situated on a caravan site (within the meaning of that Act);

c)   a residential home;

d)   premises forming part of a university or school or other educational establishment;

e)   premises forming part of a hospital or nursing home. [EPA 1990].

WASTES, INDUSTRIAL Industrial waste is defined in the Environmental Protection Act 1990 section 75 (6) as waste, subject to subsection (8), from any of the following premises:-

a)   any factory (within the meaning of the Factories Act 1961);

b)   any premises used for the purposes of, or in connection with, the provision to the public of transport services by land, water or air;

c)   any premises used for the purpose of, or in connection with, the supply to the public of gas, water or electricity or the provision of sewage services; or

d)   any premises used for the purposes of, or in connection with, the provision to the public of postal or telecommunications services. [EPA 1990].

WASTES, INERT Wastes that do not undergo any significant physical, chemical or biological transformations.

WASTES, MUNICIPAL Municipal waste is that waste that is collected and disposed of by or on behalf of a local authority. It will generally consist of household waste and some commercial waste and waste taken to civic amenity waste collection/disposal sites by the general public. In addition, it may include road and pavement sweepings, gully emptying wastes, and some construction and demolition waste arising from local authority activities.

WASTES, SPECIAL Controlled waste of any kind that is or may be so dangerous or difficult to treat, keep or dispose of, that the Secretary of State considers special provision is required for dealing with it. [EPA 1990]

The procedure to be followed is described in the Control of Pollution (Special Waste) Regulations 1980, issued under Section 17 of the Control of Pollution Act 1974, under revision 1995.

WASTES, TOXIC   In common usage referring to that class of hazardous wastes which are harmful to human health.

Appendix B
Main Legislation Affecting Landfill
Design and Construction

Appendix B
Main Legislation Affecting
Landfill Design and Construction

Planning legislation and development control

B1   Planning control is exercised through the local planning authorities. The relationship between the planning system and pollution control legislation is explained in Planning Policy Guidance Note No 23 *Planning and Pollution Control* (PPG23) (England). The planning system focuses on whether the development itself is an acceptable use of land, rather than the control of the processes or substances themselves. The function of pollution control is to control processes and substances which can have potentially harmful effects on the environment.

B2   The Town and Country Planning Act 1990[1] and the Planning and Compensation Act 1991 control the use of land for waste disposal through

- development plans
- the grant or refusal of planning permission.

Development plans

B3   Development plans are prepared at both the county and district level in England and Wales and must have regard to national and regional planning policy guidance. Any determination under the Planning Acts must have regard to the development plan, and the determination shall be made in accordance with the Plan unless material considerations indicate otherwise. Development plans must also comply with EC requirements, including the Framework Directive on Waste (75/442/EEC, as amended by 91/156/EEC and 91/692/EEC). Development plans comprise county wide *structure plans,* and district wide *local plans.* In London, the metropolitan areas and unitary authorities these are combined into *unitary development plans*[2]. Special arrangements apply in National Parks. These plans give strategic advice on the development and use of land in a particular area and include policies in respect of potentially polluting development.

B4   Other relevant plans for landfill development include *waste disposal plans* and *waste local plans*[3]. The development plan framework provides an opportunity for the requirements and constraints of waste disposal strategies to be considered in the context of the overall development and use of land and, where appropriate, set out broad criteria to be applied in identifying waste disposal sites.

Planning permission

B5   The determination of landfill applications is the responsibility of the county or unitary authorities in England and district councils in Wales and Scotland[4]. Planning permission is required for the use of land for waste disposal, except for certain permitted development under the Town and Country Planning (General Permitted Development) Order 1995[5]. Environmental matters are one of the

---

[1] In Scotland, the Town and Country Planning (Scotland) Act 1972 as amended.

[2] In Scotland, Structure Plans are prepared by the Regional and Islands Councils; Local Plans are prepared by District Councils, except within the regions of Highland, Borders and Dumfries and Galloway and the three Islands areas where they are prepared by the Regional and Islands Councils.

[3] There are no separate Waste Disposal Local Plans in Scotland. From April 1996 all planning functions will be the responsibility of the Unitary Councils.

[4] Unitary Councils from 1996.

[5] In Scotland, the Town and Country Planning (General Permitted Development) (Scotland) Order 1992, as amended.

material considerations which planning authorities have to take into account when dealing with applications.

B6   For developments which are likely to have significant effects on the environment, developers may be required to submit an *environmental statement* with their planning application, in accordance with the Town and County Planning (Assessment of Environmental Effects) Regulations 1988[6].

B7   The EA Regulations and circulars describe the process of *environmental assessment*, and the specified information to be reported in the environmental statement. In summary, this information comprises

- a description of the development, incorporating the site, the design and scale of the proposals

- baseline data necessary to identify and assess the main environmental effects of the development

- a description of the likely environmental effects of the development (direct, indirect, permanent, temporary, positive and negative) and measures proposed to mitigate adverse effects.

B8   Projects to dispose of *special waste* fall within Schedule 1 of the EA Regulations, where environmental assessment is mandatory. Other waste disposal activities fall within Schedule 2 of the EA Regulations, where environmental assessment is required if a development is judged likely to give rise to significant environmental effects. Guidance given in DoE Circular 15/88, on indicative criteria and thresholds for environmental assessment of Schedule 2 projects, indicates a threshold level of 75,000 tonnes a year waste capacity for waste disposal installations, including landfill sites. The key criterion is the *likelihood of significant environmental effects.* Many landfill proposals will fall into this category and so may require environmental assessment, even where the proposed input is less than the indicative threshold.

Waste management licensing

B9   The Environmental Protection Act 1990 prohibits the deposit of controlled (directive) waste, in or on land, unless a waste management licence authorising the deposit is in force. It also prohibits the disposal of waste in a manner likely to cause pollution of the environment or harm to human health.

B10   The purpose of licensing is to ensure that the disposal of controlled waste does not give rise to

- pollution of the environment

- harm to human health

- serious detriment to the amenities of the locality.

B11   Licences are issued subject to conditions designed to ensure that the development and operation of a landfill site will not cause any of these problems.

B12   An application for a waste management licence must be made to the Waste Regulation Authority (WRA) in whose area the site is situated. The WRA is the county/metropolitan borough council in England and district council in Wales. The WRA is required to consult both the NRA and HSE and, in certain instances,

---

[6] In Scotland, the Environmental Assessment (Scotland) Regulations 1988, SI No 1221.

the relevant nature conservation body. Guidance on the preparation and content of licences is contained in WMP4. The applicant is required to set out in a working plan how the landfill is to be prepared and operated. This should include an explanation of the basis of the landfill design, and the standards to be achieved in its preparation and operation.

B13   During the preparation and operational phases of the landfill, the WRA will inspect the site regularly to ensure that the development is in accordance with the licence and working plan.

B14   Once issued, a licence may only be surrendered if the WRA is prepared to accept it back. Normally this will be only once the WRA is assured that the site has stabilised and it is satisfied that the site is unlikely to cause pollution of the environment or harm to human health. Details of how a landfill can be assessed for completion are given in WMP26A.

Protection of water quality

B15   The Water Resources Act 1991 is concerned with the pollution of 'controlled waters', which include rivers and other inland surface and underground waters, estuaries and territorial waters. It is an offence if a person 'causes or knowingly permits any poisonous, noxious or polluting matter or any solid waste matter to enter any controlled waters'[7].

B16   To comply with the Water Resources Act 1991, a landfill development may require discharge consent in addition to planning permission and a waste management licence. Under the Water Industry Act 1991, discharges to ground and surface watercourses are the responsibility of the National Rivers Authority (NRA)[8], whilst any disposal to sewer will require consent from the relevant sewerage authority[9].

Health and safety and construction standards

B17   Every employer has a common law duty to his employees to provide a safe working environment. Engineering operations and construction processes undertaken when preparing and operating a landfill will be subject to relevant health and safety legislation. In the UK, the many different aspects of health and safety standards are to be found in a large number of statutory Regulations, Orders and Rules. The Health and Safety at Work etc. Act 1974 provides for the consolidation of these statutes, although many of the regulations which were enacted before the passing of the Health and Safety at Work etc. Act 1974 remain in force. If a landfill development is in a former or active quarry, it may also be subject to specific Mines and Quarries legislation.

B18   The Health and Safety at Work etc. Act 1974 imposes a general legal duty on employers to ensure, so far as is reasonably practicable, the health, safety and welfare at work of all employees. This is enforced by the Health and Safety Executive (HSE). The HSE has powers to supplement its duty with Regulations and Codes of Practice.

B19   The Management of Health and Safety at Work Regulations 1992 require employers to make a 'suitable and sufficient assessment of risks' to the health and safety of their employees whilst at work. The purpose of an assessment under these Regulations is to enable the employer to identify the preventative or protective

---

[7] In Scotland, pollution control is administered under the Control of Pollution Act 1974 Part II, as substituted by Schedule 26 of the Water Act 1989.

[8] In Scotland, River Purification Authorities (RPA).

[9] Water companies in England and Wales; in Scotland, the Regional and Islands Councils.

control measures necessary to control the risks highlighted in the risk assessment. The Control of Substances Hazardous to Health (COSHH) Regulations are also of relevance to many landfill developments. The COSHH Regulations impose a basic obligation to prevent or, where this is not reasonably practicable, adequately control employees' exposure to hazardous substances. The Regulations set out a basic system which should be followed to manage the risk to health.

Nuisance

B20   Nuisance from noise, odour, smoke and fumes, etc is covered in the provisions of the Environmental Protection Act 1990, and is regulated by local authority environmental health officers.

Appendix C
Waste Decomposition Processes

Appendix C
Waste Decomposition Processes

Introduction

C1   The understanding of *in situ* landfill biological decomposition has developed considerably since the publication of the original WMP26. In particular, research funded by the Departments of Energy and the Environment and the Energy Technology Support Unit has examined the fundamental microbiology of waste degradation in laboratory and field scale studies and also by means of mathematical models in conjunction with experimental data. The results from the research have confirmed the existence of many degradation pathways, and several factors affecting gas and leachate generation.

C2   Monitoring data from sites across the UK and from field trials at Brogborough landfill site have demonstrated that the organic fraction of waste present in dry landfills degrades slowly but still generates both leachate and landfill gas albeit at a low rate. In comparison, data from otherwise similar landfill sites which are wet have demonstrated that higher rates of landfill gas and leachate are generated. The data from these sites also indicate that the proportion of methane in the gas is higher within a shorter period after waste deposit and that the organic loading of the leachate measured as Total Organic Carbon (TOC) or Chemical Oxygen Demand (COD) becomes lower over a shorter time period. These data have demonstrated that management of the biological processes within the landfill can significantly alter the quality, quantity and onset of the generation of landfill gas and leachate and the timescale for waste stabilisation.

In situ composition and biodegradability

C3   Waste comprises a heterogeneous mass of material which varies according to the source and with time. Following its deposit in a landfill site, and often before, the organic fraction of the waste will begin to undergo degradation through chemical and microbiological action, resulting in the production of biochemical breakdown products and the liberation of gases. The infiltration of rainfall, ground and surface waters into the waste mass, coupled with this biochemical and physical breakdown, produces a leachate which contains soluble components of the waste, suspended solids and micro-organisms.

C4   The chemical constituents of waste, and the biodegradability of the organic fraction, vary according to both the type and source of the waste. The organic fraction of wastes characteristically comprises carbohydrates such as cellulose, lipids, proteins and fats. In domestic wastes, these account for approximately 55% by dry weight. In contrast, the organic fractions of commercial and mixed industrial wastes are 66% and 62% by dry weight respectively. The overall biodegradability of the organic fraction present in any waste and the rate of degradation depend upon its physical and chemical nature, as well as environmental factors such as temperature, moisture and pH. For example, cellulose is a constituent of many waste components, including paper and putrescible materials, and accounts for the majority of organic fraction present in waste. In circumstances where cellulose has been chemically modified, for example in textiles, or is associated with polymers such as lignin, for example in paper, the rate of degradation and overall degradability are significantly reduced.

Processes of degradation   C5   Degradation of the organic fraction of waste materials within a landfill may be described in a simplified way as a five stage process. Figure C.1 illustrates the five stages of the process and the characteristic products generated at each stage. The first and fifth stage occur under aerobic conditions (in the presence of oxygen) whilst the remaining stages take place under predominantly anaerobic conditions (in the absence of oxygen). Each stage of the process has an impact on the characteristics of the intermediate and final breakdown products and the quality and rate of generation of leachate and landfill gas. Figure C.2 illustrates the degradation process in more detail. In the first stage of the process *hydrolysis/ aerobic degradation*, which occurs both during and for a period after waste placement, a proportion of the organic fraction of waste is metabolised by aerobic micro-organisms (oxygen consumers) present in the waste. These micro-organisms convert readily degradable carbohydrates to simple sugars such as glucose, carbon dioxide and water. The intense microbiological activity during this stage generates heat (an exothermic reaction) which can cause the temperature of the waste mass to rise to 80-90°C.

C6   The duration of this aerobic stage depends on the availability of oxygen, which is influenced by management practices at the site, such as the degree of waste compaction, the depth of waste and the type of daily covering. Practices such as baling of waste, on-site consolidation of deposited materials and increasing the water content of the waste materials, all reduce the pore space available for oxygen ingress. Furthermore, as more waste materials are added to the site, oxygen flow into the underlying waste is impeded. The major decomposition products of this process are water and carbon dioxide, and the characteristic odour associated with this stage of the process is mainly due to the presence of organic esters.

C7   As oxygen becomes depleted further stages of degradation develop. The aerobic micro-organisms are superseded by groups of micro-organisms which can tolerate low levels of oxygen (facultative anaerobes) and then, as the anaerobic conditions develop, the obligate anaerobic micro-organisms which include the methane generating organisms (methanogens) gradually become established. These processes are dynamic, each new stage being dependent on the creation of a suitable environment by the preceding stage.

C8   In the second stage of the process, *hydrolysis and fermentation*, carbohydrates, lipids and proteins are hydrolysed to simple sugars and then fermented by bacteria to soluble intermediates (such as volatile acids), acetate, carbon dioxide, hydrogen and inorganic salts, such as sulphate and ammonium. The type of volatile acid generated, for example propionic, butyric, lactic and formic, depends on the initial substrate, for example carbohydrate or lipid, and the prevailing *in situ* conditions. During this stage, nitrogen is displaced by carbon dioxide and hydrogen to form leachate with a high ammoniacal nitrogen content, while the temperature within landfill drops to 30-50°C.

C9   In the third stage, *acetogenesis*, bacteria convert the soluble acids formed by the activities of the fermentative bacteria of the previous stage to acetate, carbon dioxide and hydrogen. Other bacteria convert carbohydrates, hydrogen and carbon dioxide to acetic acid. The conversion of fermentation products such as butyrate, propionate and ethanol can only be achieved at low hydrogen concentrations. If hydrogen concentrations remain higher than this, these intermediate products cannot be further oxidised to form the main food source for the methane-generating bacteria and, under these circumstances, propionic acid accumulates (propionogenesis and acid-souring). This third stage of the overall process can only be maintained if hydrogen utilising organisms such as the sulphate-reducing bacteria and methane-generating bacteria are active. During this stage, the gases generated from the waste mass in a balanced system are predominately carbon dioxide, hydrogen and methane.

C10   In the fourth stage of the process, *methanogenesis*, the methane-generating bacteria (methanogens) metabolise acetate and formate produced during the other degradation stages to form methane and carbon dioxide. Some methanogens may also be able to generate methane by the direct conversion of hydrogen and carbon dioxide. There is also evidence that formate is an important substrate for methane generating organisms. Methanogens are most active in the pH range 6.8-7.4.

C11   A balanced relationship usually occurs between the hydrogen-producing bacteria of the acetogenesis stage and the hydrogen-utilising methane generators. If concentrations of hydrogen increase, acetogenic bacteria alter their metabolism to form ethanol and lactic acids rather than acetate, which is the preferred substrate for the methanogens. If the activity of the fermentative bacteria and methanogens are not balanced, then the breakdown intermediates of the acetogenic stage accumulate. The process is known as acid-souring.

C12   Other groups of organisms are also active during the anaerobic degradation of wastes. These include a group of bacteria which convert hydrogen and carbon dioxide to acetate and the sulphate-reducing bacteria which utilise hydrogen and sulphates to generate hydrogen sulphide. These organisms can compete with the methanogens for these substances.

C13   In the final stage of the process as the degradable components are exhausted, progressive re-establishment of aerobic conditions can occur. Recolonisation of the landfill by facultative aerobic and aerobic micro-organisms such as methane oxidising organisms may then become established as prevailing conditions permit. This may release substances such as metals which were stable during the preceding anaerobic stage.

C14   Within the landfill site as a whole, all of the stages of degradation may be occurring at different rates at any one time. This is the result of different times of waste emplacement, differing biodegradabilities and spatial variability in the physical and chemical environment of the waste materials.

Landfill gas

C15   During all stages of decomposition, various gases are generated. The principal components of landfill gas are methane and carbon dioxide, although a large number of other minor components are also present. The gas is also saturated with water vapour. The changing composition of landfill gas during the different stages of degradation is illustrated in Figure C.3.

C16   During the aerobic phase of degradation, oxygen levels become depleted with the concomitant rise in levels of carbon dioxide. As the hydrolysis and fermentation stage of degradation occurs, levels of carbon dioxide and hydrogen increase and nitrogen levels fall. In some circumstances, hydrogen levels may reach 20% by volume of total gas. The concentration of methane present in the gas in this stage gradually rises as the acetogenic and methanogenic stages develop. When a balance between the amount of organic fraction hydrolysed and the activity of the methanogens is reached, steady-state methanogenic conditions occur resulting in a gas composition of about 64% methane and 34% carbon dioxide. As the degradable organic fraction within the waste becomes exhausted, methane and carbon dioxide generation decline.

C17   Landfill gas may include hydrogen sulphide, which is generated by a group of sulphate-reducing bacteria which act on sulphate within the waste. At sites with a high input of gypsum and plasterboard, concentrations up to 30% v/v have been reported although more typically concentrations in the ppm range can be expected. For landfills which do not contain sulphate wastes, hydrogen sulphide concentrations rarely exceed 5 ppm because metallic sulphides are formed preferentially. The production and control of landfill gas is discussed fully in WMP27.

Leachate

C18   Leachate is water that has percolated through emplaced waste and in so doing has extracted suspended solids, soluble constituents of waste and soluble products of the waste degradation process. The composition of leachate depends on the stage of degradation and the type of waste within the landfill (Figure C.4). Further details of leachate composition are given in Appendix I. Leachates generated during the early stages of anaerobic degradation are characterised by high concentrations of volatile fatty acids, acidic pH, high BOD to COD ratio and high levels of ammoniacal nitrogen and organic nitrogen. Ammonia is largely generated as a result of the degradation of proteinaceous materials. The low redox potential of this leachate facilitates the production of soluble reduced state metals including chromium, iron and manganese. However, as the pH rises, these metals are precipitated as sulphides, hydroxides and carbonates.

C19   Following the onset of methanogenesis, many of the fatty acids responsible for the acidic pH and high BOD have been converted to methane and carbon dioxide. Methanogenic leachates are characterised by low concentrations of fatty acids, neutral to alkaline pH, lower levels of ammoniacal nitrogen and low BOD to COD ratio. During the steady methanogenic stage, a dynamic equilibrium generally exists where organic compounds are consumed as fast as they are produced. The relationship between volatile fatty acids, cellulose degradation and gas generation is illustrated in Figures C.3 and C.4.

C20   An important factor affecting leachate generation is the absorptive capacity of the waste. This capacity may be exceeded by a combination of infiltration of surface water or rainwater, groundwater ingress due to liner failure, generation of water by microbial processes and liquid waste input. Leachate generation can also occur long before the absorptive capacity has been exceeded as a result of channelling, the heterogeneous nature of the waste or high-intensity rainfall event.

C21   The absorptive capacity of waste varies according to its type, pre-treatment and degree of compaction. Shredding and pulverisation may increase absorptive capacity by providing a more uniform fragment size and a corresponding higher voidage and a higher surface area per unit (solids) volume. In contrast, baling or increasing the emplacement density reduces the rate of percolation but increases the risk of short circuiting. The effect of compaction rates on absorptive capacity has been demonstrated in a number of laboratory and field studies. For example, it has been demonstrated that the leachate production rate of a waste mass with a density of greater than 0.7 tonnes/m^3, corresponds to 15-20% of the annual precipitation in comparison to 25-50% with similar waste, with a density of less than 0.7 tonnes/m^3.

C22   Trace levels of many chemicals have been detected in leachate from domestic, commercial, industrial and co-disposal sites including aromatics, terpenes and aliphatics.

Figure C.1 Major stages of waste degradation

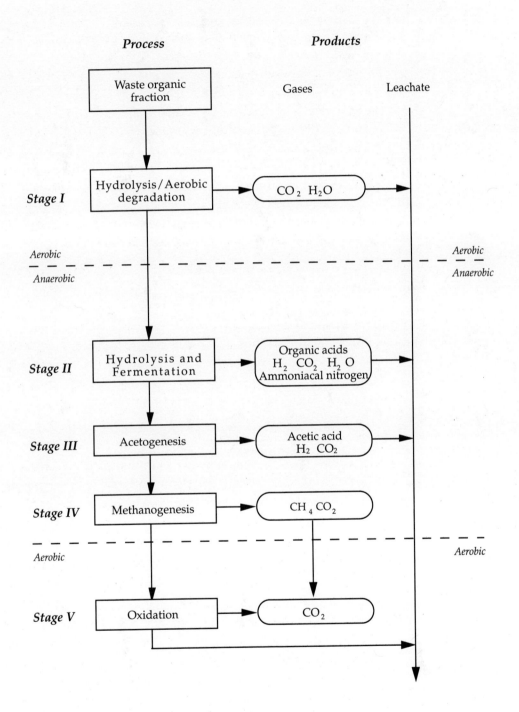

Figure C.2   Stages of waste degradation in detail

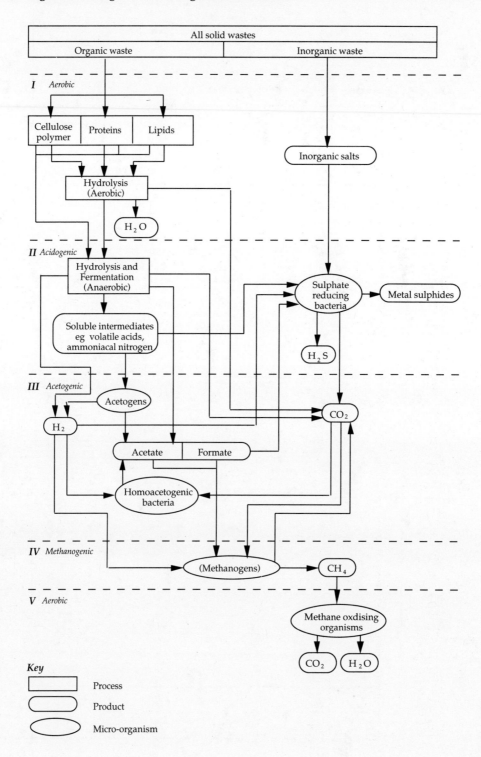

219

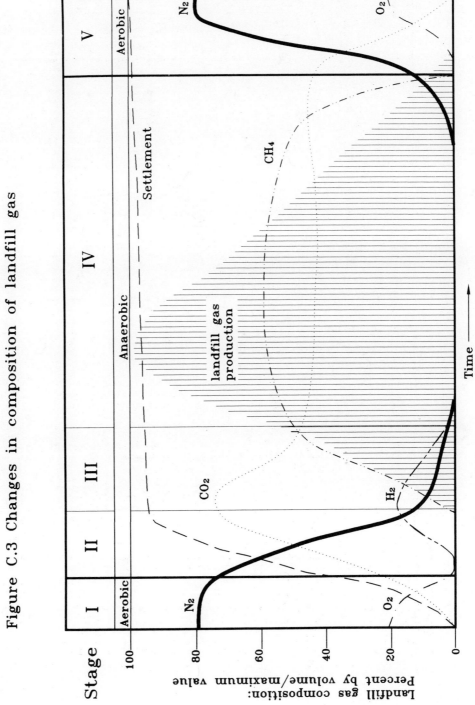

Figure C.3 Changes in composition of landfill gas

Figure C.4 Changes in composition of leachate

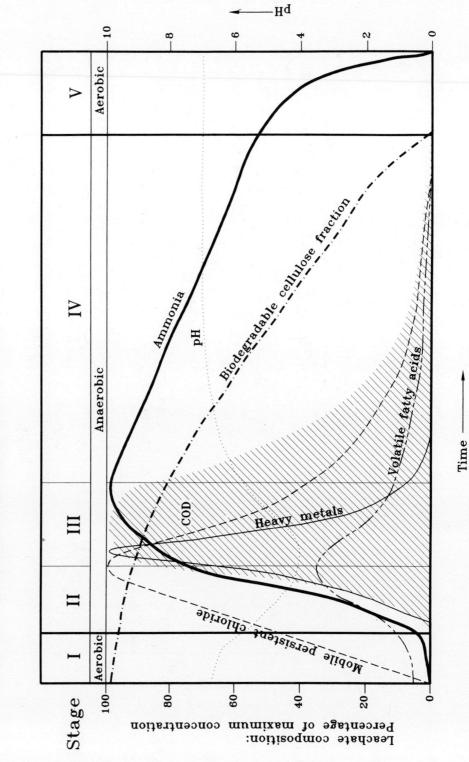

Appendix D
Issues for Accelerated Stabilisation

Appendix D
Issues for Accelerated Stabilisation

Effects on site engineering

D1   The effects of accelerated stabilisation on engineering will include

- more onerous management for acceptance of waste

- increased production rates and strength of leachate and of gas

- greater variation in composition of leachate and gas with time

- increased rate of settlement.

D2   Accelerated stabilisation is therefore likely to require, *inter alia*, changes to

- waste characteristics

- heat retention and insulation characteristics of the base, walls and cap

- surface sealing and potential for air admission

- leachate (and possibly gas) recirculation, pH adjustment and heating

- leachate removal and treatment

- gas abstraction

- daily cover usage

- barriers and bunds

- materials specifications

- filling methods.

These are discussed in turn below.

Waste characteristics

D3   There is a probable need to process the waste to a smaller maximum fraction size. It is possible that a degree of materials recovery could be incorporated at this stage, and that sewage sludge or other nutrients might be added.

Heat retention

D4   Anaerobic decomposition occurs in three temperature bands which, in ascending order of rate are psychrophilic (7-16°C), mesophilic (16-38°C) and thermophilic (38-65°C). Most UK household waste sites operate in the low end of the mesophilic range and considerable acceleration would occur if thermophilic degradation could be attained. Research has indicated that gas temperatures up to 50-60°C can be encountered in the central part of the waste in both active and closed landfills, but that temperatures are lower in the upper 20 m and lower 10 m of the waste[1]. Accelerated degradation would itself generate increased

---

[1] Department of the Environment/Aspinwall & Company (1993): Understanding Landfill Gas. CWM 040/92, April 1993.
Collins H J (1993): "Impact of the temperature inside the landfill on the behaviour of barrier systems". Proc Fourth International Landfill Symposium, Sardinia, Italy.

temperatures. **An objective of design for accelerated stabilisation should therefore be to reduce heat losses through the cap and base (and, if possible, the walls) of the landfill and via the leachate drainage and gas extraction systems**.

Surface sealing and potential for air admission

D5   Air admission, whether due to overpumping of gas or to poor sealing and atmospheric pressure changes, may reduce the rate of decomposition, both by poisoning anaerobic bacteria and by direct cooling. This can be controlled by improved design of cap and cap/walls sealing, and by completion and capping of phases more quickly. Recirculation of gas could also be used as a controlling mechanism.

Leachate recirculation and pH adjustment

D6   **The moisture content of the waste is of vital importance** for both the rate of decomposition and the flushing of inorganic components. Pre-treatment of the waste could achieve more uniform distribution of moisture content, and moisture could be added at this stage. However it is probable that many bed volumes must be exchanged to flush out chemical contaminants, particularly ammonium[2] which implies that a comprehensive leachate recirculation system would be required beneath the cap. This would also have the advantage of permitting pH adjustment[3] and heat control provided that leachate is treated, and possibly diluted, prior to recirculation. The capacity of leachate treatment facilities will also need to be much greater. There would be a need for pre-processing and possibly reduced initial compaction of the waste to attain the order of hydraulic conductivity required to permit this recirculation (equivalent to 2 000 mm/annum rainfall).

D7   **A comprehensive leachate removal system will be required**. Whilst flow rates within the drainage system would be low in hydraulic terms, averaging in the order of 1 l/s/ha, uniformity and reliability will be of great importance. A continuous under-drainage blanket with easily maintainable pipe runs, preferably discharging by gravity to points outside the landfill, is likely to be required[4]. Above-ground landforms will offer advantages in this respect.

Gas abstraction

D8   Gas generation rates will be considerably enhanced by accelerated stabilisation, and effective gas removal will aid biodegradation. The majority of loss of mass, and thereby most of the settlement, occurs through gas emissions. It therefore follows that to avoid inhibition of this process **an effective gas removal system is of fundamental importance in achieving accelerated stabilisation**. This system may be substantially larger than for where stabilisation is not enhanced, and require the provision of additional duty/standby arrangements. The composition of the gas may also be affected. The larger initial volumes of gas generated may be acidic and contain high levels of odorous trace gases.

Daily cover usage

D9   The use of inappropriate daily and intermediate cover can impede the vertical movement of leachate and gas through wastes, which will be of significant importance if accelerated stabilisation is to be achieved. **Daily cover should be restricted to high permeability or biodegradable materials only**, or removed prior to placement of subsequent wastes. This applies both to soils and to synthetic/

---

[2] Harris R C, Knox K and Walker N (1994): "A strategy for the development of sustainable landfill design and operation". 1994 Harwell Conference proceedings. Also in Proc IWM, January 1994, Vol 6. ISBN 0968-7068.

[3] If inert materials are excluded from the site, the buffering capacity may be reduced to the extent that methanogenic conditions cannot be established (acid-souring). To prevent this occurring, it may be necessary to adjust the pH of the recirculated leachate.

[4] See Chapter 6.

alternative cover materials. Pre-processing of waste may reduce or remove the need for daily cover.

D10   Cover materials may be required to reduce heat losses from the site and to prevent odour nuisance. If membrane materials are used, the operator will need to ensure that landfill gas is collected effectively from beneath the membrane to prevent it from ballooning. The operator should also be aware that large volumes of hydrogen are produced during the early stages of degradation[5]. This normally disperses to the atmosphere through the daily cover, but if membrane cover is used, it could become confined.

Bunds and barriers

D11   Barriers such as those between cells or phases may impede the lateral movement of leachate and gas through wastes. When appropriate, such as with leachate recirculation, bunds should be provided with specific interconnections to allow controlled movement of leachate across the site without compromising the lining system.

Materials specifications

D12   Changes to the decomposition process will affect the operating conditions of the construction elements of the landfill. For example, a higher rate of biodegradation may increase the operating temperatures of the liner and leachate drainage system, while stronger leachates may have a greater potential to penetrate or damage the liner system or other components.

Filling methods

D13   Increased rates of settlement, albeit for a shorter period, would be a probable result of accelerated stabilisation. This may require initial filling to a higher level than with present practice, and would require the design of a cap, and leachate and gas control systems, which can accommodate considerable vertical movement while still retaining the required properties. Alternatively, a temporary cap could be provided to allow periodic refilling to achieve final topographic levels.

D14   Particular attention will need to be paid to surface water drainage systems, leachate and gas management systems, and other aspects of site infrastructure. The designer and operator will need to take account of this when planning and constructing the site and in the site restoration and post closure management[6].

---

[5] Hydrogen is a flammable gas with an explosive range in air between 4% and 74% by volume. It is potentially more hazardous than methane, and the landfill gas management system will need to take account of this.

[6] See WMP26E *Landfill Restoration and Post Closure Management*.

Appendix E
Risk Assessment

Appendix E
Risk Assessment

General

E1   The DoE document 'A Guide to Risk Assessment and Risk Management for Environmental Protection' (HMSO, 1995, ISBN 0 11 753091 3) provides a useful discussion of the subject of Risk.

E2   The process of risk management is clearly illustrated in Diagram 1 of the document, which also provides a useful illustration of the principal terms. The diagram and terms are reproduced here.

A Simplistic Illustration of the Principal Terms

Intention: to leave Nelson's column in place as it is, unless a risk assessment reveals intolerable risks.

One **hazard** is that stones of a particular size and weight under certain circumstances might be dislodged and fall; a consequence is that a passer-by might be struck and killed or injured by falling masonry.

Risk estimation might follow the lines that the probability per unit time that a stone will fall is very low whilst the probability that if it does fall it will hit a passer-by is low most of the time; the magnitude of the consequence is high for the person affected but overall the risk to the passer-by is estimated to be low.

Risk evaluation determines whether the risk is significant in relation, for example, to other risks to pedestrians in Trafalgar Square and taking account of perception *ie* the fact that people do not perceive a risk of being hit by a falling stone in Trafalgar Square.

The **risk assessment** would probably be that the risk was negligible.

If the risk were judged to be significant, **risk management** would lead to consideration of actions taken to reduce the level of risk and the cost of such actions. Those actions and the reduction in risk thereby achieved would be subject to a like process of evaluation. Possible actions are: to demolish the column (for which there is the difficulty of valuing the loss of benefit of a Trafalgar Square without a Nelson's column); to strengthen the column; to leave the column alone but to erect fencing to preclude people from the area around the base of the column; to manage the risk by monitoring and maintaining Nelson's column; or leave it alone. The last two actions should take account of the possible development of a greater risk due to, for example, underground works or vibration caused by heavy lorries.

230

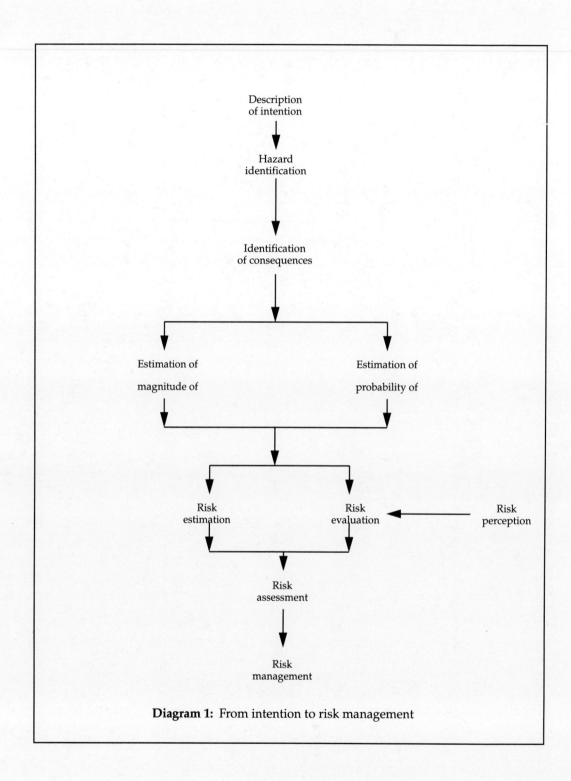

Diagram 1: From intention to risk management

Summary of a Methodology for Probabilistic Risk Assessment for Landfill Leachate Migration

Introduction

E3   Landfill regulators and developers within the UK are using probabilistic risk assessment techniques to assess proposals for waste disposal sites. The probabilistic methodology allows proper quantification of uncertainty within the geological environment, the performance of any landfill lining system, and varying leachate chemistry. The Department of the Environment and the National Rivers Authority have undertaken a development project to establish a standard methodology of probabilistic risk assessment suitable for regulatory use within the UK[1].

E4   The methodology will assist the regulators in assessing the multitude of liner systems and leachate management systems offered by developers at the licensing stage. It also allows full consideration of the variety of geological and hydrogeological regimes beneath and around the landfill sites.

Risk assessment methodology

E5   The chosen methodology is to break the problem down into a series of interconnected modules. The modules deal with the calculation of leachate head in the landfill, assessment of leakage volumes from the site, and allowance for variations of leachate strength. It then computes migration of contaminants into the unsaturated zone and assesses the attenuation processes that may occur. The migration of contaminants within the saturated zone is then computed. A Monte Carlo numerical scheme propagates uncertainty and for each output type, results are represented as probability distributions.

E6   The model has been designed to be user friendly so that regulators and designers, who are familiar with the specification of liner systems and have an understanding of potential leachate impact, can generate the required model input from information readily available from the design and information obtained from a site investigation. Virtually all types of landfill liner can be accommodated within the model along with a variety of leachate collection methods and landfill geometrics. The geological environment is described purely by hydrogeological, geological, physical and geochemical properties.

E7   The need to use probabilistic methods is dictated primarily by the need to incorporate the reality of variation in the performance of geomembranes within a liner system. Having developed methods for dealing with this uncertainty, it has become apparent that virtually the entire system including infiltration, leachate production, leachate chemistry, leakage rates and geological characteristics contains either uncertainty or known variation.

E8   User-friendliness has been achieved by programming the probabilistic model as a Microsoft Windows© based package adhering to all the usual Windows standards. Values are therefore entered into the model typically as minimum credible values, most likely values and maximum credible values. In each case it is intended that the input properly describes the viable range of possible values weighted such that the overall distribution matches that expected. Where a greater degree of certainty surrounds the variation of a particular property then a more confined distribution of values is entered.

Basis of methodology

E9   There are five elements to the probabilistic model. The output of one element forms the input to the next. These are:

---

[1] The development of this model has been undertaken by Golder Associates (UK) Ltd under contract to the Department of the Environment (Contract Ref: EPG 1/7/04) and funded jointly by the Department of Environment and the National Rivers Authority.

- source term

- engineered barriers

- geosphere

- biosphere

- receptors.

E10   The source is a supply of contaminants, in this case the contents of the landfill. Factors for consideration in the source model include a description of the waste stream, its decay processes, management strategies etc. The output of the source term is a list of contaminants, together with their concentrations and volumes. Both concentrations and volume release rates will vary with time.

E11   With landfills, the engineered barrier will comprise the geomembrane and/or clay layers together with the drainage system, and also the capping system and soil cover. Issues for consideration here include the reliability of the design equations, the degree to which construction achieves the design objectives, and subsequent degradation of the constructed elements. The output from the engineered barrier is a release rate for the source term.

E12   The geosphere is all of the pathways which transport the contaminants from the release point of the engineered barrier to the receptors in the biosphere. For one of the pathways, i.e. the potential transport of leachate to groundwater, factors to be considered include advection and dispersion of contaminants, retardation and possible breakdown of the contaminants to other species. The output of such a geosphere module is a possible time delay and attenuation of the contaminants reaching the biosphere.

E13   The biosphere is the final link in the chain and is the point at which the health risk could be calculated for the target population groups, who are referred to as the receptors.

E14   A probabilistic risk assessment describes the inputs and processes involved in terms of a distribution of values reflecting the uncertainties associated with them. Software can make use of the Monte Carlo simulation technique which randomly chooses inputs to the assessment according to their distribution. For each realisation, the output is calculated. Repeating the process many times produces a distribution of outputs that reflects the uncertainty in the system. The results can be displayed as a series of probability distributions for the variables under consideration. Such displays can assist when making decisions on the acceptability of releases from landfills and the need for additional measures to control them. Probabilistic risk analysis can quantify how the landfill may perform and provides a basis for making consistent judgements.

Application

E15   The model output does not give a yes or no answer for the acceptability of a specific design within a certain geological environment. What it does do is provide decision makers with information on probable leakage rate and resulting impacts. This information can then form the basis of rational, well formulated judgements based on an assessment, which due to the nature of the model requires full consideration of all the processes involved. Also it allows designers to fine-tune various aspects of the containment system in order to ensure an appropriate performance for a specific location. It steers both designer and regulators to reviewing the appropriateness of existing site investigation data collected, and highlights those aspects which might need further investigation.

E16   The tool is equally useful for the assessment of existing and closed landfill sites.

E17   The model will underpin a policy of developing engineering barriers which are designed specifically for a certain geological and hydrogeological environment. This approach is preferred to the prescription of a minimum overall standard with little or no regard to the valuable contribution that the natural geological formations can provide to the additional safeguarding of the environment.

Appendix F
Landfill Costings

Appendix F
Landfill Costings

Landfill cost tables (see Chapter 3)
Introduction

F1   The economics of landfill disposal need to be understood by those involved in order that the true cost of development, operation, restoration and aftercare of a site can be evaluated prior to development; only by so doing can it be demonstrated that the site is financially viable and that proper environmental protection can be assured. This Appendix provides information on

- the types and order of cost encountered in developing, operating, restoring and providing aftercare for landfills

- a method of comparing and assessing costs on a common basis over the lifetime of the site.

F2   The detail and accuracy of the cost rates are intended for preliminary assessment of site costs and more accurate figures may be needed for those sites subsequently selected for development. Users should satisfy themselves of the adequacy of the rates used, or substitute rates of their own derivation.

F3   The rates have been derived from actual tenders, reference guides to construction costs, and industry experience. They may be considered to be national figures and regional weighting may be applied if appropriate.

F4   It has been assumed that plant will be leased and the operator will be responsible for repairs and maintenance of the plant. However, if the operator chooses to purchase the plant then, as well as including the cost of the compactor in the capital requirements, it would be necessary to allow for the purchase of subsequent items of plant in later years. Plant life will depend on its rate of utilisation.

F5   The scale of environmental monitoring will depend on the size of site and also on site specific factors such as proximity to housing, susceptibility of groundwater or surface water systems.

Financial assessment of landfills based on unit costs

F6   Each table represents a list of the types of work that may be required at that stage of a landfill's construction. Users should consider which items are appropriate to their case, and whether other aspects specific to their site should also be included. For each item there is a rate or range of rates, which is intended to include all aspects of construction relative to that item. For example, the rate for a surface water channel includes all aspects of excavation, trimming, headwalls, outfalls, and field drain interception, likely to arise in a typical channel. Users should therefore use their judgement to select an appropriate rate, and apply it to the relevant site quantity to produce an overall total. Division of this total by the site's volume or tonnage (or input rate for operational costs) will yield the unit cost of that item, ie the total cost expressed per tonne (T) or m³ of waste. The application of unit costs for each element of the site's life can be used to identify the principal costs to be incurred during the life of the site. The indication of relative significance thus provided can enable the rapid evaluation of alternative construction or development options, or of the effects of varying rates of waste input, to provide a sensitivity analysis.

F7   Tables have been prepared covering each element of site assessment, development, operation, restoration and aftercare in terms of cost per appropriate unit (Tables 1-5). All costs are at mid 1995 prices.

F8   The layout of the tables is designed for easy translation into spreadsheet calculations. Users may also wish to extend the tables by considering the work to be carried out per year or per phase over the site's life, and thereby facilitate the generation of cash flow projections.

F9   The tables do **not** include for projection of **income** over the site's life. However it is recommended that the effects on cost of potential long-term aftercare should be evaluated to ensure that sufficient funds can be generated for its provision. Discounted cash flow techniques are frequently of assistance in this respect.

Discussion   F10   The table can be used to consider typical landfill costs. The RCEP Report 1993[1] indicated the following breakdown of costs for a 200,000 tpa landfill

Acquisition	43.4%	(Excluding acquisition	–
Assessment	0.8%	these become:)	1.4%
Development	13.2%		23.4%
Operation	33.6%		59.4%
Restoration	4.9%		8.6%
Aftercare	4.1%		7.2%

This breakdown indicates that operational costs are by far the largest element, that site assessment and aftercare costs are a very small proportion, and that the marginal cost of high quality liner systems is relatively low, when taken in terms of the overall site volume.

F11   Table 5 has been arranged as 'first 30 years' and 'following 30 years' post cessation of waste acceptance, to align with the sustainable development proposals discussed in Chapter 1. The cost rates given for these two periods are similar, but users should consider the extent to which they expect the costs of leachate and gas management to reduce over time. This will be to a large extent dependent on the degree to which accelerated stabilisation is to be adopted at a site.

---

[1]   RCEP (1993): Incineration of Waste. Tables B1 and B4 in Appendix B. 17th report of RCEP Cm 2181. London, HMSO, May 1993. ISBN 0 10 121812 5.
The model from which this breakdown is derived assumed
- 12 phases of operation over a 20 year life
- a 30 year aftercare period
- composite lining of 2 mm HDPE on 1 m of clay and geotextile, at a rate of £12.50 per m^2
- a discount rate of 10%
- unit costs are discounted costs.

Appendix F Landfill Costings

Table F.1 Site assessment costs

Item no	Item	Cost £/unit	unit	Site quantity	Site costs	Cost /(m³ or t)		Item no
	Type of waste:							
	Input rate (t/yr or m³/yr):							
	Duration of filling (yr):							
1	Reconnaissance - including data collection, detailed walk over survey, preliminary consultation with statutory authorities, and assessment of site's suitability and problems	5,000 to 15,000	site					1
2	Market survey - types and quantities of waste available, competition, potential landfill gas users etc	4,000 to 12,000	site					2
3	Preliminary ground investigation:- including eg trial pits, shallow drill holes, water sampling:							3
	Fees	3,000 to 10,000	site					
	Plant hire	1,000 to 5,000	item					
4	Topographical survey (and calculation of void)	250 to 500	ha				5 ha minimum	4
5	Site selection	2,000 to 5,000	site				Excludes need, in market survey	5
6	Full geological and hydrogeological SI , modelling, and outline landfill design:							6
	Fees	10,000 to 50,000+	site					
	SI Contract	2,000 to 5,000	ha					
7	Planning and site licence consultations and applications, advertising and public meetings (excludes application, waste management licence and planning fees)	10,000 to 20,000	site					7
8	Environmental assessment (including eg ecological, noise, traffic, air and dust, visual and/or other surveys and modelling)	20,000 to 80,000	site					8
9	(Possible) Public inquiry	50,000 to 300,000	site				A sum is allowed for PI. But may be better spent at planning stage	9
	Total site assessment costs:							
	Total site assessment costs(£/t or m³):							
	NB: Some items may need to be iterated							

Appendix F Landfill Costings

Table F.2 Site development costs

Item no	Item	Cost £/unit	unit	Site quantity	Site costs	Cost /(m³ or t)		Item no
	Type of waste:							
	Input rate (t/yr or m³/yr):							
	Duration of filling (yr):							
1	Acquisition of site : purchase, lease, or royalty							1
	Remote sites	0.1 to 2	m³					
	Closer to cities	2 to 3	m³					
	Co-disposal	3 to 7	m³					
2	Surface water interception channel :							2
	1m deep	12	m					
	2m deep	17	m					
	Extra over (E/O) for lining or pitching	5 to 15	m²					
3	Groundwater cut-off (fin) drain :							3
	3m deep	100	m					
	5m deep	190	m					
	6.5m deep	250	m					
	E/O for well point and dewatering	70	m					
4	Groundwater cut-off:							4
	Cement-bentonite cut-off wall	50 to 70	m²					
	Sheet piled wall	150	m²					
	E/O for membrane in cement-bentonite wall	10 to 15	m²					
5	Groundwater separation (on base)							5
	Geotextile on granular with pipes	3 to 5	m²				(depends on source of stone and thickness)	
	Geonet	1 to 2	m²					
6	Groundwater drainage							6
	Gravity pipe	20	m					
	Submersible pump	5,000 to 20,000	item					
	Pumping main	30	m					
	Cabling	20	m					
7	Culvert (eg twin 1m diameter up to 2m deep below original ground level under landfill)	550	m					7
	Culvert not under landfill (1m dia)	200	m					
8	Lining (Ref Table 7.1)							8
	Clay, material on site: (No of layers x thickness)	2 to 4	m³					
	Clay, imported: (No of layers x thickness)	5 to 10	m³					
	BES (300 mm thick)	5 to 9	m²					
	GCL (x No of layers)	6	m²					
	Geomembrane FML (Primary)(x No of layers)	5	m²				Assume 2 mm HDPE	
	Geomembrane FML (Secondary)(x No of layers)	4 to 5	m²				Assume 1.5 mm HDPE	
	Hydraulic asphalt	50	m²					
	Protective geotextiles:							
	600 gsm	2 to 3	m²					
	1200 gsm	4 to 5	m²					
	Sand protection	3 to 8	m²					
	Separation geotextile:	0.6 to 1	m²					
	Seepage detection layer:							
	Geonet:	1 to 2	m²					
	Granular blanket:	3 to 5	m³				Assumes imported	
	Geogrid reinforcement:	2.5 to 4	m²					

Appendix F Landfill Costings

Table F.2 Site development costs

Item no	Item	Cost £/unit	unit	Site quantity	Site costs	Cost /(m³ or t)		Item no
	E/O for vertical installation:	50 to 120	m² of wall					
	CQA, CQC, Liner leakage detection survey(LLDS) (min 1.5% of liner costs)	10,000 to 20,000	ha					
9	Leachate collection:							9
	Drainage blanket plus manholes and pipes:	3 to 5	m²					
	Herringbone drains:	35	m					
	Leachate manhole:							
	Vertical	2,000 to 4,000	No				1st 3 m	
	Side slope riser	upto 15,000	No				for 15 m deep	
10	Leachate removal :							10
	Pump:	500 to 3,000	No				Includes pump and controls, life of pumps can be short	
	Electricity cable:	20	m					
	Delivery pipe:	30	m					
11	Leachate treatment facility	150,000 to 700,000	No				depends on eg flow rate, quality, variability, temperature of leachate	11
12	Leachate pumping or gravity pipes(c.150/250 dia):	20 to 50	m					12
13	Passive gas vents:							13
	Single vents:	400	No					
14	Gas abstraction wells:	25 to 60	m					14
	Well head chambers:	300 to 1,500	No					
	Extraction pipe	15 to 35	m					
	Condensate traps	500 to 1,000	No					
	Compound incl. pumping plant, flare & access:	60,000 to 120,000	item					
15	Gas utilisation plant:	500,000 to 4,000,000	Sum					15
	Power generation	50,000 +	MW					
	Connection	varies					poss. 60,000 to 120,0000	
16	Gas monitoring boreholes	35 to 60	m					16
17	Topsoil stripping (thickness x area):	1 to 2	m³					17
18	Excavate materials to stockpile:	1 to 2	m³					18
19	Excavate from stockpile or within site to:							19
	Compact in bulk fill or screen bunds	1 to 2	m³					
	Place in bunds or road embankments	1.5 to 2.5	m³					
	Place in liner (if not included above)	0 to 2	m³					
20	Import earthworks materials (if not included above):							20
	indicative prices only,							
	actual cost depends on availability							
	Granular:	5 to 20	m³					
	Cohesive:	7.5 to 10	m³					
	Topsoil	3 to 8	m³					
	Subsoil	2 to 6	m³					
	Sand:	5 to 10	m³					
	General:	2.5 to 5	m³					
21	Access road (embankments included in 4):							21
	Tarmac	20	m²					
	Hardcore	5	m²					
	(Also allow for compactor travel routes)							

Appendix F Landfill Costings

Table F.2 Site development costs

Item no	Item	Cost £/unit	unit	Site quantity	Site costs	Cost /(m³ or t)		Item no
22	Fencing :							22
	2 m security, cranked tops	25	m					
	1 m stockproof	5	m					
	close boarded	30	m					
23	Landscape planting :							23
	Standard trees	20	No					
	Transplants	0.5 to 2	No					
	Shrubs	0.5 to 3	No					
	Hedges	1 to 2	m					
24	Grass seeding:	0.2 to 0.5	m²					24
								25
25	Site offices :	5,000 to 60,000	item					
26	Laboratory (geotechnical and chemical):	15,000 to 40,000	item					26
27	Wheelcleaner	15,000 to 30,000	item					27
28	Weighbridge (allow for appropriate type):	20,000 to 50,000	item				including office	28
29	Fuel stores/garages/workshops	8,000 min	item					29
30	Site specific requirements: For example;							30
	Mineshaft capping	5,000 to 25,000	No					
	Entrance from highway	15,000 to 25,000	item					
	Services diversion	varies	item					
	Rail sidings	varies	m					
	Civic amenity site	40,000 to 80,000	item					
31	Site services :							31
	Water	varies	item					
	Electricity	varies	item					
	Telephone	varies	item					
32	Other site specific costs (list :)		item					32
33	Preliminary items (25%)							33
	Contingencies (10%):							
34	Detailed landfill design and supervision	(allowance: 5 to 15%)						34
	Total site development costs:							
	Total site development costs (£/t or m³):							

Appendix F Landfill Costings

Table F.3 Costs of site operation

Item no	Item	Cost £/unit/yr	unit	Site quantity	Site costs	Cost /(m³ or t)		Item no
	Type of waste:							
	Input rate (t/yr or m³/yr):							
	Duration of filling (yr):							
1	Wages and salaries	17,000	employee					1
2	Plant lease:							2
	Compactor	46,000	item					
	Bulldozer	20,700	item					
	Wheeled loader	16,100	item					
	Tracked loader	16,100	item					
	Motor scraper	51,750	item					
	Tracked hydraulic excavator	20,700	item					
	Dump truck	20,700	item					
	Pumps	2,300	item					
	Bowser	2,300	item					
	Mobile lighting	2,875	item					
	Jet cleaner	1,725	item					
	Tractor and attachments	5,750	item					
	Other (miscellaneous):							
3	Machine repair and maintenance:							3
	Compactor	9.00	hour				total compactor cost including items 2 and 3 reported to be £29/hr	
	Bulldozer	4.50	hour					
	Loader	3.50	hour					
	Motor scraper	16.00	hour					
	Tracked backacter	4.50	hour					
	Dump truck	6.00	hour					
	Pumps	0.60	hour					
	Bowser	0.20	hour					
	Mobile lighting	0.50	hour					
	Jet cleaner	0.40	hour					
	Tractor and attachments	2.30	hour					
	Other (miscellaneous):							
4	Fuel, oil and lubricants	0.30	tonne of waste deposited					4
5	Imported soils materials:							5
	Daily cover:	2.5 to 5	m³					
	Roadmaking:	5 to 20	m³					
	Granular drainage:	5 to 20	m³					
6	Site maintenance (roads, grass cutting, drainage)	10,000 to 50,000	site					6
7	Environmental control (pests, wind, etc)	5,000 to 35,000	site					7
8	Environmental monitoring	5,000 to 20,000	small site					8
		15,000 to 35,000	medium site					
		25,000 to 50,000	large site					
9	Surveying	150 to 250	ha					9
10	Leachate:							10
	On-site treatment incl. maintenance:	0.5 to 1.0	m³/yr					
	Disposal to sewer of pre-treated leachate:	0.3 to 1.0	m³/yr					
	Disposal to sewer of untreated leachate:	1.0 to 4.0	m³/yr					

Appendix F Landfill Costings

Table F.3 Costs of site operation

Item no	Item	Cost £/unit/yr	unit	Site quantity	Site costs	Cost /(m³ or t)		Item no
	NB Include all discharge consent charges. Trade effluent costs may rise in real terms							
11	Gas:operation and maintenance of system and plant:							11
	Gas abstraction	14000	ha					
	Gas flare and compound	5000	site					
	Utilisation:	less than 0.04	kW					
12	Rates	0.4 to 0.45	tonne of waste deposited					12
13	Annual waste management licence fee	650 to 12,375	item				1995 cost - use current rate	13
14	Landfill levy (details to be released)		tonne of waste deposited					14
15	Financial bond or surety		tonne of waste deposited					15
16	National Aftercare Fund (if EC approved)		tonne of waste deposited					16
17	Site overheads including admin, insurance, professional office salaries, power, utility supply Allow 20% of annual operation costs	Allow 20% of annual operation costs	item					17
	Total annual operating cost							
	Total annual operating cost (£/t or m³):							

Appendix F Landfill Costings

Table F.4 Capping and restoration Costs

Item no	Item	Cost £/unit	unit	Site quantity	Site costs	Cost /(m³ or t)		Item no
	Type of waste:							
	Input rate (t/yr or m³/yr):							
	Duration of filling (yr):							
1	Granular blanket for gas collection/leachate drainage or recirculation (plus separation geotextiles):	3 to 5	m³					1
2	Insulation layer		m³				not yet used	2
3	Capping: clay:							3
	Clay obtained from stockpile:	2 to 4	m³					
	Imported clay :	5 to 10	m³					
4	Capping: bentonite enhanced soils :	5 to 9	m²					4
5	Capping: geosynthetic clay liner :	4 to 7	m²					5
6	Capping :							6
	Membrane: LDPE, MDPE, VLDPE etc:	1.5 to 3	m²					
	Sand protection	3 to 8	m³					
	Protective geotextile:	2 to 5	m²					
7	Drainage:							7
	Granular layer:	3 to 5	m³					
	Geonet:		m²					
8	Subsoil replacement from:							8
	Stockpile	1 to 3	m³					
	Imported source	2 to 6	m³					
9	Topsoil replacement from:							9
	Stockpile	1 to 3	m³					
	Imported source	3 to 8	m³					
10	Soil improver/conditioner for subsoil/poor topsoil	650	ha					10
	Grass seeding	0.2 to 0.5	m²					
11	Field drainage (may also be in (7))	3000	ha					11
12	Landscape planting :							12
	Standards	20	No					
	Transplants	0.5 to 2	No					
	Shrubs	0.5 to 3	No					
	Hedges	1 to 2	m					
13	Grass cutting, maintenance inc. fertiliser and weedkiller etc.	0.3	m²					13
14	Fencing :							14
	2 m security, cranked tops	25	m					
	1 m stockproof	5	m					
	Close boarded	30	m					
	Total capping and restoration costs:							
	Total capping/restoration costs (£/t or m³):							

Appendix F Landfill Costings

Table F.5 Aftercare costs

Item no	Item	Cost £/unit/yr	unit	Site Quantity	Site Costs	Cost /(m³ or t)		Item no
	Type of waste:							
	Input rate (t/yr or m³/yr):							
	Duration of filling (yr):							
	A: FIRST 30 YEARS POST COMPLETION OF FILLING							
1	General maintenance of restoration and of capping	200	ha					1
2	Treatment of differential settlement	100	ha					2
3	Leachate: collection and extraction:							3
	On-site treatment incl. maintenance:	0.5 to 1	m³					
	Disposal to sewer of pre-treated leachate:	0.3 to 1.0	m³					
	Disposal to sewer of untreated leachate:	1.0 to 4.0	m³					
	NB Include all discharge consent charges							
	NB Include for replacements							
4	Gas:operation and maintenance of system and plant:							4
	Gas abstraction	9000	ha					
	Gas flare and compound	5000	site					
	Utilisation:	less than 0.04	kW					
	NB Include for replacements							
5	Environmental monitoring	1000	ha					5
6	Surveying	250 to 500	ha					6
7	Rates		tonne of waste deposited				or per ha ?	7
8	Annual waste management licence fee	100 to 650	year				1995 cost - use current rate	8
9	Financial bond or surety		tonne of waste deposited					9
10	National Aftercare Fund (if EC approved)		tonne of waste deposited					10
	Total aftercare costs (first 30 years):							
	Total aftercare costs (first 30 yrs) (£/t or m³):							
	B: AFTER 30 YEARS POST COMPLETION OF FILLING							
1	General maintenance of restoration and of capping	100	ha					1
2	Treatment of differential settlement	30	ha					2
3	Leachate: Collection and extraction:							3
	On-site treatment incl. maintenance:	0.5 to 1.0	m³					
	Disposal to sewer of pre-treated leachate:	0.3 to 1.0	m³					
	Disposal to sewer of untreated leachate:	1.0 to 4.0	m³					
	NB Include all discharge consent charges							
	NB Include for replacements							
4	Gas:operation and maintenance of system and plant:							4
	gas abstraction	9000	ha					
	gas flare and compound	5000	site					
	Utilisation:	less than 0.04	kW				assume utilisation complete ?	
	NB Include for replacements							

Appendix F Landfill Costings

Table F.5 Aftercare costs

Item no	Item	Cost £/unit/yr	unit	Site Quantity	Site Costs	Cost /(m³ or t)		Item no
5	Environmental monitoring	1000	ha					5
6	Surveying	50 to 100	ha					6
7	Rates		tonne of waste deposited					7
8	Annual Waste Management licence fee	100 to 650	year				1995 cost - use current rate	8
9	Financial Bond or Surety		tonne of waste deposited					9
10	National Aftercare Fund (if EC approved)		tonne of waste deposited					10
	Total aftercare costs (second 30 years):							
	Total aftercare costs (second 30 yrs) (£/t or m³):							

Appendix F Landfill Costings

Table F.6 Summary

Table F.1	Total site assessment costs:	
	Total site assessment costs (£/t or m³):	
Table F.2	Total site development costs:	
	Total site development costs (£/t or m³):	
Table F.3	Total annual operating costs:	
	Total annual operating costs (£/t or m³):	
Table F.4	Total capping and restoration costs:	
	Total capping and restoration costs (£/t or m³):	
Table F.5A	Total aftercare costs (first 30 years):	
	Total aftercare costs (first 30 yrs) (£/t or m³):	
Table F.5B	Total aftercare costs (second 30 years):	
	Total aftercare costs (second 30 yrs) (£/t or m³):	
	OVERALL SITE TOTAL:	
	OVERALL SITE TOTAL (£/t or m³):	

Appendix G
Site Investigation Techniques

Appendix G
Site Investigation Techniques

Scope of site investigations

G1　A wide range of techniques are available for site investigation. This appendix provides general comments on a number of the more common techniques available and highlights a number of potential difficulties to be avoided.

G2　It is not the intention of this document to provide a comprehensive list of techniques or to advise on their use, as each has different merits depending upon the situation and information required. Furthermore, technology is developing at a rapid pace and new techniques and equipment are constantly appearing. This must be taken into account in the design of the site investigation.

Common techniques

G3　Table G.1 lists a number of the more commonly used techniques and gives advantages and disadvantages applicable to each.

Difficulties to be considered

G4　Many of the techniques utilised in site investigations contain inherent limitations which must be recognised. These range from sampling techniques which may, or may not, provide samples of the required integrity to piezometer installations which may be inappropriate to the hydrogeology in which they are installed. An example is piezometers which are often used as a source of primary data and whose design must allow for potential response times and other aquifer characteristics.

G5　Any site investigation must also consider the end use of the data. Much of the data will be used to provide background information against which later data is compared. Discrepancies in measured levels may indicate leakage. In such cases it is paramount that the base data are accurate and have not been compromised by cross contamination between samples or the introduction of contaminants into the ground during the investigation. Both of these aspects are discussed below.

G6　Where drilling is proposed into existing waste or land adjoining established sites as part of the site investigation, particular care will be required to avoid damage to existing liner and control systems.

a)　Cross contamination

G7　Cross contamination occurs when contaminants present in any one geological horizon are introduced into another horizon by the investigation techniques. This can come from

> contaminated material spilling off the borehole wall and falling into the bottom of the hole before advancement of the casing

> the borehole acting as a vertical conduit allowing vertical movement of contaminated fluids

> unclean equipment transferring contaminants between samples or between boreholes.

G8　These apply primarily to site investigations on or near existing contaminated ground. Nevertheless, they should be considered in all cases. The problem can be minimised by careful selection of investigation methods and cleaning of equipment between sampling and moving of rigs. Sampling equipment now available is designed to overcome these problems. A form of contamination can also be caused if clean water-bearing horizons are interconnected by borehole. This will confuse the results and may produce fundamental changes to the hydrogeological regime.

G9   With regard to potential vertical movement of fluids along the borehole, all boreholes should be carefully grouted to full depth on completion using cement/bentonite grout.

G10   When drilling through contaminated ground, the borehole casing must extend through any suspected contaminated material and be sealed into any underlying bedrock before drilling continues below the contaminated horizon.

b)   Self contamination

G11   Self contamination occurs when the site investigation process introduces contaminants into the ground. Potential sources of self contamination are:

(i)   Drilling machine and associated fluids

G12   Drilling fluids can contain/introduce contaminants into the ground, such as

- hydrocarbons from lubricants in an air flush compressor

- machine lubricants dropping down the hole

- anti-frost compounds leaking down the hole

- drill rod joint lubricants

- water flush additives such as polymers, foams and other forms of artificial drilling.

G13   If water has to be added to the borehole to assist boring it must come from a source of known quality with samples analysed to provide a reference against which groundwater samples can be compared.

(ii)   Borehole installations

G14   Equipment such as samplers, pumps or monitoring points installed within the borehole is a potential source of contamination. This can arise from spillage of contaminants onto the equipment while stored on-site, including

- contaminated filter pack material which should not be stored on-site but should be delivered in sealed containers

- solvents or coatings leaching from installation materials

- solvents from glued joints

- heavy metals from galvanised or brass fittings

- grout mixed with contaminated water.

G15   While the potential degree of contamination likely from the above is small, it may be sufficient to distort background levels required as a benchmark for future readings. Most, if not all of the above problems may be minimised by careful site control and selection of materials to suit the required end use.

G16   Site investigation techniques, laboratory analytical methods and knowledge of the effects of contaminants are continually developing. The future interactions of materials installed in boreholes may therefore not be known or understood. To allow for this, consideration should be given to the long-term storage of samples of materials installed including

- liner

- filter

- standpipe

- bentonite.

Table G.1

Commonly used site investigation techniques

Technique	Advantages	Disadvantages
Cable percussion boring	Commonly available Casing follows hole reducing cross contamination	Non continuous sampling Disturbance to base of hole
Hollow stem auger	Speed of boring Forms a "casing" as auger advances Ability to grout hole as auger removed	Limitations on sampling through hollow stem, notably sample diameter (although some modern augers allow up to 100 mm dia sampling)
Rotary cored drilling	Provides continuous sample in the form of a core	Inappropriate to soft ground and granular horizons May require a system for casing to follow the drill bit
Rotary open hole drilling	Speed of drilling	Lack of sample Mixing of returns Potential for cross contamination of returns
Trial Pits	Relatively cheap Rapid coverage Allows visual examination of strata In situ macropermeability testing	Limited to 4 - 5 m depth
Cone Penetration Test	Continuous data with depth In situ testing for permeability Profiling of soil Special undisturbed samples for continuous or spot sampling	No sample Not applicable to hard ground and some granular horizons May leave a vertical conduit on extraction Localised permeability assessment
Dynamic Cone Penetration Test	Continuous data	No sample Needs correlation with borehole data Probe stopped by obstructions or cobbles
Surface Geophysics	Two/three dimensional Rapid coverage	Specialist interpretation required Need correlation with borehole data
Borehole Geophysics	Relatively cheap Range of useful information Reduces need for coring	Specialist interpretation required Need correlation against cores

Appendix H
Seepage through Liners

Appendix H
Seepage through Liners

Introduction

H1   This appendix provides basic information on the mechanisms of leakage through the principal types of liner as components of an overall liner system. **Actual calculations of leakage should be carried out on a probabilistic basis using an agreed risk assessment methodology, and considering the other variables in the system.** This is described in paragraphs 3.27 to 3.34 and Appendix E.

Mineral liners

H2   Where mineral liners are constructed above the level of groundwater, they essentially comprise part of the unsaturated zone. Determination of flow rates is therefore uncertain due to complex flow paths and variations in permeability between unsaturated and saturated strata. However, seepage rates through mineral liners are typically approximated to flow according to Darcy's Law in saturated strata[1]. This yields the equation:

$$q = k\frac{(h+d)}{d}$$

where

q = seepage rate $(m^3/s/m^2)$
h = leachate head above top of liner (m)
d = thickness of liner (m)
k = hydraulic conductivity (m/s)

H3   Thus for a mineral liner 1 m thick with a hydraulic conductivity of 1×10^{-9} m/s and a leachate head of 1 m, the seepage rate is equivalent to $1.7 \, m^3/ha/day$. Increasing the hydraulic conductivity of the mineral liner or the head of leachate, or decreasing the thickness of the liner (for example, for BES or GCL liners), will all increase the seepage rate though the liner. Conversely, decreasing the hydraulic conductivity of the liner (for example, for BES or GCL), or the leachate head, or increasing the thickness of the liner, will decrease the seepage rates.

H4   The assessment of flow rates through mineral liners should also take into account the presence of localised flaws in the liner. These are generally considered in terms of a global increase in the ascribed k value. The magnitude of this increase depends on the quality of the construction, the effectiveness of the CQA programme, and any changes which may affect the liner after its emplacement (for example, desiccation, damage or deformation).

H5   The chemistry of landfill leachate may also affect flow rates, particularly if the leachate is unusual, for example highly acidic or basic or including significant concentrations of organic chemicals, oils or red list substances.

H6   Landfill gases will also move through mineral liners. Darcian flow rate is inversely proportional to viscosity; as landfill gas is of lower viscosity than leachate, flow rates would be accordingly higher for the same pressure gradient, although pressure gradients will normally be lower. Landfill gas may also seep through a mineral liner by diffusion[2].

Geomembrane liners

H7   Seepage through geomembrane liners can occur by two mechanisms, permeation/diffusion through the intact membrane, and leakage through holes.

---

[1] Seymour K J (1992): "Landfill lining for leachate containment". J Inst Water Env Management.
[2] See WMP27.

Due to the extremely low permeabilities of geomembranes, permeation rates are generally very low with the majority of seepage due to leakage through flaws in the liner.

H8   Seepage through geomembrane liners is, therefore, controlled by the number, size and location of the defects. Giroud[3] has suggested that the number of flaws likely to be present in a geomembrane depends on the effectiveness of the CQA programme as follows[4]:

Very good CQA   2 to 3 holes/ha

Average CQA   10 to 20 holes/ha

Poor CQA   30 to 50 holes/ha.

H9   Holes may be either pinholes $(0.1 - 5 \text{ mm}^2)$, small holes $(5 - 100 \text{ mm}^2)$ or large holes $(100 - 10,000 \text{ mm}^2)$. CQA programmes will tend to preferentially detect the larger holes, so the number of such holes will generally be smaller. Hall[5] has suggested the following mean values:

Pinholes 5 per hectare

Small holes 2 per hectare

Large holes 0.15 per hectare.

H10   The location of holes can also be important; if most of the holes are at low points of the site, leachate head and hence leakage rates may be higher.

H11   A number of theoretical and experimental studies have evaluated flow rates through defects in geomembrane liners[6,7]. Where the material directly under the geomembrane has a high permeability, this approach is helpful. In landfill liners, where the geomembrane usually lies directly on, and in intimate contact with, a medium or low permeability material (for example, mineral liner or subgrade), it may be less helpful. Leakage rates through holes in the membrane are best determined by considering the membrane as part of a composite liner system; see below.

Composite liners

H12   Where a geomembrane material is placed in intimate contact with a mineral liner, or even a subgrade material, leakage rates through the flows in the geomembrane will be controlled by the permeability of the mineral liner. Giroud et al[8] have empirically derived the following equation to determine flow rates through flaws in a composite liner:

[3] Giroud J P and Peggs I D (1990): "Geomembrane Construction Quality Assurance" in *Waste Containment Systems: Construction, Regulation and Performance*. Geotechnical Special Publication No 26, ASCE, pp 190-225.

[4] Peggs has suggested that 70% of the holes in membranes occur at or near seams (Reference: Peggs I D (1990): "Detection and investigation of leaks in geomembrane liner". Geosynthetics World, Vol 1, Issue 2, pp 7-14).

[5] Hall D H and Marshall P (1991): "The role of construction quality assurance in the installation of geomembrane liners" in *The Planning and Engineering of Landfills*. Midland Geotechnical Society, 1991, pp 187-192.

[6] Walton J C and Sagar B (1990): "Aspects of fluid flow through small flaws in membrane liners". Environ Sci Tech, Vol 24, No 6.

[7] Giroud J P & Bonaparte R (1989): "Leakage through liners constructed with geomembranes: Part I, Geomembrane Liners" in *Geotextiles and Geomembranes*, Vol 8, No 1, pp 27-67; also Giroud J P & Bonaparte R (1989): "Leakage through liners constructed with geomembranes: Part II, Composite Liners", in *Geotextiles and Geomembranes*, Vol 8, No 2, pp 78-111.

[8] Giroud J P, Khatami A & Badu-Tweneboath K (1989): "Evaluation of the rate of leakage through composite liners" in *Geotextiles and Geomembranes*, Vol 8, pp 337-340.

$$q = c.a^{0.1} h^{0.9} K_s^{0.74}$$

where q=flow rate (m^3/s)

c=a constant depending on the contact between the membrane and the subsoil (0.21 for good contact, 1.15 for poor contact)

h=head of leachate (m)

a=area of holes (m^2)

K_s=hydraulic conductivity of subgrade (m/s)

Appendix I
Leachate Quality

Table I.1

Summary of composition of acetogenic leachates sampled from large landfills with a high waste input rate, relatively dry (35 samples in all)

Determinand	Samples	Minimum	Maximum	Median	Mean	SD
pH-value	34	5.12	7.8	6.0	6.73	—
COD	35	2,740	152,000	23,600	36,817	32,718
BOD_5	29	2,000	68,000	14,600	18,632	15,643
ammoniacal-N	34	194	3,610	582	922	802
chloride	34	659	4,670	1,490	1,805	910
BOD_{20}	13	2,000	125,000	14,900	25,108	32,870
TOC	24	1,010	29,000	7,800	12,217	10,028
fatty acids (as C)	26	963	22,414	5,144	8,197	6,786
alkalinity (as $CaCO_3$)	24	2,720	15,870	5,155	7,251	4,390
conductivity ($\mu S/cm$)	28	5,800	52,000	13,195	16,921	11,602
nitrate-N	30	<0.2	18.0	0.7	1.80	3.41
nitrite-N	25	0.01	1.4	0.1	0.20	0.30
sulphate (as SO_4)	24	<5	1,560	608	676	549
phosphate (as P)	21	0.6	22.6	3.3	5.0	5.47
sodium	26	474	2,400	1,270	1,371	631
magnesium	28	25	820	400	384	196
potassium	28	350	3,100	900	1,143	760
calcium	31	270	6,240	1,600	2,241	1,656
chromium	26	0.03	0.3	0.12	0.13	0.08
manganese	26	1.40	164.0	22.95	32.94	37.29
iron	32	48.3	2,300	475	653.8	566.2
nickel	24	<0.03	1.87	0.23	0.42	0.48
copper	24	0.020	1.100	0.075	0.130	0.216
zinc	34	0.09	140.0	6.85	17.37	29.56
cadmium	24	<0.01	0.10	0.01	0.02	0.03
lead	24	<0.04	0.65	0.30	0.28	0.16
arsenic	19	<0.001	0.148	0.010	0.024	0.039
mercury	15	<0.0001	0.0015	0.0003	0.0004	0.0004
heavy metals excl Zn [2]	24	0.34	2.57	0.95	1.03	0.56

Notes: 1. Results in mg/l except pH-value and conductivity.
2. Represents the sum of concentrations of chromium, nickel, copper, cadmium, lead, arsenic and mercury.

Source: DoE: *A Review of the Composition of Leachates from Domestic Wastes in Landfill Sites.* DoE Research Report No CWM 072/94 (in preparation 1995).

Table I.2

Summary of composition of methanogenic leachates sampled from large landfills with a high waste input rate, relatively dry (29 samples in all)

Determinand	Samples	Minimum	Maximum	Median	Mean	SD
pH-value	29	6.8	8.2	7.35	7.52	–
COD	29	622	8,000	1,770	2,307	1,527
BOD_5	29	97	1,770	253	374	378
ammoniacal-N	29	283	2,040	902	889	396
chloride	29	570	4,710	1,950	2,074	9,870
BOD_{20}	24	110	1,900	391	544	459
TOC	29	184	2,270	555	733	470
fatty acids (as C)	29	<5	146	5	18	29
alkalinity (as $CaCO_3$)	29	3,000	9,130	5,000	5,376	1,664
conductivity (μS/cm)	25	5,990	19,300	10,000	11,502	3,890
nitrate-N	27	0.2	2.1	0.7	0.86	0.53
nitrite-N	27	<0.01	1.3	0.09	0.17	0.26
sulphate (as SO_4)	16	<5	322	35	67	83
phosphate (as P)	28	0.3	18.4	2.7	4.3	4.3
sodium	29	474	3.650	1,400	1,480	691
magnesium	29	40	1,580	166	250	308
potassium	29	100	1,580	791	854	387
calcium	29	23	501	117	151	106
chromium	28	<0.03	0.56	0.07	0.09	0.11
manganese	29	0.04	3.59	0.30	0.46	0.66
iron	29	1.6	160	15.3	27.4	32.8
nickel	29	<0.03	0.60	0.14	0.17	0.13
copper	27	<0.02	0.62	0.07	0.13	0.15
zinc	29	0.03	6.7	0.78	1.14	1.30
cadmium	27	<0.01	0.08	<0.01	0.015	0.02
lead	27	<0.04	1.9	0.13	0.20	0.35
arsenic	27	<0.001	0.485	0.009	0.034	0.093
mercury	23	<0.0001	0.0008	<0.0001	0.0002	0.0002
heavy metals excl Zn [2]	27	0.15	2.78	0.51	0.61	0.49

Notes: 1.   Results in mg/l except pH-value and conductivity.

2.   Represents the sum of concentrations of chromium, nickel, copper, cadmium, lead, arsenic and mercury.

Source: DoE: *A Review of the Composition of Leachates from Domestic Wastes in Landfill Sites.* DoE Research Report No CWM 072/94 (in preparation 1995).

Bibliography

Bibliography

The references in this bibliography are grouped by chapter. Within chapters they are sequenced in alphabetical order, by the name of the first author.

Legislation, departmental reports and other such corporate publications usually have no named author. For sequencing purposes, the corporate author has been used here, and in the abbreviated form where appropriate. The commonly used abbreviations are:

BSI	British Standards Institution
CIRIA	Construction Industry Research and Information Association
DE	Department of Employment
DoE	Department of the Environment
DoT	Department of Transport
EC	European Communities
HMIP	Her Majesty's Inspectorate of Pollution
HSE	Health and Safety Executive
ICE	Institution of Civil Engineers
NRA	National Rivers Authority
NWWDO	North West Waste Disposal Officers
NWWRO	North West Waste Regulation Officers
USEPA	United States Environmental Protection Agency

References given as footnotes in the main text are repeated here.

Chapter 1: Background and Concepts

DoE: *Waste Management Licensing*. Circular 11/94 (DoE), 26/94 (Welsh Office), 10/94 (Scottish Office Environment Department). London, HMSO, 1994. ISBN 0 11 752975 3.

DoE: *Landfilling in the UK and Landfill Containment*. Wastes Technical Division/ Waste Management Division Note, June 1994.

DoE: *Landfilling Wastes*. A Technical Memorandum for the Disposal of Wastes on Landfill Sites. Waste Management Paper No 26. London, HMSO, 1986 ISBN 0 11 751891 3.

DoE: *Planning and Pollution Control*. Planning Policy Guidance Note PPG23. London, HMSO, 1994. ISBN 0 11 752947 8.

DoE: *Sustainable Development - The UK Strategy*, Summary Report. Cm 2426 London, HMSO, 1994.

DoE: *Sustainable Waste Management: A Waste Strategy for England and Wales*. DoE/ Welsh Office (in preparation 1995).

DoE: *The Control of Pollution (Special Waste) Regulations 1980*. SI 1980 No 1709.

DoE: Waste Management Paper No 4A, *Licensing of Metal Recycling Sites*. London, HMSO, 1995 ISBN 0 11 751194 2

EC: Directive 75/442/EEC, as amended by 91/156/EEC and 91/692/EEC, *The Framework Directive on Waste*.

EC: Directive 91/689/EEC on *Hazardous Waste*

EC: *Towards Sustainability, A European Community Programme of Policy and Action in Relation to the Environment and Sustainable Development*, published by the Office for Publications of the European Communities, 1992.

NRA: *Policy and Practice for the Protection of Groundwater* Bristol, National Rivers Authority, 1992. ISBN 1 873160 37 2. Available from National Rivers Authority, Newcastle-upon-Tyne X, NE85 4ET.

Chapter 2: An Overview of the Legislative Framework

DE: *Control of Substances Hazardous to Health Regulations 1988*. SI 1988 No 1657.

DE: *Control of Substances Hazardous to Health Regulations 1994*. SI 1994 No 3246.

DE: *Health and Safety at Work etc. Act 1974*.

DE: *The Management of Health and Safety at Work Regulations 1992*. SI 1992 No 2051.

DE: *Work Place (Health, Safety and Welfare) Regulations 1992*. SI 1992 No 3004.

DoE: *Waste Management Licensing*. Circular 11/94 (DoE), 26/94 (Welsh Office), 10/94 (Scottish Office Environment Department). London, HMSO, 1994. ISBN 0 11 752975 3.

DoE: *Environmental Assessment*. Circular 15/88. London, HMSO, 1988.

DoE: Control of Pollution (Amendment) Act 1989.

DoE: Environmental Protection Act 1990.

DoE: *Planning and Pollution Control*. Planning Policy Guidance Note PPG23. London, HMSO, 1994. ISBN 0 11 752947 8.

DoE: *Planning, Pollution and Waste Management*. DoE Research Report. London, HMSO, 1992: ISBN 0 11 752668 1.

DoE: *The Construction (Design and Management) Regulations 1994*. SI 1994 No 3140.

DoE: *The Controlled Waste (Registration of Carriers and Seizure of Vehicles) Regulations 1991*. SI 1991 No 1621.

DoE: *The Controlled Waste Regulations 1992*. SI 1992 No 588, amended by SI 1993 No 566.

DoE: *The Environmental Protection (Duty of Care) Regulations 1991*. SI 1991 No 2839.

DoE: The Planning and Compensation Act 1991.

DoE: *The Reclamation of Mineral Workings*. Minerals Planning Guidance Note MPG7. DoE/Welsh Office. London, HMSO, 1989.

DoE: *The Special Waste Regulations 1995*. London, HMSO, 1995.

DoE: *The Town and Country Planning (Assessment of Environmental Effects) Regulations 1988*. SI 1988 No 1199 and subsequent amendments 1994.

DoE: The Town and Country Planning Act 1990.

DoE: *The Town and Country Planning General Development Order 1988*. SI 1988 No 1813, Amendment Order 1991, and subsequent consolidated general development orders: *The Town and Country Planning (General Permitted Development) Order 1995*. SI 1995 No 418, and *The Town and Country Planning (General Development Procedure) Order 1995*. SI 1995 No 419.

DoE: *The Waste Management Licensing Regulations 1994*. SI 1994 No 1056. London, HMSO, 1994. ISBN 0 11 044056 0.

DoE: Waste Management Paper No 4, *Licensing of Waste Management Facilities*. London, HMSO, 1994. ISBN 0 11 752727 0.

DoE: Waste Management Paper No 26A, *Landfill Completion*. London, HMSO, 1994. ISBN 0 11 752807 2.

DoE: Waste Management Paper No 26D, *Landfill Monitoring*. (in preparation 1995)

DoE: Waste Management Paper No 26E, *Landfill Restoration and Post Closure Management*. (in preparation 1995).

DoE: Waste Management Paper No 26F, *Landfill Co-disposal*. (in preparation 1995).

DoE: Waste Management Paper No 27, *Landfill Gas*. London, HMSO, 1991. ISBN 0 11 752488 3.

DoE: Water Industry Act 1991.

DoE: Water Resources Act 1991.

HSE: *COSHH Assessments*. HSE Booklet 1988. London, HMSO. ISBN 0 11 8854704.

HSE: *Occupational Exposure Limits*. HSE Guidance Note EH40. London, HMSO (current edition).

NRA: *Policy and Practice for the Protection of Groundwater* Bristol, National Rivers Authority, 1992. ISBN 1 873160 37 2. Available from National Rivers Authority, Newcastle-upon-Tyne X, NE85 4ET.

NRA: Position Statement on *Landfill and the Water Environment*. Bristol, National Rivers Authority, 1995.

Chapter 3: Design Objectives and Considerations

Aiken M and Roberts I (1994): "Construction quality assurance of composite liners". *Waste Management*, February 1994.

CESMM3 Price Database (current edition). London, Thomas Telford Services Ltd. ISBN 0 7277 1834 7.

Collins H J (1993): "Impact of the temperature inside the landfill on the behaviour of barrier systems". Proc Fourth International Landfill Symposium, S Margherita di Pula, Sardinia, Italy, 1993.

Department of Energy/AERC, (1993): *The Sustainable Landfill*. ETSU B/B3/00242/REP, 1993.

DoE: *A Guide to Risk Assessment and Risk Management for Environmental Protection*. London, HMSO, 1995. ISBN 0 11 753091 3.

DoE: *A Review of the Composition of Leachates from Domestic Wastes in Landfill Sites*. DoE Research Report No CWM 072/94 (in preparation 1995).

DoE: *Waste Management Licensing*. Circular 11/94 (DoE), 26/94 (Welsh Office), 10/94 (Scottish Office Environment Department). London, HMSO, 1994. ISBN 0 11 752975 3.

DoE: *Guidance on Good Practice for Landfill Engineering*. Second draft, December 1993. DoE Research Report No CWM 106/94 (in preparation 1995).

DoE: *Landfilling in the UK and Landfill Containment*. Wastes Technical Division/Waste Management Division Note, June 1994.

DoE: *Sustainable Development - the UK Strategy: Summary Report*. London, HMSO 1994.

DoE: *The Waste Management Licensing Regulations 1994*. SI 1994 No 1056. London, HMSO, 1994. ISBN 0 11 044056 0.

DoE: *Understanding Landfill Gas*. DoE Research Report No CWM 040/92, April 1993.

EC: Directive 80/68/EEC: *Council Directive of 17 December 1979 on the protection of groundwater against pollution from certain dangerous substances*. Official Journal of the European Communities L 020, January 1980.

EC: Draft Landfill Directive (Ref 4103/95, 9 January 1995).

Gross B A, Bonaparte R and Giroud J P (1990): "Evaluation of Flow from Landfill Leakage Detection System". Proc Fourth International Conference on Geotextiles, Geomembranes and Related Products. The Hague, Vol 2, pp 481-486.

Harris R C, Knox K and Walker N (1994): "A Strategy for the Development of Sustainable Landfill Design and Operation". 1994 Harwell Conference Proceedings. Also in Proc IWM, January 1994, Vol 6. ISBN 0968-7068.

Jessburger H L (1994): "Geotechnical Aspects of Landfill Design and Construction". Part 1. Proc Inst Civ Engrs. Geotech Engng 1994. **107** Apr, pp 99-104.

Landreth R E (1990): "Service life of geosynthetics in hazardous waste management facilities" in *Geosynthetics: Microstructure and Performance*. ASTM STP 1076, ed I Peggs, 1990, pp 26-33.

Latham B (1994): "The Everlasting Question of Landfill Settlement" in *Waste Management*, June 1994, pp 23-26.

McKendry P (1994): "Engineered landfills: Comparative risk assessment of containment designs". Proc IWM April 1994, Vol 6.

NRA: *Landfill Liners*. Internal Guidance Note No 7, 1994.

NRA: *Leachate Management*. Internal Guidance Note No 8, 1995.

NRA: *Policy and Practice for the Protection of Groundwater*. Bristol, National Rivers Authority, 1992. ISBN 1 873160 37 2. Available from National Rivers Authority, Newcastle-upon-Tyne X, NE85 4ET.

NRA: Position Statement on *Landfill and the Water Environment*. Bristol, National Rivers Authority, 1995.

NWWDO (1991): *Leachate Management Report*. Lancashire Waste Disposal Authority, Preston, 1991.

NWWRO Technical Sub-group (1995): *Pollution Control Objectives for Landfill Design, Development and Operation*. Available from North West Waste Regulation Officers.

Parkinson C D (1991): "The permeability of landfill liners to leachate" in *The Planning and Engineering of Landfills*. Midland Geotechnical Society, 1991, pp 147-152.

Peggs I D, Carlson D S and Peggs S J (1990): "Understanding and preventing shattering failures of polyethylene geomembranes". Proc Fourth International Conference on Geotextiles, Geomembranes and Related Products, 1990. A A Balkema Rotterdam, Vol 2, p 549.

Reeds J (1994): "Anaerobic Workout". Article in *Surveyor*, June 1994.

Robinson H D (1993): "Timescale for completion". Article in *Surveyor*, May 1993.

Spon: Spon''s Landscape and External Works Price Book (current edition), ed Derek Lovejoy Partnership and Davis Langdon & Everest. London, E & F N Spon Ltd. ISBN 0 419 17390 0.

Spon: Spon''s Civil Engineering and Highway Works Price Book (current edition), ed Davis Langdon & Everest, Chartered Quantity Surveyors. London, E & F N Spon Ltd. ISBN 0419 19380 4.

Stegmann R and Ehrig H (1989): Leachate production and quality results of landfill processes and operation.

USEPA: *Guide to Technical Resources for the Design of Land Disposal Facilities*. Technical Guidance Document EPA/625-6-88/018, December 1988. Office of Research and Development, Washington DC 20460.

Wallis S (1991): "Factors affecting settlement at landfill sites" in *The Planning and Engineering of Landfills*. Midland Geotechnical Society, 1991, pp 183-186.

Water Authorities Association: *Civil Engineering Specification for the Water Industry* 3rd Edition 1989. Water Research Centre plc, Henley Road, Medmenham, PO Box 16, Marlow, Bucks SL7 2HD. ISBN 0 902156 73 X.

Chapter 4: Quality and Contracts

BSI: BS 4778 : Part 1 : 1987 (1993): Quality vocabulary - international terms.

CIRIA: *A Client''s Guide to Quality Assurance in Construction*. CIRIA Special Publication 55.

CIRIA: *Quality Assurance in Construction - The Present Position*. June Special Publication 49, 1987.

CIRIA: *Quality Management in Construction, Contractual Aspects*. Special Publication 84, 1992.

CIRIA: *Quality Management in Construction, Interpretation of BS 5750 (1987) - "Quality Systems" for the Construction Industry*. Special Publication 74, 1990.

DoE: *The Construction (Design and Management) Regulations 1994*. SI 1994 No 3140.

ICE: *Civil Engineering Procedure*, 3rd Edition.

ICE: *Conditions of Contract for Minor Works,* 1st Edition.

ICE: *Conditions of Contract, 6th Edition.* Conditions of Contract and Forms of Tender, Agreement and Bond for Use in Connection with Works of Civil Engineering Construction. Institution of Civil Engineers, Association of Consulting Engineers and Federation of Civil Engineering Contractors, 1991. ISBN 0 7277 16174.

ICE: *Design and Construct Conditions of Contract,* 1st Edition.

ICE: *The New Engineering Contract: Guidance Notes,* 1st Edition.

Institution of Chemical Engineers: *An Engineer''s Guide to the Model Forms of Conditions of Contract for Process Plant,* 1st Edition.

USEPA: *Quality Assurance and Quality Control for Waste Containment Facilities.* Technical Guidance Document EPA/600/R-93/182 September 1993. Office of Research and Development, Washington DC 20460.

Chapter 5: Site Investigation

Applied Geology (1993): *A Review of Instability due to Natural Underground Cavities in Great Britain.* DoE Research Report (in preparation 1995).

Arup Geotechnics (1991): *Review of Mining Instability in Great Britain.* DoE Research Report.

British Drilling Association (Operations) Limited (1992): *Guidance Notes for the Safe Drilling of Landfills and Contaminated Land.*

BSI: BS 1377 : 1990 : Methods of Test for Soils for Civil Engineering Purposes.

BSI: BS 5930 : 1981 : Code of Practice for Site Investigations.

BSI: DD 175 : 1988 : Code of practice for the identification of potentially contaminated land and its investigation.

DoE: *Planning and Pollution Control.* Planning Policy Guidance Note PPG23. London, HMSO, 1994. ISBN 0 11 752947 8.

DoE: *Waste Management Licensing Regulations 1994.*

DoE: *Waste Management Licensing.* Circular 11/94 (DoE), 26/94 (Welsh Office), 10/94 (Scottish Office Environment Department). London, HMSO, 1994. ISBN 0 11 752975 3.

Dumbleton M J and West G (1976): *Preliminary Sources of Information for Site Investigation in Britain.* Transport and Road Research Laboratory Report LR 403.

Dumbleton M J (1979): "Historical investigation of site use". Conf Proc on Reclamation of Contaminated Land, Eastbourne, October 1979. Society of Chemical Industry, London, 1980. B3/1-B3/13.

EC: Directive 80/68/EEC: *Council Directive of 17 December 1979 on the protection of groundwater against pollution from certain dangerous substances.* Official Journal of the European Communities L 020, January 1980.

Harper J: "The importance of investigation in the design and development of landfill sites" in *The Planning and Engineering of Landfills.* Midland Geotechnical Society, 1991, pp 177-182.

ICE: *Conditions of Contract for Ground Investigations (1st Edition) 1983.* London, Thomas Telford 1983. ISBN 0 7277 0178 9.

Leach B A and Goodger H K (1991): *Building on Derelict Land.* CIRIA Special Publication 78.

Site Investigation Steering Group (1993): *Planning, Procurement and Quality Management.* Site Investigation in Construction Series No 2. London, Thomas Telford.

Site Investigation Steering Group (1993): *Specification for Ground Investigation.* Site Investigation in Construction Series No 3. London, Thomas Telford.

Site Investigation Steering Group (1993): *Guidelines for the Safe Investigation by Drilling of Landfills and Contaminated Land.* Site Investigation in Construction Series No 4. London, Thomas Telford.

USEPA: The Groundwater Monitoring RCRA Technical Enforcement Guidance Document 1986.

Chapter 6: Engineering Design and Construction

Biddle A (1985): 'Evaluating landfill compactors' presented at conference of The Institute of Wastes Management 1985.

Bing C Y and Scanlon B (1975): 'Sanitary landfill settlement rates'. J Geotechnical Eng Div, ASCE.

Bjarngard A and Edgers L (1990): "Settlement of Municipal Solid Waste Landfills". Thirteenth Annual Madison Waste Conference, pp 192-205.

BSI: BS 1722 : — : Fences.

BSI: BS 6031 : 1981 : Code of Practice for Earthworks.

CIRIA (1986): *Control of Groundwater for Temporary Works*: Report No 113. London, CIRIA, 1986.

Davies J and Hammonds J (1991): "The Control of Leachate" in *The Planning and Engineering of Landfills.* Midland Geotechnical Society, 1991, pp 157-164 .

Di Stefano A B (1993): "Settlement of Beddingham Landfill" in pre-prints of papers for the 29th Annual Conference of the Engineering Group of the Geological Society of London, ed S P Bentley.

DoE: *Guidance on Good Practice for Landfill Engineering.* DoE Research Report No CWM 106/94 (in preparation 1995).

DoE: *Landfilling Wastes.* A Technical Memorandum for the Disposal of Wastes on Landfill Sites. Waste Management Paper No 26. London, HMSO, 1986. ISBN 0 11 751891 3.

DoE: *The Reclamation of Mineral Workings.* Minerals Planning Guidance Note MPG7. DoE/Welsh Office. London, HMSO, 1989.

DoE: *Water balance methods and their applications to landfill in the UK.* DoE Research Report No CWM 031/91.

Golder & Associates (1984): *Geotechnical Engineering and Refuse Landfills.* 6th National Conference on Waste Management in Canada, Vancouver, BC.

Harrison N H (1985): "Compaction and effective densities in landfill sites". Proc Inst WM. North West Centre meeting, Leyland, February 1985.

Hydraulics Research (1990): *Charts for the Hydraulic Design of Channels and Pipes.* 6th edition 1990.

Institute of Hydrology (1978): *Flood Prediction for Small Catchments*. FSR Suppl Report No 6. Institute of Hydrology, Wallingford, UK.

Koerner R M (1993): "Collection and Removal Systems". Chapter 9 in *Geotechnical Practice for Waste Disposal*, ed David E Daniel, pp 187-213. London, Chapman & Hall. ISBN 0 412 35170 6.

Landva & Clark (1990): "Geotechnics of Waste Fill" in *Geotechnics of Waste Fill - Theory and Practice*. ASTM STP 1070.

Latham B (1994): 'The Everlasting Question of Landfill Settlement' in *Waste Management*, June 1994, pp 23-26.

Nature Conservancy Council/M J Carter & Associates (1990): *Design Options for the Development of Landfill Sites in Quarries which contain Geological Sites of Special Scientific Interest:* Research report available from English Nature, Northminster House, Peterborough PE1 1UA.

NRA North West Region (1989): *Earthworks on landfill sites*. NRA North West Region, Warrington.

NRA: *Landfill Liners*. Internal Guidance Note No 7, 1994.

NRA: *Leachate Management*. Internal Guidance Note No 8, 1995.

NWWDO (1991): *Leachate Management Report*. Lancashire Waste Disposal Authority, Preston, 1991.

NWWRO Technical Sub-group (1995): *Pollution Control Objectives for Landfill Design, Development and Operation*. Available from North West Waste Regulation Officers.

Oweis I S and Khera R P (1990): *Geotechnology of Waste Management*. Cambridge, University Press, 1990. ISBN 0 408 00969 1.

Parkinson C D (1991): "The permeability of landfill liners to leachate" in *The Planning and Engineering of Landfills*. Midland Geotechnical Society, 1991, pp 147-152.

RPS Clouston and Wye College (1993): *Reclamation of Landfill Workings to Agriculture: Phase 2 Report to DoE*. DoE Research Report (in preparation 1995).

Singh & Murphy (1990): "Evaluation of the Stability of Sanitary Landfills" in *Geotechnics of Waste Fill - Theory and Practice*. ASTM STP 1070.

Wall D K and Zeiss C (1995): "Municipal Landfill Biodegradation and Settlement". J Environmental Engineering, Vol 121 No 3, pp 214-224.

Wallis S (1991): "Factors affecting settlement at landfill sites" in *The Planning and Engineering of Landfills*. Midland Geotechnical Society, 1991, pp 183-186.

Chapter 7: Landfill Liners

Alther G R (1983): "The Methylene Blue Test for Bentonite Liner Quality Control". Geotechnical Testing Journal, GTJODJ, Vol 6 No 3, Sept 1983, pp 128-132.

ASTM Standard D5514.

Benson et al (1994): "Estimating Hydraulic Conductivity of Compacted Clay Liners". ASCE, Jn of Geotech Eng, Vol 120, No 2.

Bonaparte R & Gross B A (1990): "Field behaviour of double liner systems" in *Waste Containment Systems: Construction, Regulation and Performance*, ed Bonaparte. ASCE Geotechnical Special Publication No 26, 1990, pp 52-83.

BSI: BS 1377 : — : Methods of test for soils for civil engineering purposes.

Building Research Establishment (1994): *Bentonite Walls.*

Daniel D E (1993): "Keys to the successful design, construction, testing and certification of soil liners for landfills". GRCDA Journal of Municipal Solid Waste Management.

Daniel D E, (ed) (1993): *Geotechnical Practice for Waste Disposal.* London, Chapman & Hall. ISBN 0 412 35170 6.

DoE: *Guidance on Good Practice for Landfill Engineering.* DoE Research Report No CWM 106/94 (in preparation 1995).

DoT: *Specification for Road and Bridgeworks 1991.* London.

Elsbury et al (1990) "Lessons learned from compacted clay liner". ASCE, Jn of Geotech Eng, Vol 116, No 11.

Giroud J P & Bonaparte R (1989): "Leakage through liners constructed with geomembranes: Part I, Geomembrane Liners" in *Geotextiles and Geomembranes*, Vol 8, No 1, pp 27-67; also Giroud, J P & Bonaparte, R (1989): "Leakage through liners constructed with geomembranes: Part II, Composite Liners", in *Geotextiles and Geomembranes*, Vol 8, No 2, pp 78-111.

Giroud J P and Peggs I D (1990): "Geomembrane Construction Quality Assurance" in *Waste Containment Systems: Construction, Regulation and Performance.* ASCE Geotechnical Special Publication No 26, pp 190-225.

Giroud J P, Khatami A & Badu-Tweneboath K (1989): "Evaluation of the rate of leakage through composite liners" in *Geotextiles and Geomembranes*, Vol 8, pp 337-340.

Hall D H and Marshall P (1991): "The role of construction quality assurance in the installation of geomembrane liners" in *The Planning and Engineering of Landfills.* Midland Geotechnical Society, 1991, pp 187-192.

NRA, North West Region (1991): Guidance Note on Composite Lining Systems for Landfill Sites (Letter to Waste Regulation Officers).

NRA: *Landfill Liners.* Internal Guidance Note No 7, 1994.

NRA: *Leachate Management.* Internal Guidance Note No 8, 1995.

NWWDO (1991): *Leachate Management Report.* Lancashire Waste Disposal Authority, Preston, 1991.

NWWRO Technical Sub-group (1995): *Pollution Control Objectives for Landfill Design, Development and Operation.* Available from North West Waste Regulation Officers.

Peggs I D (1990): "Destructive testing of polyethylene geomembrane seams" in *Geotextiles and Geomembrane*, Vol 9, No 4-6, pp 405-414.

Peggs I D (1990): "Detection and investigation of leaks in geomembrane liner". Geosynthetics World, Vol 1, Issue 2, pp 7-14.

Rowe, Quigley and Booker (1995): *Clayey Barrier Systems for Waste Disposal Facilities.* London, E & F N Spon Ltd, 1995.

Seymour K J (1992): "Landfill lining for leachate containment". J Inst Water Env Management.

USEPA: *Quality Assurance and Quality Control for Waste Containment Facilities.* Technical Guidance Document EPA/600/R-93/182, September 1993. Office of Research and Development, Washington DC 20460.

Walton J C and Sagar B (1990): "Aspects of fluid flow through small flaws in membrane liners". Environ Sci Tech, Vol 24, No 6.

Chapter 8: Planning and Design of Site Operations

HSE: *Avoiding Danger from Underground Services.* HSE Booklet HS(G)47.

HSE: *COSHH Assessments.* HSE Booklet 1988. ISBN 0 11 8854704.

HSE: *Occupational Exposure Limits.* HSE Guidance Note EH40/91, 1991.

Surveyor/National Association of Waste Regulation Officers: *Waste Management Licensing: A Practitioners" Guide to the 1994 Regulations.* Published by Surveyor, 32 Vauxhall Bridge Road, London SW1V 2SS.

Chapter 9: Operational Practice

BSI: BS 5378: — : Safety signs and colours.

DoE/Scottish Office/Welsh Office: *Waste Management: The Duty of Care: A Code of Practice.* London, HMSO, December 1991. ISBN 0 11 752557 X

DoE: *A Review of Leachate Composition*: DoE Research Report No CWM 072/94 (in preparation 1995)

DoE: *The Environmental Protection (Duty of Care) Regulations 1991.* SI 1991 No 2839.

DoE: *The Safety Signs Regulations 1980.* London, HMSO.

DoE: Wildlife and Countryside Act 1981.

DoT: Highways Act 1990.

Knox K (1987): "Design and operation of a full scale leachate treatment plant for nitrification of ammonia". Proc First International Landfill Symposium, S. Margherita di Pula, Sardinia, Italy, 1987.

Knox K and Gronow J (1993): "A review of landfill cap performance and its application for leachate management". Proc Fourth International Landfill Symposium, S. Margherita di Pula, Sardinia, Italy, 1993.

Morris J (1993): "Royal Reeds Reap Rewards" in Water Bulletin 565, 9 July 1993.

National Association of Waste Disposal Contractors: NAWDC Guidance Notes:

1.   *Control and reception of wastes at landfill sites*

2.   *Safety procedures at landfill sites*

3.   *Monitoring of landfill gas*

4.   *Landfilling of liquid and sludge wastes delivered in tankers*

5.   *Disposing of asbestos to landfill*

6.   *Prevention of the accumulation of mud on the road*

7.   *Landfill disposal of drummed wastes*

8.   *Monitoring landfill site preparatory works and operations and surrounding ground and surface water quality*

9.   *Use of computers in the design, development and operation of landfill sites*

10.   *Drilling in waste materials on landfill sites*

11.   *Use of landfill liners*

12.   *Bird control at landfill sites*

13.   *Control of environmental noise at landfill sites*

14.   *Leachate treatment*

15.   *Control and utilisation of landfill gas*

16.   *Use of computerised weighbridge systems*

17.   *Litter control*

18.   *Daily cover.*

Parr T (1989): *1988 Survey of Reed Growth in the UK Reed Bed Treatment Systems.* WRC/NERC Contract Report TO2058el. Medmenham, UK.

Robinson H D, Barr M J and Last S D (1992): "Leachate Collection, Treatment and Disposal". Journal of the Institution of Water and Environmental Management, Vol 6, No 3, June 1992.

Robinson H D (1994): "Treating Landfill Leachate". Landfill Completion Seminar, IBC Technical Services Ltd, Industrial Division, 27 October 1994.

Whalen S C, Reeburgh W S and Sanbeck K A (1990): "Rapid Methane Oxidation in a Landfill Cover Soil". Applied and Environmental Microbiology, Vol 56, pp 3405-3411.

Young A (1994): *Applications of computer modelling to landfill processes.* DoE report CWM 039A/92.

Chapter 10: Capping Design and Construction

Alexiew D, Berkhout H and Kirschner R (1995): "On the slope stability of landfill capping seals using GCLs" in *Geosynthetic Clay Liners*, ed Robert M Koerner, Erwin Gartung & Helmut Zanzinger; published by AA Balkema/Brookfield. ISBN 90 5410 5194.

Knox K and Gronow J (1993): "A review of landfill cap performance and its application for leachate management". Proc Fourth International Landfill Symposium, S. Margherita di Pula, Sardinia, Italy, 1993.

INDEX

Printed in the United Kingdom for HMSO
Dd. 301510 C30 11/95 9385 3329